John Seltz

HUMAN SEXUALITY

HUMAN SEXUALITY

Physiological and psychological factors of sexual behavior

JAMES LESLIE McCARY, Ph. D.

Professor of Psychology
University of Houston

D. VAN NOSTRAND COMPANY, INC.
Princeton, New Jersey

TORONTO   NEW YORK   LONDON

Van Nostrand Regional Offices: *New York, Chicago, San Francisco*

D. Van Nostrand Company, Ltd., *London*

D. Van Nostrand Company (Canada), Ltd., *Toronto*

D. Van Nostrand Australia Pty. Ltd., *Melbourne*

Library of Congress Catalog Card No. 67-28290

PRINTED IN THE UNITED STATES OF AMERICA

Foreword

RALPH D. EICHHORN, M.D.

Clinical Associate Professor of Medicine
Baylor University School of Medicine

There are few thoughtful members of the medical profession who have not long recognized the need for an authoritative and incisive volume on the subject of human sexuality—one that goes beyond a chilly clinical exposition of the mechanism of human reproduction, and above a mechanical description of the gymnastics of the human mating rites.

I have just put down the final galleys of Dr. McCary's book, and find myself enthusiastically convinced that, at last, the void on our bookshelves is now filled. *Human Sexuality* is not only for those people who have a general (and very human) interest in the subject. The volume will, I am certain, prove to be of immense value to the students who seek straightforward sex information; and to the psychotherapists, marriage counselors, clergy, and, particularly, the members of the medical profession who seek to impart as sound and wholesome guidance on sexuality as they can. These professional people are frequently called upon to act as advisors—or arbiters, even—in a realm of human relations where they feel themselves uncomfortably at sea for lack of proper information. The tragedy of their ignorance is compounded in many instances by prejudices imposed upon them by their own religious and moral upbringing, prejudices which can lie dangerously, like so many icebergs, beneath the surface of the advice they impart and which can render that advice useless, if not downright dangerous.

Physicians are in an especially unique position to offer help to those who have any of a thousand sexual difficulties or, simply, questions to present to them. The patient expects the doctor to keep his confidence; he also expects him to be a fount of knowledge. I do not suppose that a patient can often accuse his doctor of breaking his confidence; but I *do* suspect that many patients leave their doctor's office, when the subject under discussion has been sex, more bewildered than when they entered. The physician, no less than the marriage counselor or clergyman, tends to commingle his emotional prejudices with the prescriptions and advice he metes out to his patient. Often he is quite aware of his lack of objectivity and dispassionate knowledge, and this is the physician who will welcome Dr. McCary's book.

The text is medically sound, and reflects the latest available data on subjects ranging from conception to parturition. The detail is concise without being ponderous, and the illustrations are excellent. The biology is presented concisely, and once more, many misconceptions are set to rights—for example, aphrodisiacs, sexually connected physical disorders, and orgasm.

Although the psychology of the "why" and "how" of successful sexual interaction is presented sanely and frankly, it will hardly serve those whose interest in such a volume is only salacious. It is, on the other hand, an ideal reference book and marriage manual, and should probably be the very first book a prospective bride and groom buy. Furthermore, older couples who need to reeducate themselves, or who have youngsters requiring sex information, will not find a more thorough examination of the entire subject of human sexuality in any other book.

The literature in the field of human sexuality is, as almost anyone can attest, either lurid and pornographic, or frantic and pedantic, or reflective of incredible ignorance of what sex *really* means. One therefore welcomes Dr. McCary's book because of its singular candor and scope. He is not afraid to discuss his subject in unequivocal language, thankfully avoiding such pedantic references as "integumentary frictional apposition," which render the usual volume on sex ludicrous as well as useless.

Human Sexuality is a book I am happy to recommend.

Foreword

EDWIN DE F. BENNETT, A.B., B.D., S.T.M.
*Coordinator, Religious Activities and
Student Leadership Development
University of Houston*

One can only give thanks for such a book as this, which takes seriously the quest for knowledge and reveals a trust in freedom so vital in the area of human sexuality. Dr. McCary's aim is to equip the reader with data with which to confront his or her own life's situation; these data are comprehensive in scope and thorough in detail. The attempt to combine clinical accuracy and a burning concern for human dignity is evident throughout. The author does not fall prey either to facile answer-giving or to the temptation to encase his subject in mere cold objectivity. His positive evaluation of the total human being and the place of the sexual dimension in being human provides the fundamental framework for all that is said.

It is clear that we live in times of transition, and that we are a bit uncomfortable with the changes taking place. There are forces that would seek solutions by restricting freedom, that basically do not trust human beings to determine their own destinies. Those with such mentalities may find the openness and frankness of this book threatening. Those, however, to whom freedom of inquiry poses no threat can only find Dr. McCary's volume a welcome addition to their library. The candor with which the author confronts his subject indicates a genuine hopefulness in human possibilities worthy of the best in the humane tradition. At times one might wish for a little less broad generalization when the relationship between religion and sexuality is dealt with. Yet one senses constantly the author's trust that the reader will enter into dialogue with him about these essential facets of human existence.

And that we need dialogue in this, as in so many other areas of human concern today, is clear. One of the great good effects of living in times of rapid change is the growing awareness that all the answers are not in—that we have the capacity to reshape social order so that fuller, more creative human potentialities may emerge. We must move forward not in destructive rebelliousness against the past, but with thoughtful awareness that modes of sexual behavior are the product of adjusting to given realities of time and place—and that as the life situation changes, modes of behavior relative to current realities and to the needs of human beings must be shaped.

This book offers a careful presentation of data on the human condition that are an essential possession of that person who wishes to participate in this reshaping. Those willing to enter into a dialogue with this material and these times will find here something intrinsic to the development of an awareness of what is at stake in building a more humane framework within which sexuality is integrated meaningfully and joyfully in human relationships.

Preface

Many prestigious private and governmental organizations, seeing the need, have urged the development and extension of sex education in schools. Progressive educators through newspaper and magazine articles have repeatedly advocated that sex education be accorded a prominent position in the curricula of both secondary schools and colleges. Some universities are beginning to meet the challenge of pervading ignorance in the realm of human sexuality by introducing courses designed to educate the students in the physiological and psychological aspects of sexual behavior.

One of the pioneers in this field of education has been the University of Houston. A course which encompasses lectures, discussions, films, and question-and-answer sessions, and which deals exclusively with sexual matters was presented for the first time in the spring of 1964. The scope and nature of the course were announced at the time of registration, and initial enrollment was 185 students. Next semester, the enrollment grew to 350, and in the succeeding semesters, to 550 and 750, respectively. When the course was offered for the fifth time, 1169 students registered, and the section had to be closed during the latter part of registration because the lecture hall, the largest on campus, could not accommodate any more students. Enrollment has remained at capacity since that time.

This book is an outgrowth of my experiences in teaching the course in sexology at the University of Houston: its contents are based on the needs of the students as I perceived them through questionnaires, examinations, questions, and comments. The students are vitally interested in the subject matter, and have displayed remarkable maturity in accepting the straightforward manner in which the material has been presented to them.

The aim of the book is to explore the physiological, sociological, and psychological components of human sexuality in a readable yet sufficiently detailed manner so that the mystery and confusion enveloping this needlessly hypersensitive subject can be dispelled. It is my earnest hope that each reader will be able to integrate these components in a meaningful pattern into his own life. I further hope that he not only will be able better to understand and accept his own sexual needs and behavior, but also, at the same time, will be more accepting and understanding of his fellowman whose sexual attitudes and behavior might differ from his own.

A word of caution might be extended to those unfamiliar with the difficulties encountered by researchers in attempting to make an accurate assessment of any facet of human behavior or motivation. The reader will do well to remember that no research conclusion in the behavioral sciences is ever universally applicable to all people, and it becomes even less widely applicable when there are added any of the many pertinent qualifying variables, such as age, sex, religion, subculture, education, and on and on.

No book can be made ready for publication without the help of many people, and I feel that I have had an extraordinary amount of cooperation from many sources. Many publishing houses, for instance, have been most generous in permitting the use of their pictures and illustrations.

My good friend Dr. Ralph Eichhorn has read the manuscript for accuracy in the medical areas, a time-consuming job which he some-how managed to work into a busy practice and heavy teaching schedule. Dr. Lee Anderson Smith also examined the material and made many valuable suggestions, as did Drs. Patricia Perry Corke, Gerhard Neubeck, and Kenneth E. Ware. To each of you I extend my heartfelt gratitude.

The often tedious but nonetheless important tasks of sorting, compiling, typing, and retyping the manuscript have been efficiently handled by Ellen Brochstein. Thank you again, Ellen. The art work of Fran Morehead and the indexing by Marguerite Barfield are greatly appreciated. My secretaries, Carmen Perez and Eleanor Underhill, have given valuable assistance by way of proofreading and juggling appointments and teaching schedules so that I would have maximum time for writing. Each of you has exhibited incredible patience; I hope you know how grateful I am.

A genuine word of thanks must also be extended to Mary Elizabeth Sieber who with much grace and good humor joined our hectic staff in the days just preceding the publication deadline. We would never have made the deadline without her skillful efforts and ever-watchful eye.

The outstanding milestone in the literary meanderings of this writer has been the opportunity to work with Elizabeth Miremont Smith, my editor supreme. Mrs. Smith is a gentle soul who can crack a fierce whip when the appropriate occasion arises. Her energy and enthusiasm have a unique way of inspiring extra effort from all those who fall under her influence. I am grateful for that influence and for all her guidance, assistance, and hard work, all of which have contributed so significantly to the production of this book.

My wife LaVirle has made more contributions to this book than I can ever recount. Both of us know what those contributions have been, and that is what really matters.

JAMES LESLIE McCARY
University of Houston
Houston, Texas
September, 1967

Contents

Dedicated to that person
who wishes both to better understand
his own sexual needs and behavior,
and to be more accepting of his neighbor
whose sexual attitudes and behavior
might be different from his own

CHAPTER 1 ✓

Why Sex Education ?

IN A RECENT survey, high school honor students criticized their parents most for having failed to discuss with them the subject of human sexuality. Two-thirds of these students had never been told anything about sex by their parents. The others had received only cursory information, and that was faulty and garbled.[339]

Information about sex—frequently erroneous and steeped in negative emotionalism—is most often received from young people's peer groups, usually through the medium of bad jokes, and then from their parents; very little comes from public schools and similar institutions. Most of those who learn the basic facts of their sexuality learn them too late to help them through the initial period of sexual adjustment; for example, in another survey, about two-thirds of the boys who were told about sexual intercourse by their parents already knew about it. About 70% of the women canvassed in another study reported that they had been led to believe (chiefly by their mothers) that sex was dirty.[43]

Why this distressing situation is so common is quite simple: parents are filled with shame and guilt about sex, and are themselves painfully uncertain in what they genuinely believe about sexuality and sexual behavior. They are reluctant to admit to this confusion, and they often have little valid information on the subject. Rectifying this state of affairs is, however, not a simple matter. One might readily ask how young people can be trained in a healthy attitude toward sex when the adult society in which they live is unable to reach a consensus on sexual matters. If agreement, for instance, cannot be reached on the moral right of married adults to have free access to contraceptive information, or to engage in whatever kinds of sexual activity they wish in the privacy of their bedrooms, how can agreement on a moral or legal code of sexual behavior for the young and unmarried be expected? It is indeed unfortunate, but nonetheless true, that to date there is no clearly accepted or acceptable code of sexual beliefs and behavior in our society.[290] Adults will have to resolve their own illogical and guilt-ridden sexual attitudes before the young in their charge can

1

become educated rather than indoctrinated. Until such time, perplexity and irrationality in the sexual sphere are liable to be perpetuated from one generation to another.

Laymen and scientists alike too often are strangely reluctant to accept scientific findings, or even to give unbiased examination to new data in the field of human sexuality. When new investigations appear to lend support to time-honored prejudices, they are quickly accepted as being scientifically impeccable. However, when contemporary research fails to confirm cherished theories, the research tends to be discounted as suspect, its conclusions judged as being quite likely distorted by sample- and examiner-bias. Such suspicious attitudes have been seen in certain public reactions to the recent works of the Kinsey investigators and to the work of Masters and Johnson on the subject of human sexual response. The Kinsey workers were especially harassed.

> During the first year or two we were repeatedly warned of the dangers involved in the undertaking, and were threatened with specific trouble. There was some organized opposition, chiefly from a particular medical group. There were attempts by the medical association in one city to bring suit on the ground that we were practicing medicine without a license, police interference in two or three cities, investigation by a sheriff in one rural area, and attempts to persuade the University's administration to stop the study, or to prevent the publication of the results, or to dismiss the senior author from his university connection, or to establish a censorship over all publication emanating from the study.[180]

The many approaches to sex education range from advocating the avoidance of sexual experiences altogether to openly approving complete sexual freedom.[171, 290] At one extreme is the ostrich-like position that there should not be any sex education: a problem not faced squarely, it is hoped, will quietly disappear. Sexual conflicts, unhappy marriages, premarital pregnancies, abortions, and a general anxiety in sexual matters are all sad testimonials to the fallacy of this premise.

Next on the continuum of sex education theories is the "thou shalt not" approach, which treats sexuality as a gift from God that is to be used solely for the purpose of procreation. Judged from such a viewpoint, sexuality used for any other reason becomes immoral, animalistic, and defiling. The "thou shalt not" approach, however, obviously denies the basic fact that man's biological sex drive will, one way or another, find expression. It is thus less than realistic and probably produces more conflict than the total ignorance imposed by the first theory. It is not an exaggeration to suggest that the guilt-ridden, moralistic patients crowding the offices of marriage counselors, ministers, and psychotherapists have largely been molded by the "thou shalt not" philosophy of sex education.

The next approach on the continuum is that the fledgling should be inundated with facts. Sex is hereby stripped entirely of its veil of seclusiveness and sanctity, and is presented in an unembellished fashion without any suggestion of its emotional content. According to this approach, since sex is a physical drive, it should be discussed in terms of physiological data and in a straightforward manner, omitting any psychological considerations or emotional overtones. What this approach ignores is the incontestable fact that sexual activity is far more meaningful when it takes place between people who love or at least admire one another than it is, say, in masturbation or when love or affection is absent.

At the far end of this continuum is a viewpoint which might be called "sexual anarchy." This theory of sex education urges the removal of all blocks to sexual freedom and would grant unrestrained license to any act that individual sexual needs and desires might dictate, the only qualification being that no hurt or injury befalls others. Such permissiveness, of course, challenges the value of virginity and monogamy, as well as the other popularly approved sexual conditions. This precept implies that sexual activity should be regarded as fun and uninhibited by shame, guilt, tradition, or any code of morality. To a degree, such a permissive sexual ethic has much to commend it because so many of our taboos are senseless and act only to inhibit emotional growth, development, and happiness. However, man does not pass his days in isolation from his fellowman, and he cannot therefore expect to defy openly and consistently the mores of society, especially those of such emotionally laden content, without encountering society's wrath. Since most of us are influenced—willingly or not, directly or indirectly, consciously or unconsciously—by our associates, it is wiser to conduct ourselves in a manner that is fairly closely related to expected patterns of behavior (at least insofar as others know). Otherwise we shall find ourselves reprimanded, rejected, or even jailed, with a painful backwash of sociological and psychological problems.

The safest solution to this dilemma would appear to be a course of compromise and selectiveness among the various philosophies of sex education. Certainly sexual needs should be permitted expression; unadorned information about the physiological and psychological aspects of sex should be presented to all; and the Judeo-Christian traditions within which we live must be understood and dealt with sensibly in the framework of present-day society. Relative freedom of expression in sexual matters is justifiable because of individual differences in sexual preferences. Emotional and personality factors should be considered in striving for greatest sexual satisfaction and happiness. There are few absolutes in this world, and only bigots establish an inflexible code of sexual morality based solely on the rightness or wrongness of the commission or omission of a specific sexual act. Generally speaking, the consequence of a certain act upon society is a far better criterion in judging its morality.[182]

To expect healthy males and females to avoid or to inhibit all expression of their sexual needs and drives is unrealistic, to say the least. It is true that different cultures and subcultures permit varied means of expressing sexuality, and hardly any group fails to recognize that the need is present and that it *will* be expressed. It is well recognized that if these sexual needs are not expressed in one way, they will be in another. Thus, by denying healthy expressions of the sexual impulse, we are in reality encouraging its expression through the guise of psychoses, neuroses, personality maladjustments, guilt, inadequacy feelings, and true sexual perversions. (In the last part of the 19th century, a physician wrote in a medical journal that he did not believe that one bride in a hundred married with the expectation of sexual gratification.[47] What direction the expression of the denied sexual impulses took is a question the physician failed to answer.)

Much of a normal person's behavior is influenced by the inhibition of sexual impulses and the displacement of the expression of these needs into other channels. For example, we consciously are disturbed by the thought of premarital or extramarital sexual relationships, yet we show our unconscious interest in and perhaps desire for these very acts by joking about them or otherwise showing excessive interest. Consider how many of us laugh at or express horror over, yet voraciously follow every detail (however exaggerated) of, the less than conventional behavior of certain luminaries in the entertainment world. We thereby satisfy our own desires, conscious or unconscious, by identifying with these people, yet at the same time, by pointing an accusing finger at them, we avoid self-guilt. The tensions accrued from a denial of our own desires are thus drained off through joking and laughter.[119] Certainly this is not to say that control and appropriate expression of our sexual needs according to time and place are not desirable and necessary. But to set up unrealistic and unreasonable prohibitions, whether directly or through the mechanism of guilt, is setting the stage for trouble now or later.

In his two-volume survey of contemporary American attitudes on sex, love, marriage, and family relations (*The Folklore of Sex* and *The*

American Sexual Tragedy), Albert Ellis made a painstaking examination of stories, advertisements, books, magazines, newspapers, movies, and other mass communication media. His conclusion was that our woefully inadequate sex education, with the resulting neurotic repression and inhibition of normal sexual expression, has had a greatly deleterious effect on our lives and behavior.[121, 123] There is little doubt that our guilt, shame, and unrealistic demands and expectations in the realm of sex cause our distorted approach to and interest in this normal human need. Pictures of near-nudes on paperback books, the burgeoning sales of "girlie" magazines, the use of attractive women with seductive voices and voluptuous figures as modern-day hucksters to sell everything from shoe polish to salad dressing, the suggestive "Adults-only" ads for many films—all these point up the manner in which our mishandled sexual drives are being expressed. We allow this displaced sexual force to pervade almost every aspect of our lives. In a recent incident, the only way a department store owner of Birmingham, England, could quell the indignation of window shoppers inspecting his negligee-clad mannequins was to put wedding rings on the mannequins. This sort of prudery has been matched in America by the Society for Indecency to Naked Animals, which has fought to protect children from the sight of naked animals, particularly cattle, dogs, and cats.[306] The society (SINA) advocates the clothing of animals, at least if they appear in public or are in the presence of children.

A current slogan states: "Movies are better than ever." Why? Because films, according to their advertisements, contain more bedroom scenes and more snide sexual innuendoes than ever. If an enterprising producer were to make a motion picture of *Little Red Riding Hood* and wanted to assure its financial success, he need only designate it as an adult movie, with no children's tickets to be sold. (Mind you, this does not mean no tickets will be sold to children — just no children's tickets; after all, children are fair prey in this game also.) The advertisements might well portray Miss Hood as a buxom Lolita, being almost (but not quite) seduced by a lustful bare-chested human wolf. The wood-chopper, axe in hand, would be prominently displayed in the ads for those who like aggression tinged with sadism in their sexual fantasies. It follows that Grandmother is shown languishing on her queen-sized bed, dressed in a flimsy nightgown, her expression suggestive more of longing and sexual deprivation than of illness.

The sad conclusion to be drawn from all these particulars is that our thinking in sexual matters has become warped by the residuals of guilt, ignorance, and inappropriate means of contending with aggressive and erotic urges. It is not that the questionable advertisements, fiction, illustrations, and the like in our mass communication media have a strong effect upon our aggressive or sexual behavior;[178] to the contrary, they merely mirror our sexual anxieties. For instance, millions of Sunday School children have studied and know the gruesome details of a crucifixion, but not many youngsters play crucifixion games with their friends.[236] Confusion begets confusion, and we find a disturbing conflict in our social order: we live in an era in which illicit sexual relationships are severely condemned by society in general, while on the other hand these very acts are rendered enticing and desirable by purveyors of advertising.[53]

Too often parents rely on the supposition that if their children do not know about sex they will avoid it, and will consequently lead a sexually unblemished life. Nothing could be further from the truth. For example, parents will frequently withhold information on contraception and venereal diseases, or will recount only the dangers and shame of illegitimate pregnancy and VD, expecting these approaches to keep their children from engaging in premarital coitus. Yet the findings of the Kinsey group disclosed that only 44% of the unmarried women interviewed listed "fear of pregnancy" as a deterrent to sexual intercourse, and only 14% listed "fear of venereal disease" as a deterrent.[179]

Before the modern, swiftly effective cures for venereal diseases were available, and when these "social diseases" were greatly feared, people nonetheless readily engaged in sexual relations even with partners whose freedom from infection was not determined. Investigating the correlation between fear of VD and its incidence, one study showed that of psychologically normal men who had no fear of venereal infection, 15.4% contracted one of the diseases; of those who had moderate fear, the percentage rose to 20.8%; and of those who had a very strong fear, 15.3% became infected.[286]

A recent study of unmarried pregnant girls showed that they had received little or no sex education either from home or school, and that their mothers either lacked proper sex knowledge themselves or were unable or unwilling to give proper instruction to their daughters.[342] It by no means follows, however, that a girl's having an adequate knowledge of contraceptive devices is an assurance that she will use one of them if and when she has premarital sexual intercourse.[382] The evidence is to the contrary: many girls reason that contraception is the boy's responsibility, and that if they took it upon themselves to ensure that some contraceptive method were available, it would appear that they were both overly willing for coitus and premeditated in their behavior. Contraception apparently should become somebody's business, inasmuch as one in six brides in America is pregnant when she marries.[286] Curiously, many of these unwanted pregnancies occur among the religiously devout who, despite their determination to "refrain from sin," somehow lose control of their emotions and get swept into the act of sexual intercourse.[170]

The World Health Organization states that ignorance, not knowledge, of sexual matters is the cause of "sexual misadventure."[55] The clinical experience of most psychotherapists and marriage counselors certainly lends support to this viewpoint, as does the subsequent strife and heartbreak of parents and their children who become victims of "sexual misadventure." That parents possess little enough accurate information on sex may be true; but what they do have should be shared in an open and honest manner with their children, even though their own guilt and confusion in the area often make this a most difficult task. The important thing, nevertheless, is their openness with their children on this most crucial subject. For parents who do not have accurate or adequate information, or who are actually afraid or ashamed to talk with their children on the subject of sex, there are books, physicians, psychologists, and various agencies from which the children (and parents for that matter) can get a sex education with a minimum of emotional stress. Even here, however, there is danger of unwittingly selecting an emotionally oriented, factually unscientific book or a counselor who has his own problems. It is unfortunately true that except for adequate knowledge of reproductive processes, physicians as a group are grievously ignorant and actually rather prudish in matters of human sexuality.[230] Furthermore, it has been established that because training of ministers in marriage counseling is grossly inadequate, and because they are lamentably uninformed or plainly misinformed, only 15% of such counseling service can be considered competent.[317]

The impact on marriages of adequate early sex information can be judged from Clifford Kirkpatrick's analysis of the components of successful marital adjustment.[186] The subjects of his survey ranked "adequate sex information in childhood" third in importance among the leading ten factors considered fundamental to a successful marriage, falling behind only "happiness of parents' marriage" and "adequate length of acquaintanceship, courtship, and engagement."

It has been speculated that ancient man's need for religion developed as a result of his discovering that there were various elements in the world with which he could not cope (severe weather, famine, etc.). To overcome these types of misfortune, he conjured up a supreme being who had the power to solve problems by being able

to do those things which man could not do for himself.[114] In order
to be able to call on his deity in time of danger, man had to pay a
price — to give up pleasures, as well as remain good and pure. By
forswearing pleasures, he underwent a self-sacrificial process which

*"The Board of Education requires me to give you some basic
information on sex, reproduction and other disgusting filth."*

Fig. 1-1.   Reproduced by special permission of *Playboy* magazine. Copyright
1967 by HMH Publishing Co., Inc.

somehow was supposed to please his god. Furthermore, through punishing himself in minor ways, he mystically transferred to his godhead the responsibility for the solution of difficulties beyond his capabilities. Needing his god's help, and recognizing the surpassing pleasure of sexual activity, man quite naturally made his sexuality a focal point in his efforts to please or appease the deity. In effect, man might have said, on the one hand, "Protect and help me, and I shall sacrifice my sexuality for your protection"; and on the other hand, "I have sinned, I have been evil, and I offer the sacrifice of my sexuality in expiation for my sinfulness."

Few people who have been in the position to observe the results would deny that probably the greatest detriment to the sexual-mental health of mankind is certain rigid, puritanical, guilt-instilling religions. Protagonists of such religions have succeeded remarkably well in indoctrinating their followers in the belief that sex is dirty and animalistic, to be looked upon only as a necessary evil—with emphasis placed on the word "evil."[103] This attitude is best exemplified in the prudery of the Victorian era, when "decent" women, not daring to expect pleasure from the sexual act, suffered it only because of their "duty" to their husbands.

It is somewhat surprising to find rigidity and bigotry still permeating even the most orthodox of present-day religions, considering the series of changes, however belated, in attitudes toward sex and marriage that have occurred throughout history commencing with the Old and New Testaments of the Bible. Early Israelite tribes permitted polygynous marriages, and women were regarded as little more than chattel; marriages were primarily of legal rather than of religious concern. Some men were left without female partners as a result of polygyny, and a more equal distribution of women became necessary; thus was monogamy evolved. Mosaic laws (detailed in the books of Leviticus, Deuteronomy, and, to a lesser degree, Exodus), which are the foundations of prevailing Christian-Judaic morality, were assumed to have divine inspiration; gradually marriage, together with sex, came to be regarded as belonging to a sphere higher than simple legality. These laws, however, have been reinterpreted many times over the centuries and, generally, they have been made to conform to the requirements of changing times, although too often change has lagged behind need by several generations.

We are resistant to a reexamination and reinterpretation of religious precepts, despite the fact that in retrospect we see that those changes which have managed to come about have been necessary and beneficial. We would not think of buying servants or slaves today, and we certainly would not keep the wife and children of the servant while freeing the man, but these were acceptable practices in early Judaic tradition (Exodus 21). Present-day civil law prohibits marriage between close relatives, yet Abraham in good conscience married his half-sister Sarah (Genesis 20). Jacob, Abraham's grandson, would be arrested today for bigamy, yet in his day his having two wives was wholly permissible.

Much of the ancient interpretation of Mosaic laws—indeed, the necessity for the laws in the first place—was based on the need for larger and stronger tribes. The rule that women were to be considered unclean and untouchable during the five days of menstruation and for seven days afterwards (Leviticus 15) was undoubtedly based on the fact that these twelve days were (and are) generally considered to be unfavorable for conception; man should not, therefore, waste his sperm lest he be punished by God for not adding to the strength of his tribe. It also appears that the laws prohibiting bestiality and homo-sexuality, and the judgment that such sexual acts among men were considered to be much more reprehensible than if women were the participants, were based on the need not to waste precious sperm and thereby perhaps impede tribal growth. Since there is no loss of sperm in lesbianism, no such rigid prohibitions against it developed as they did concerning male homosexuality

Much has been said about Onan's "spilling his seed on the ground," as recorded in Genesis. This story involved Onan's being ordered by God to marry, as was the custom, and have children by his deceased brother Er's wife. Onan refused to do so, apparently employing *coitus interruptus* (premature withdrawal) as a birth control method—"spilling of his seed on the ground"—because any children born of the union would have borne Er's name and not his own. God was angered by Onan's defiance of His orders, and struck him dead. The misinterpretations of this story have had severe repercussions on Western sexual stability over the centuries. Onanism somehow became enlarged to imply a method of birth control. Furthermore, some time during the 17th century the "spilling of seed" and masturbation became equated, masturbation thenceforth being condemned as sinful and producing devastation (see Chapter 14).

Traditionally, the temptations of the flesh have been attributed to women and their presence. The preferential position of men in society apparently influenced the unconscious mind of early lawmakers and the traditions emanating from their decrees. A typical example is the Old Testament assertion that when a woman gave birth to a male child she was "unclean" for forty days, but when she gave birth to a female child she was "unclean" for eighty days (Leviticus 12). Woman's role as a sexual temptress is portrayed early in the Old Testament. In Chapter 3 of Genesis, Adam and Eve succumb to temptations and Eve is designated as the instigator of the evil act. Later in Genesis (Chapter 19), Lot and his daughters, who had survived the destruction of a sinful city, found themselves involved in incestuous relationships. Once more the onus for illicit sexuality, in this instance incest, was placed on women—the daughters—because they supposedly gave Lot sufficient wine to render him incapable of knowing what he was doing, and forthwith seduced him. Lot would appear to be absolved of any responsibility for the act, and the whole story but another attempt to assess women with the blame for illicit sexual acts and to portray them as vehicles of sinfulness. But the story of Lot and his daughters is not convincing: if Lot was so drunk that he did not know what he was doing, the chances are that he could not have performed the sexual act anyway, because male sexual functioning is severely repressed by heavy intake of alcohol.

Contrary to common belief, Jesus Christ himself taught very little on the subject of sex. The vast majority of sexual proscriptions associated with and attributed to Christianity are actually outgrowths of the thought and writings of later Christian theologians, and most of this moral theology was not actually propounded until long after Christ's death. Paul was probably the first Christian to speak out specifically on sexual morality. He emphasized the need for marriage as a means to avoid fornication, although he apparently considered sexual abstinence a more admirable goal in life (I Corinthians 6 and 7). The writings of St. Augustine during the 4th century A.D. have probably had as much impact upon prevailing 20th-century sexual attitudes as any other single force, in that he severely condemned premarital and extramarital sexual outlets, including bestiality, homosexuality, and especially masturbation. The Roman Catholic Church in time came to idealize celibacy, with the highest level of male achievement being total rejection of all life's pleasures, while women could expect to reach their greatest glory only through permanent virginity.

Virginity and purity have long been regarded as one and the same thing; the virgin birth of Jesus, the springing of Athena full grown from Zeus's forehead, and the atypical genesis of other deities are testimonials to that view.[10] It is therefore not difficult to understand why concepts of sex and sin (impurity) are so closely bonded, or how indulgence in sexual acts, or even thoughts, in marriage or out— however licit the acts may be—can easily produce feelings of guilt and emotional stress. When young people are given harsh and rigid

instruction in sexual matters, which is not counterbalanced with a
rationale for sexual morality, then guilt must be relied upon to control
sexual behavior. Young people incorporate the rules into their emotional makeup, but if and when the rules are broken, emotional stress
often results. Far too frequently, the marriage ceremony does not serve
as a conjurer's wand to eradicate the "thou shalt not" and "sex is
dirty and should be avoided" attitudes handed down from parents

MARRiAGE

Fig. 1-2.   Used by permission from VOICES—*The Art and Science of Psychotherapy,* Vol. 1, No. 1: one of the Seven Ages of Man. Artist, John Severin.

(and society) to children. Consequently, brides and grooms too often find themselves caught up in the conception that sex equals sin, and hence suffer from such unfortunate reactions as guilt, pain, frigidity, impotency, and premature ejaculation. These reactions persist long after the marriage ceremony, even when on a conscious level the couple regards sex as something permissible and proper. It is expecting too much to think that sex can be transformed from something vile and sullying into something beautiful and ennobling by a mere recitation of the words of the marriage ceremony.

With the development of Christian and Judaic theology came the evolution of an ethical code governing marriage, which limited morally acceptable sexual activity to the marriage bed and considered sinful any deviation from this limitation. When a code is unrealistic and unyielding and stands as an unavoidable obstacle in an individual's pathway, some sort of suffering is almost inevitable. Furthermore, recent research findings in England give little comfort to those who believe that religious convictions alone are necessarily a deterrent to premarital sexuality: the atheists interviewed had had less sexual experience than either Protestants or Roman Catholics.[337] An individual should judge rationally the many ramifications of a moral code, and arrive at his own dispassionate conclusions regarding the probable effects of various sexual behavior on himself, his partner, and society. He will then be much more likely to manage his sexuality in a manner which is normal and healthy, and which is also free from anxieties, guilt, and abnormalities.

Fortunately for the mental health of society, the outmoded and oftentimes harmful dictates of certain rigid religious groups are being analyzed more and more on a plane of objectivity, their validity being assessed according to their pertinence to present-day circumstances of life. When we mature to the point that we no longer feel compelled to impose our personal biases on others, and when we are able to abide by the Golden Rule, that farsighted and sensible guide to all human behavior in its unequivocal emphasis on the equal rights of all men—"Therefore all things whatsoever ye would that men should do to you, do ye even so to them: for this is the law and the prophets" (Matthew 7:12)—we will encounter and engender fewer emotional difficulties, including those of a sexual nature.

An extension of the precepts of the Golden Rule is the granting of relative freedom of behavior in sexual matters because there *are* individual differences in sexual drives and preferences. Perhaps this aspect of sex education would better be termed "sexual democracy" or "freedom from sexual fascism." In his excellent discussion on sexual fascism,[110] Albert Ellis points out that some people arbitrarily evaluate certain sexual behavior—their own, of course—as being right and superior to other sexual behavior, and will go to great lengths in imposing their viewpoints on other people. An individual's failure to comply with these arbitrary standards is tantamount to his being an anti-Christ, a pervert, or a sexual inferior. The sexual fascist neither understands nor cares that women respond to sex relations differently from men; he therefore expects women to employ and respond to the same sexual techniques that men do. These bigots live by the traditional double standard of morality for men and women. For example, girls must be virgins until marriage, while boys are allowed, even expected, to have many premarital experiences; women are much more condemned for having children out of wedlock than the men who father the children. This unfair dichotomy in values is an obvious outgrowth of the patriarchal customs of early biblical days, but it is nonetheless perpetuated by the code of the modern-day sex fascist.

It has long been recognized by authorities in the field of mental health that a crucial factor in people's emotional health and adjustment is the maintenance of "a reasonable degree of flexibility and freedom from fixation in the major aspects of their lives."[119] We do not expect all people to eat or even to like asparagus; and indeed we do not expect those who do eat asparagus to want to eat it all the time. However, when it comes to sex, the bigot's philosophy does not allow for any behavioral flexibility, or for the experimentation that adds so much to the adventuresomeness and spice which the normal, sexually mature person incorporates into his sexual expression.

Any student of human sexual behavior soon recognizes the extreme difficulty encountered in trying to define precisely what is, and what is not, sexual deviation, perversion, and abnormality. For instance, coitus accomplished in any position other than the husband's being above his wife is too often condemned out of hand as deviant, and something not to be practiced either occasionally or regularly. By extension, non-coital sexual activities, such as masturbation, petting, and oral-genital contact, would be ruled out. Such rigidity poses a unique problem, in light of research findings which indicate that masturbation is commonly practiced by most men and women, both single and married; that oral-genital contact is found to occur in most marriages in the upper socio-economic-educational stratum of society; and that more than one-half of women prefer, and respond more intensely to, non-coital methods of stimulation than to sexual intercourse.[119, 179, 180, 215]

The man-above coital position is not widely assumed anywhere except in the United States and a few other countries; among boys of

Arab countries, masturbation is little practiced and is considered a less acceptable activity than homosexuality.[122] These are only two examples of the significant differences found in attitudes and evaluations concerning sexual behavior in various cultures. No one is justified in saying that the sexual practices of one culture are proper and normal, while a different set of practices in another culture is improper and abnormal. It cannot be overemphasized that there are individual human differences which extend into every aspect of life, including expression of sexuality; and any valid program of sex education must take into account these differences. The rights of others must be respected, which means an acceptance of their tastes and pleasures, however different they may be from our own. No one has the moral (and should not have a legal) right to force his ethical views, any more than his aesthetic ones, on others.

Finally, there must be an appreciation of the role which emotions and personality play in the creation of sexual attitudes. In a meaningful study by A. H. Maslow,[200] the importance of emotions and of personality factors in marital happiness and sexual adjustment is clearly indicated. Following are some of his related findings.

Women who rate high in dominance feelings (or self-esteem) are considered to be self-confident, self-assured, and to possess a high evaluation of the self. They display feelings of superiority while showing a lack of shyness, self-consciousness, and embarrassment. Women who empirically rate low in dominance feelings (low self-esteem) show the opposite personality characteristics, while middle-dominance subjects fall some place midway between the two extremes. Because dominance traits affect behavior as well as feelings, high-dominance females are much more likely than low-dominance subjects to masturbate, to have premarital sexual intercourse, to volunteer for sex research studies, not to shun pelvic examinations, and such like.[200]

Despite, however, the fact that Jewish women are generally found to be higher in both dominance feelings and dominance behavior than Catholic and Protestant women, they show a higher percentage of virginity than either of the other two religious groups. Women who are *strongly* religious—whether Jewish, Catholic, or Protestant—are more likely to be virgins, not to masturbate, and to have lower ratings for "sex attitude" (a term used by Maslow to describe personal reactions to sexuality) than women with less pronounced religious feelings.

Women of low dominance feelings avoid the upper position during sexual intercourse while those with very high dominance feelings frequently prefer that position. The low-dominance man or woman often dislikes or is afraid of sex. The most satisfactory marriages are those in which the husband equals or is somewhat (but not markedly) superior to his wife in dominance feelings. On the other hand, if the wife has higher dominance feelings than the husband, or if the husband is very markedly more dominant than the wife, social and sexual maladjustments are likely to be found, unless both are very secure persons. Moderately sexed women are more likely to reach orgasm during sexual activity if they feel loved and secure than if these components are weak or lacking entirely. In the matter of sheer sexual satisfaction, a monogamous state is preferable to a promiscuous choice of sexual partners, but monogamy does not satisfy the emotional needs of ego-insecure people.

A high-dominance woman is attracted only to a high-dominance man and wants him to be straightforward, passionate, and somewhat violent or animalistic in their lovemaking. She wishes him to proceed quickly without prolonged wooing. The middle-dominance woman prefers gentle, prolonged wooing where sex, as such, is woven into a pattern of loving words, tenderness, soft music, and low lights. As Maslow puts it, "The high-dominance woman unconsciously wants to be raped; the middle-dominance woman wants to be seduced."[207] He might have added that the low-dominance woman wishes to be left alone.

People who are rated high in "sex attitude" appreciate sex for its own sake and wholeheartedly approve of it, while people who are rated very low are highly puritanical and inhibited in their sexual attitudes, and reject sex as something disgusting. A large portion of the high-dominance subjects like and engage in oral-genital activity; and generally speaking, the higher the dominance (with ego-security held constant), the greater attractiveness the external genitalia of the sexual partner hold for them. In marriages of high-dominance people, the couples very frequently have experimented with almost every form of sexual activity known to sexologists. While these sexual acts would likely be considered pathological by low-dominance subjects, they contain no pathological connotation for high-dominance subjects. Maslow is thus led to conclude: "It would appear that no single sexual act can *per se* be called abnormal or perverted. It is only abnormal or perverted individuals who can commit abnormal or perverted acts. That is, the dynamic meaning of the act is far more important than the act itself."[207] Maslow's work fairly well shows the importance of the emotions and personality factors in both sexual and marital adjustment.

Repressions and inhibitions, which apparently have their inception in very early childhood, are the most active agents in female sexual unresponsiveness. There are, in addition, marked differences in many of the factors incorporated in the "marital happiness" and "sexual adjustment" scales[2] of two groups of college wives (one, sexually responsive, and the other, sexually unresponsive).

Marital happiness depends to an important degree upon sexual adjustment, and sexual adjustment in turn is related to sexual responsiveness. (Clinical observation is that there can be marital happiness and sexual adjustment even with low sexual responsiveness.) A prominent early researcher in the field of marriage, G. V. Hamilton,[152] found that almost three-quarters of divorced women interviewed did not have orgasms during their first year of marriage. Another renowned researcher in this field, H. J. Locke,[202] found that 90% of happily married women found pleasure in sex while only about 50% of divorced women had done so. The evidence is clear that early sex education and certain experiences relating to childhood and family background are related to orgasm adequacy in women.[309]

Certain physiological anomalies have also been found to be related to sex education and to emotions. For example, most women who suffer from premenstrual tension and difficult menstruation have a background of parental discord and sex education from a mother who presented it in a deprecating manner.[313] Many other scientifically controlled studies point clearly to the fact that sexual adjustment and satisfaction are directly correlated with emotional stability and maturity, and having received an adequate sex education.

The only way our society is going to achieve proper sexual stability and mental health, which are undisputed requirements for maturity, is to instigate and persevere with a sound sex education for everyone. This goal means that those who are in a position to instruct must freely admit to what they do not know, at the same time teaching that which they know to be the truth. They must educate, not indoctrinate; teach facts, not fallacies; formulate a code of ethics, not asceticism; be objective, not subjective; be democratic, not autocratic; and seek knowledge, not emotionally biased constructs. This will be difficult because most people have grown up in a culture which produces and espouses most or all of the negative agents in sexual ignorance and maladjustment. Richard Starnes in the *New York World Telegram and Sun* sums up this problem fairly well with his comment that "never in the history has a nation talked so much about prudery from a basically horizontal position."

It is incumbent upon each individual to develop his own code of acceptable sexual behavior, and each must decide how he is to present that ethic in the sex education of his children — an instructional process, incidentally, that begins at a far earlier age for the child than many suspect. There is clear scientific evidence that sex education begins long before nursery school,[54] the first intimate mother-infant contact after birth being the start of it.

Experiments, in which infant monkeys were raised in isolation except for wire "mother substitutes," and were deprived of the usual early affectional relationships with the mother and other monkeys, demonstrated that without interaction with their own kind, monkeys displayed disorganized and psychotic-like behavior. They became so confused in what was expected of them by way of comportment that even as physically mature animals, they could not engage in sexual intercourse because they did not know how to assume coital positions.[154, 155] However, when terrycloth coverings were placed over the wire "mothers" so that the infant monkeys might have a softer "mother" to which they could cling and cuddle up, they did not become so sexually disorganized. Furthermore, when the baby monkeys were allowed to play and to cuddle one another, they at least learned to perform the coital act, even though the consummation was still far from normal because of the social and maternal deprivation. It is evident from these studies that the sexual training of these primates commenced at birth.[54, 154, 155]

Sex education of the human infant also begins at or shortly after birth. The way in which mothers and fathers love, fondle, and even hold their infant; the soothing or harsh sound of parents' voices, which comes to be associated with love or with rejection and hostility; the feel of the parents' skin; the smell of their bodies—all these factors significantly affect a child and influence his emerging sexual attitudes and conduct. Parents initiate a child's sexual tutelage in the earliest days of his life, whether they realize it or whether it is their intention to do so. Even when parents avoid discussing sex altogether, the child nevertheless detects their attitudes, stressful or happy, through non-verbal communications.[54]

Hopefully, the material in this book will assist the reader toward a better knowledge of himself and his sexuality, and will encourage him to prepare others for a healthy, well-adjusted sex life. There follows an article[232] by the author setting forth his personal attitudes (as well as his biases) about human sexuality.

WHAT I WOULD TELL MY DAUGHTER ABOUT PREMARITAL SEX*

As a part of the course in Marriage and Family Life which I teach at the University of Houston, students ask frank questions about sex and receive equally frank and direct answers. One question which is asked each semester is "What would you tell your daughter about

*Reprinted by permission of *Sexology* magazine. ©Sexology Corp., 1966.

premarital sex?" My answer was recorded last semester by one of the students and a written transcript is presented here as one view which parents might consider when giving sex information and training to their children.

This question about one's daughter, I tell my students, is often received by psychologists who talk on problems of sex. Most often it is meant to embarrass the psychologist, the questioner assuming that the psychologist will talk out of both sides of his mouth; that is, he might make certain liberal statements about sexual matters to the public, but when it comes to his own daughter he will forget his academic views and become as rigid, as demanding, as moralistic as the next father.

This question, "What would you tell your daughter about premarital sex?" is one which cannot be answered with one short statement because a whole lifetime of living sets the stage for the answer. But let me at least give you some of my own thinking and views on the question you raise.

I will assume you mean a daughter who is roughly of your age—that is college-level. Basically, of course, there must first be a healthy attitude toward sex in the home. If the parents are well adjusted in the area of sex, if they have a healthy attitude toward sex, then the children, also, will likely have a healthy attitude toward sex and will, in general, react about sex in much the same manner as have the parents.

Parenthetically, I might add that the converse of this is also true—if the parents have an unhealthy attitude towards sex, if they are filled with guilt and repressions in this area, then their children are also likely to learn the same disturbed attitude and suffer from it throughout their lives.

I would want my daughter to know the biological and physiological sexual structure of the male and of the female and I'd want her to thoroughly understand the similarities and differences between these two sexes.

I'd want her to know not only the biological and physiological makeup but the psychological makeup. I'd want her to know that males, for example, are made more easily sexually excited than are females and are made easily excited by different methods and different techniques than are females. I'd want her to know what these techniques are so she might avoid their use in many situations, but, also, so she could make use of them in appropriate situations.

I'd want consistency in all matters if possible, but certainly I would want consistency in sexual matters in the home. I think that a parent has to be consistent within himself in order to produce sane and predictable ideas in the daughter; a parent must feel at ease with his sexual ideas if he is to present the same attitude and approach to sex day in and day out. He should come to his own conclusions as to what is proper before he makes a statement or shows his attitude which his children are to adopt.

I furthermore would wish that both parents would be consistent between themselves; that is, that the mother and the father would have consistent ideas about sex—that the father should not make certain demands and present one set of ideas while the mother makes different demands and presents a different set of ideas.

Inconsistency can only produce confusion and insecurity within the child. If a child accepts the ideas of the father, frequently he feels guilty about not accepting the ideas of the mother, and on the other hand, if he accepts the ideas of the mother, he feels guilty about rejecting the ideas of the father. The child has to learn to depend upon one set of rules and regulations, not a new set with each parent.

Equally important with these first two points covering consistency is the fact that the home should be somewhat consistent with the outside world. Now, this certainly cannot always be done in sexual matters because society is too varied in the demands it makes and what it expects of its members, depending upon what sub-culture and area one encounters.

Therefore, I would want my daughter to understand that there will be some inconsistencies in society's expectations with what she is taught in our home and that she must understand what it is that society expects and demands. She must understand the attitudes of bigots, the people whom Dr. Albert Ellis has called the sexual fascists; she must understand that these people disagree with any person who does not conform to their way of thinking, demanding and behaving, and that they are ready to condemn and even persecute those who do not follow to the letter their unbending ideas.

I'd want her to know of methods and techniques of sexual outlet other than sexual intercourse, and I'd want her to know the values of these methods. I would want her to know that masturbation and petting are perfectly normal modes of behavior which can and will satisfy sexual urges and which at the same time do not carry with them some of the same problems that are found resulting from sexual intercourse.

I would want my daughter—and my son, too, for that matter— to have a kind and fair attitude toward her fellow man. I'd want her to be fair and ethical in all relationships, including sex. There should be no cheating, no lying, no taking advantage of others. I'd want her to understand that, when her behavior in any way harms another person or harms herself, that this is behavior which should be reconsidered because it is oftentimes behavior which is truly evil.

I'd want her to understand that sex is a game for many boys and young men, and that she must be prepared for lies and trickery. Seduction is an ego boost for boys and for men who feel sexually inferior. She must understand how boys get this attitude from a society which has a disturbed attitude toward sex, and that this behavior is not a personal thing directed toward her.

For these boys and emotionally disturbed men, seduction is an act which is designed to increase, albeit only momentarily, their ego strength, and they are not necessarily after sex as such. When she finds men behaving in such a manner, she must understand that this is their problem and deal with it accordingly.

I'd want her to understand the views of various religions and to understand how the unwise use of some of the ideas and ideals from these religions can produce guilt and repressions. I'd furthermore want her to understand guilt and repression, and if she avoids sex to do so because of rational factors and not guilt, because guilt in this area, as well as in others, leads to many problems, and sexual conflicts resulting from guilt can be devastating.

If, with all this information, along with the attitude and background of her home, she still decided on sexual intercourse, then I would want her to certainly know about and have access to contraceptive devices. This would include information on pregnancy and venereal diseases, which, incidentally, should be made available to all children at an early age.

I'd want her to know that, basically, I think one is usually significantly better off if he or she avoids premarital sexual intercourse, especially if in the teens, and would in most cases, be better off to use masturbation or petting when sexual expression is necessary.

But, if she makes the other decision, that is, to have sexual intercourse before marriage, I would want her to know that, while I might think she has made a foolish mistake, no matter what she does along these lines, so long as she does not hurt herself or others, I am with her and my respect and love will not change. And I would hope, and I believe it would follow, that, if she ever needed a friend, that she would turn first to her father and/or mother and know that she would receive support from either of us.

These are the principles in which I believe and are the ones by which I raised my daughter who is now happily married. I do not know whether or not she had premarital sexual intercourse—and frankly, I couldn't care less; I respect her and love her too much even to question her, although I could ask and she could answer without embarrassment to either of us.

I am pleased that she has an open and healthy attitude toward sex and that she does not have the guilt or shame or fear which causes sexual repressions which can later build to such an intense peak that they erupt into sexual or neurotic acting out. Because of her views on sex—among other things—she is likely to remain emotionally stable and healthy.

CHAPTER 2

The Development and Differentiation of Male and Female Genitalia

ALTHOUGH it is commonly held that men and women are vastly different creatures, the truth of the matter is they are quite similar. Martians, for instance, would undoubtedly encounter considerable difficulty in discerning the difference, when such externals as clothing and hairstyles are often so nearly identical. Generally speaking, the concept of a "typical male" and a "typical female" reflects more of customs and cultural attitudes than of actual anatomical differences.

Even the sexual systems, where the primary differences lie, are quite similar. From the early embryonic through the mature adult stages of human development, there is a marked likeness both in the structure and function of the male and female reproductive systems. The completely developed genitalia (internal and external sexual or reproductive organs) of the adult man and woman maintain homologous (similar) but modified structures and have complementary functions. The most obvious of the original homologous structures are the male penis and female clitoris. The makeup of the two sexual systems correspond and are counterparts of one another more than they are different in development, structure, and function. Furthermore, Kinsey and his co-workers concluded from their monumental investigations into human sexual behavior that "in spite of the widespread and oft-repeated emphasis on the supposed differences between female and male sexuality, we fail to find any anatomic or physiologic basis for such differences."[170]

The development of the human sexual systems is quite complicated. The genitalia of both sexes originate from the same anatomical structure, or cell mass. In the early days of the embryonic stage—the first eight weeks after conception—the reproductive system appears to be merely a genital thickening on the posterior outer layer (epithelium) of the embryonic body cavity. In a very young embryo, there is no distinguishable difference between the two sexes in this thickening, and the sexual system is said to be in an indifferent, or undifferentiated, stage. In time, the genital thickening or cell mass grows and the specific organs of the two sexual systems develop and become differentiated (structurally distinguishable). This differentiation, whether in the male or the female, results from a special chromosomal pattern which was established in the embryo at conception.

Male sperm contain either one X (female) or one Y (male) chromosome; and sperm containing X- and Y-bearing chromosomes are, in a unique way, produced in exactly equal numbers. The male sperm is the sex-determinant of the offspring, in that of the 200,000,000 to 500,000,000 sperm contained in the average ejaculate, only one will penetrate and fertilize the female ovum or egg. If an X-bearing sperm fertilizes the ovum, an XX, or female, child is conceived; a Y-bearing sperm will produce an XY, or male, child.

In their early formative periods, the internal organs *(gonads* and *ducts)* of both sexes follow an identical course of development and are sexually indistinguishable. Most of the structures in the embryonic generative system either disappear, degenerate, or are replaced by new developments long before the end of the fetal life. During the undifferentiated period, a genital gland (gonad) originates from the genital ridge which has developed from the early epithelial cell mass. As the gonad grows, it pulls away from the ridge and later partially forms the male or female sex structure.

The primitive genital ducts are exceptions to the process of early degeneration of the embryonic generative system. All embryos develop two systems of ducts, *Wolffian* and *Mullerian,* before ultimate sex is established. These ducts serve as forerunners for specific sexual development. The Wolffian ducts will evolve into the male genital structure, and the Mullerian into the female genitalia.

The embryo of about six weeks possesses undifferentiated sex glands and both male and female genital ducts. The internal sexual transformation, first observable about six weeks after conception, starts with the differentiation of the gonads into male *testes* or female *ovaries.* The gonads produce procreative "seeds," the male *sperm* and the 'female *ova,* and are also involved in the hormonal interplay of the body. After maleness or femaleness has been established by the gonads' development, the ducts of the opposite sex for each embryo—that is, Mullerian in the male and Wolffian in the female—remain rudimentary or began to degenerate.

When the male embryo is four to six weeks old, a series of primordial tubules develop and grow to make connection with the Wolffian (mesonephric) duct which terminates in the urogenital sinus (opening). From this mesonephric network the male sex system is partially formed.

In the male, the testicle is the first sexual structure to be developed from the genital ridge. Some of the mesonephric or Wolffian ducts and tubules persist and grow to form another network of tubes called the *epididymis.* The epididymis is a swelling attached to each testicle; within the swelling is a compactly wound tube, approximately twenty feet in length. The coiled tube is positioned at the side and top of the testicle, and serves to receive, house until maturity, and then convey the sperm to the *vas deferens,* a small connecting tube approximately eighteen inches in length. The vas deferens takes a circuitous path from the epididymis of each testicle in the scrotum, through the inguinal canal and into the abdominal cavity, where it connects with the *seminal vesicle* ("seed" reservoir) to form the ejaculatory duct.

The seminal vesicles are pouch-like structures located behind the bladder and adjacent to the top of the prostate gland. The ejaculatory duct from each side passes through the prostate and ends in the urethra. The *prostate gland,* composed of muscular and glandular tissues, surrounds the upper portion of the urethra and is located between the bladder and base of the penis. The male *urethra,* a canal within the penis, conveys urine from the bladder and semen from the seminal vesicles. Within the prostate gland, the connection is made between the canal from the bladder and the genital ducts at a small elevation on the floor of the prostatic urethra known as the *verumontanum* or *prostatic utricle,* and they then continue as one tube through the length of the penis.

While the male genital-urethral system is in the process of formation, the Mullerian ducts, for the most part, degenerate and disappear. The proximal ends, however, are preserved and become appendages to the testes *(appendix testes),* and the fused distal ends become a tiny pouch *(prostatic pouch)* in the floor of the prostatic portion of the urethra. The pouch is part of the elevated area, the verumontanum.

In the female embryo, the Mullerian ducts follow the pattern of the Wolffian ducts in appearance and development. The upper ends of these ducts become the uterine *(Fallopian)* tubes, projections which grow eventually to cup over the ovary and in some way pick up each ovum as it is discharged from the ovary. In the embryo's seventh

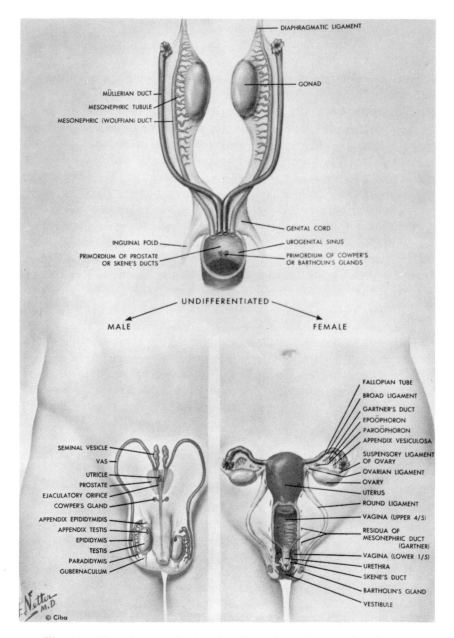

Fig. 2-1.   Homologues of internal male and female genitalia; development from undifferentiated into differentiated stage. Copyright *The Ciba Collection of Medical Illustrations* by Frank H. Netter, M.D.

week, the Mullerian ducts fuse and terminate in the urogenital sinus, forming the Mullerian tubercle, which is destined to become the uterus (womb), the upper four-fifths of the vagina, and the hymen (maidenhead).

The *uterus,* a heavily muscled structure shaped somewhat like a flattened pear, is the organ in which the fetus develops. The uterus has a lateral-anterior opening on each side leading to the Fallopian tubes, which are the passageways for transport of the ova from the ovaries and the structures in which fertilization takes place. In the female, the atrophied Wolffian ducts are functionless. They form a tiny vestigial line which is involuted in the roof of the vagina and runs parallel to the urethra.

Certain accessory genital glands are homologous in the male and female. For instance, that part of the sexual structure which becomes the prostate in the male becomes the *Skene ducts* (para-urethral ducts) in the female. That part which develops into a woman's *Bartholin glands*—major vestibular glands which open on the labia majora just within the vestibule of the vagina—differentiates into a man's *Cowper's glands,* which secrete a precoital fluid in preparation of the urethra for easy passage of the sperm. The Cowper's glands of the mature male are located just below the prostate, and each is about the size of a pea.

The growth, development, and differentiation of the external genitalia of both sexes are similar to what has been described for the internal genitalia. In the male, the developing penis with its penile urethra parallels the development in the female of vagina, uterus, and intrauterine formations. The external genitalia are first defined at about the sixth week of embryonic formation, and for a period of another week or so they are indifferent in appearance. By the end of the seventh week the sex of the embryo becomes distinguishable by external characteristics. These first criteria for sexual distinction are not entirely reliable, however, and errors are sometimes made in distinguishing male from female at this early stage.

The external genitalia of male and female arise at a common site, located between the umbilical cord and the tail of the embryo. This site becomes the *genital tubercle*. It is at first an undifferentiated area, then becomes a phallus-like projection which eventually develops into male or female external sexual organs. In about the fourth week of prenatal life, the front area of the genital tubercle begins to form a vertical groove. This produces a separation of the anal pit from the genital ridge, the separating area being known as the *primitive perineum*.

Two urethral folds or swellings *(labioscrotal swellings)* develop on the elevated margin (lateral and parallel) of the urethral groove, and differentiate into the female labia majora or into the male scrotal pouch. Although sex can now, at the seventh embryonic week, be distinguished with a moderate degree of accuracy, there is about a three-week lag before the external genitals assume a really distinct form. Once commenced, the genital development is rapid, and by the fourth month the sex of the fetus is easily recognizable.

The male embryo reaches a definitive stage about the tenth week when the edges of the urethral groove fold and grow together. The previously open urogenital sinus is thus closed and transformed into a tubular urethra within the penis, the fused edge being referred to as the *penoscrotal raphe*. The evidence of this fusion appears in the adult male as a scar line on the underside of the penis, running from the anus to the *glans* (head of the penis). The penis, which has evolved from a phallic tubercle projection, elongates and grows rapidly. By the end of the third month the male urethra is fully formed. The prepuce (foreskin) develops over the *glans* (Latin: acorn) of the penis simultaneously with the formation of the urethra. The outside opening of the urethra at the end of the penis is called the *penile meatus*.

The female external genitalia are less complicated, yet slower to develop than those of the male. A phallus-like tubercle projection slowly develops into the body and glans of the *clitoris,* the most important organ for female sexual stimulation. The labioscrotal swelling becomes the *labia majora,* the outer protective lips of the vaginal region, and continues anteriorly to terminate in the *mons veneris,* or *mons pubis*, the fatty tissue on the upper exterior of the female genitalia.

In its early stages, the female urethral groove follows the same pattern of formation as the male's. However, the groove never closes to form a tube; instead, part of it deepens to fashion the *vestibule,* the area surrounding and including the opening of the vagina. The urethral folds fail to unite in the female, and they gradually develop into the *labia minora,* the inner protective and highly erogenous lips of the vagina.

The female *urethra,* or bladder outlet, is homologous to the prostatic portion of the male urethra; it is just above the vagina, and both open into the vestibule. A prepuce (foreskin), often referred to as the *hood,* also develops over the glans of the clitoris. *Vulva* is a collective name used for the whole of the external female genitalia, as is the term *pudendum,* which derives from the Latin word *pudere,* "to be ashamed." The derivation of this word suggests the guilt and the psychological difficulties which too often become associated with anything sexual.

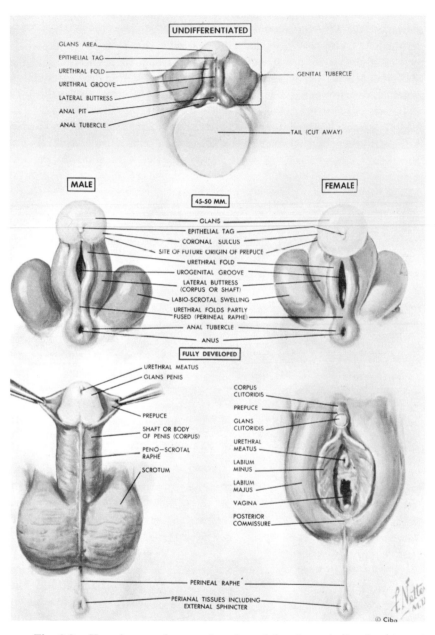

Fig. 2-2. Homologues of external male and female genitalia; development from undifferentiated into differentiated stage. Copyright *The Ciba Collection of Medical Illustrations* by Frank H. Netter, M.D.

A peculiar and marked difference in the development and differentiation of the Wolffian system and of the Mullerian system has been outlined.[19, 391] The Wolffian ducts, which give rise to most of the male reproductive system, are stimulated by fetal testicular hormones; and the Mullerian ducts, which give rise to most of the female reproduction system, are suppressed by the androgenic (male hormone) substance of the testes. However, the opposite situation is *not* the case—that is, the Mullerian system develops into the basic female structure (vagina, Fallopian tubes, uterus) even in the absence of female gonadal secretion.

CHAPTER 3

The Endocrine System in
Sexual Differentiation

PUBERTY is that stage of life at which sexual reproduction becomes possible and secondary sexual characteristics commence their development. The period of rapid change occurring just before the body reaches maturity is known as *pubescence,* and is often referred to as the pubic growth cycle. The pubescent growth spurt, with its anatomical, sexual, and endocrine transformations, is the second period of accelerated growth in human development, the first having been in infancy. It is more of a transition than a state, more a becoming than being. Sexual glands mature, and differences between the sexes become more marked. Body chemistry as well as physical appearance and functioning becomes more distinctively male and female in pubescence, and as these differences widen, a girl becomes ready for womanhood and a boy for manhood.

There is no "typical" pubescence. Every boy and girl has his or her own periods of transition, and the range of individual differences is broad. The antecedents to puberty-pubescence appear earlier for girls than for boys and the development is more swift, girls beginning the rapid maturing process at about ten to twelve years, approximately two years before boys do. The earlier development of girls gives them a temporary superiority over boys, physically, sexually, and socially. Most girls reach their full stature by their sixteenth year, while boys continue to grow in height until eighteen or later.

This is a period of "sexual awakening" which is met with ambivalent reactions by both sexes. Attitudes, emotions, and interests change. Experimentation and new physical gratifications, such as masturbation, begin to occur or increase in frequency. Possessing a positive attitude toward the biological sexual urge and condition, as well as an understanding of society's expectations of the newly emerging self, is essential to the emotional well-being of both sexes at this time.

Elaboration on the subject of sexual attitudes, both adolescent and adult, follows in later chapters.

The first evidences of pubescence in a girl are changes that occur in the breasts; the small conical buds increase in size, and the nipples begin to project forward. A girl now becomes quite aware of breasts, not only because of the physical changes in her, but because of the psychological implications in the attitudes of men and women of our culture towards breast size. As development continues with the growth in size and sensitivity of breast tissue, the body contour gradually rounds out and the pelvic area broadens. The bony structure of the pelvis widens, a growth of fatty pads on the hips develops, and the vaginal epithelium, or lining, thickens. There then appears soft, downy, rather colorless pubic hair, together with some axillary (underarm) hair growth. The pelvic hair thickens and coarsens, becoming curly and dark in color. It grows downward to the pubic area into the inverted triangular shape peculiar to women. With these bodily changes, and the unfolding of the classic feminine form, menstruation is imminent.

About two years after the breasts begin budding and about one year after the appearance of pubic hair (approximately thirteen years of age), menstruation begins. The *menarche,* the beginning of menstrual functioning, is the first real indication that a youngster is becoming a woman. There is considerable variation in the age at which girls reach the menarche because of individual differences in general health, developmental maturation, and heredity factors. A girl cannot have a child until she actually starts *ovulation—i.e.,* until the ovaries commence releasing mature ova—and this process usually does not take place for a year or so after menstruation first occurs. When a young girl's ovaries produce their first mature eggs, at about fourteen years, it can be said that puberty has been reached.

There are obvious exceptions both to the age at which this development begins and to its sequence. In 1939, for example, at the incredible age of five a Peruvian girl gave birth to a normal and healthy son. (The baby, fathered by a mentally retarded teen-age stepbrother, was delivered by Caesarean section.) In spite of the fact that the mother was so very young, she was sexually mature, and physicians confirmed that she had menstruated since she was perhaps one month old. Furthermore, there are cases on record in which a girl became pregnant and produced a child without ever having menstruated. The explanation here appears to be that the girl, contrary to the usual sequence of events, released a mature ovum just before she would have started menstruating, and the resulting pregnancy delayed menstruation until after delivery.

Female genital changes continue to occur from pubescence on into adolescence. The thickened, darkened pelvic hair continues to spread; the mons pubis (fatty pads just above the vulva) becomes prominent; the outer lips (labia majora) develop and become more fleshy, hiding the rest of the vulva, which is ordinarily visible during childhood; and the inner lips (labia minora) also develop and grow. The glands of Bartholin, which are just to each side of the opening of the vagina, are now capable of secreting a fluid, especially during sexual excitement; the clitoris rapidly develops its extensive system of blood vessels; the vagina turns a deeper red color, and its mucous lining thickens and will remain so until the *menopause,* or "change of life," when it reverts to the thinness of childhood. The vaginal secretions now become acid. The uterus commences its rapid growth rate when a girl reaches ten or twelve years of age, and doubles in size by her eighteenth year (although the wombs of 60% of fifteen-year-old girls have already reached their adult size).

It is interesting to note that when a female infant is born, her uterus is still under the influence of the hormonal secretions of the mother, and is at that time larger than it will be until the ovaries start to produce hormones as a prelude to the menarche. Because of the abrupt withdrawal of maternal hormones at the time of birth, the infant's uterus shrinks within a few days after birth, and sometimes the change is significant enough to result in some vaginal spotting or staining. The uterus then remains the same size until the ovaries start their own hormone production. Pregnancies will later on increase the permanent size of the uterus slightly more.

When a youngster is around ten, her ovaries begin to secrete female sex hormones (in particular, estrogen) and they begin a rapid growth. At the time of the menarche, they are approximately one-third their adult size, reaching maximum size and weight by the time a girl is nineteen or twenty.

The age at which girls begin to menstruate has dropped sharply in the last few centuries.[338] For example, in Germany the average age in 1795 was 16.6 years, but by 1920 was 14.5 years. In the United States in the late 1930s, the average age was 13.5, while data from the mid-1960s indicate a drop in this average to 13 years. It is concluded by some authorities that approximately one-half of American girls become capable of bearing children between 12½ and 14½ years of age.

Because she is unaccustomed to it, a girl often does not feel secure or adequate in her new role as a sexually mature person. She stands in critical need of support and guidance to help her learn to evaluate puberty and sexual maturity as a normal, healthy process. She has many problems to solve and challenges to meet during the next few years, not all of them sexual; if they are not dealt with properly during this crucial period, they can easily lead to emotional difficulties which have adverse effects on later personal and marital adjustments.

A boy's pubic growth curve lasts from four to seven years and parallels that of a girl's, but as has been said, lags behind hers by a year or two. Progress to and through puberty varies considerably from boy to boy, and the process of maturing physiologically occurs later, moves more slowly, and continues longer than a girl's. His physical superiority does not develop until after puberty; in fact, boys of thirteen are usually smaller than girls of the same age. Even so, boys of today are considerably better developed physically than in the past. For example, a nine-year-old boy today is 3.8 inches taller and 18.7 pounds heavier than a lad that age living in 1881.[355] The most obvious changes, and the greatest variability in physical size and physiological development, are first observed at the age of twelve or thirteen, and the developmental transformation continues to or beyond his seventeenth year.

At the age of eleven, a boy shows few outward signs of puberal alteration. He may first blossom into a "fat period," often a precedent to male pubescence. Penile erections occur spontaneously at this early age, but from various sources of stimulation, not all of which are sexual. By the age of twelve, the penis and scrotum begin to show an increase in size, one of the earliest indicators of approaching puberty. Erections occur more often, but still spontaneously; and while a boy might know about ejaculation, he has yet to experience it.

Pubic hair commonly appears at the age of thirteen or fourteen, following the genital spurt of growth by a year or so, but it can become discernible as early as the twelfth year. Ejaculation is now possible; secretion of sperm begins about this time, a process equated with ovulation in a girl, although neither sperm nor ova are yet necessarily mature. The growth of axillary and facial hair follows that of the pubic hair. Nocturnal emissions ("wet dreams") are now probable if a sexual outlet of another nature is not utilized. The change of voice occurs about the fourteenth or fifteenth year (the voice of a mature boy is usually about an octave lower than that of a mature girl), even though in many cases a boy may not attain full stature and mature sexual development until he is college-age.

What brings about these remarkable transformations in boys and girls to make them sexually mature? Certainly it is not mere physical growth, because there are many adult men and women who lack the proper primary and/or secondary sexual characteristics associated with full sexual capability. And in contrast, boys and girls far short of their teens, who would not be considered adult by ordinary standards, have been known to have mature sexual organs and to show sexual behavior usually found only in adults—for example, fathering or giving birth to babies.

The primary control in sexual maturation is the secretion of sex *hormones* (Greek: to arouse). These chemical substances are produced by the *endocrine glands* which, acting rather like small chemical laboratories, take materials from the bloodstream, convert them into hormones, and then secrete the hormones directly into the bloodstream to be distributed throughout the entire body.

Because hormones are secreted directly into the bloodstream without passing through any duct or canal, endocrine glands are also referred to as ductless glands or glands of internal secretion. The endocrine system is quite complex and contributes to many of the physiological functions and behavior patterns of humans. In this discussion, however, only those hormones which more or less directly influence both sexual systems' development, growth, and functioning will be considered.

It would appear that sex has been a subject of man's fascination since prehistoric times. While even primitive creatures recognized the external differences between male and female, it has only been in very recent years that scientists have begun to understand more clearly the basic physiological differences and the glands which influence these differences.

The *pituitary gland* at the base of the brain is about one-half the size of a thimble, and contains three lobes: the anterior, the intermediary, and the posterior. The anterior pituitary lobe is known as the "master gland"; it serves as a coordinator of the functions of the other endocrine glands, and is therefore important to sexual growth and functioning. Not only does the pituitary have a harmonizing influence on the other endocrine glands, but if it functions abnormally, it can have a disturbing effect on any or all of them.

Specifically, the anterior lobe of the pituitary gland controls both the cytogenic (the beginning of a cell) function concerned with the production of sperm and ova, and the endocrine secretory function of the gonads of both sexes—testes in men and ovaries in women.[20] The anterior lobe secretes at least six hormones, three of which are

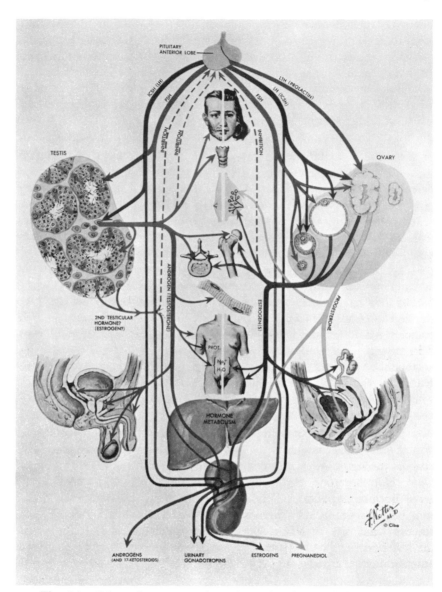

Fig. 3-1. Schematic representation of the functional relationships between pituitary and male and female gonads, together with effect of hormonal secretion on bodily parts and functions. Copyright *The Ciba Collection of Medical Illustrations* by Frank H. Netter, M.D.

directly related to gonadal function and are classed as *gonadotropic*. They are (1) the follicle stimulating hormones (FSH); (2) the luteinizing hormone (LH) in the female, and its counterpart, the interstitial cell-stimulating hormone (ICSH) in the male; and (3) luteotropic hormone (LTH), containing the lactogenic hormone, prolactin, which prompts the secretion of milk by the mammary glands (although prolactin apparently plays no part in the development of the mammary glands themselves). These gonadotropic hormones exert great influence on the growth, development, changes, and sexual activity of both males and females.

Men in early recorded history, perhaps sensing the special function of the testicles which we now identify as hormonal, have been known to attempt increasing their sexual prowess by eating the testicles of a defeated enemy. Indeed, as late as 1889, the renowned French physiologist, Charles E. Brown-Sequard, was apparently dissatisfied with his sexual vigor at the age of seventy-two and tried to outwit nature by injecting himself with extracts from the testicles of dogs. This famous scientist was apparently barking up the wrong tree, because despite the fact that he reported spectacular rejuvenation, any benefits he actually derived must surely have been the result of psychological factors related to autosuggestion—especially when one considers that the injection of the extract from approximtely 500 pounds of bull testicles would be needed to furnish what is considered an average dose of male sex hormones.[300] The one thing that Brown-Sequard did accomplish, however, was to stimulate a considerable amount of research in this area. Since his time, well-controlled experimentations with hormones have shown that we are physically, mentally, and emotionally dependent upon the action of our endocrine glands.

Based on chemical and physiological differences, there are three groups of sex hormones: the *estrogenic* hormone group and the *corpus luteum* hormone group (both female hormones), and the *androgenic* hormone group (male hormones). The action of these three hormonal groups differs greatly, although their chemical structure is quite similar; all are classed as steroids and are natural substances which are among the basic components of living cells. Once the sex hormones have been used by the body, they are broken down and eliminated, usually in the urine.

Estrogen (Greek: to produce mad desire) is the hormone responsible for stimulating the sexual urge in a female animal's reproductive organs during *estrus,* her mating period, which is also called *heat* or *rut.* In humans, where estrus does not exist, estrogen hormones are highly important in controlling body structure, and in the development and functioning of genital organs. Estrogen also influences the menstrual cycle, especially its first half.

In addition to their role in reproductive functions, estrogenic hormones aid in (1) maintaining the normal size and function of the uterus, its tubes, and the vagina; (2) controlling the production of gonadotropic and other hormones by its actions on the pituitary gland; (3) influencing the growth, development, and maintenance of the secondary sexual characteristics such as distribution of fat; (4) maintaining normal condition and function of nasal and oral mucous membranes; (5) influencing normal uterine contractions; (6) controlling the growth of breast duct tissue; and (7) developing and maintaining physical and mental health in the mature, normal female.

Recent experimental research[238] has uncovered evidence that certain neural centers of the brain are directly affected by sex hormones. For example, female test animals show an intensification in smell acuity during certain stages of the estrous cycle. In female animals, body odors become much stronger during the estrous cycle, which accounts for the attraction of male animals to them while they are in heat. In addition, it has been shown that body odor of animals varies at different stages of maturation. Studies of humans have revealed that women have greater smell acuity than men, and that the peak of their olfactory sensitivity is reached midway between menstrual periods when estrogen levels are the highest. Smell acuity decreases after an ovariectomy, but can be restored following administration of estrogen.

As a part of the developmental process, either the pituitary gland begins to secrete more of its follicle stimulating hormone (FSH), or the ovaries of the growing girl develop to the point where they become more sensitive than before to the already existing level of FSH secretion. Whichever the cause—perhaps a combination of the two—the FSH gonadotropic hormones of the anterior lobes of the pituitary gland stimulate the growth of the immature ovaries and their *Graafian follicles* (small sacs, each of which contains an ovum), which, in turn, initiate the production of estrogen from the cells of the cavity lining of each follicle. Further discussion of the value and place of estrogen, especially in ovulation and menstruation, is presented in greater detail in another section.

When an egg is discharged from a follicle in ovulation, the remaining follicular cells multiply rapidly and fill the cavity of the follicle just ruptured. The new cell growth is yellow in color and is known as the *corpus luteum* (yellow body). The second female hormone, more popularly known as *progesterone,* is produced by the corpus luteum, which is stimulated by the pituitary gland's luteinizing hormone (LH). The cells of the yellow body produce progesterone for about thirteen days following the peak of development of the cells which fill the follicular cavity after the discharge of the ovum. If the ovum has not been fertilized by the sperm by about the twenty-seventh day after the first day of the previous menstrual period (fourteen days preceding ovulation, plus the thirteen days just discussed), the corpus luteum involutes into a wasted body known as a *corpus albicans,* and the secretion of progesterone ceases.

Progesterone is the hormone of primary importance in preparing the uterus for pregnancy and in maintaining the pregnancy itself. When impregnation does not occur, the lining of the uterus, which had been readied during the month by progesterone, begins to break down, since that hormone is no longer produced. The degeneration of the uterine tissue is the onset of the monthly flow of blood known as *menstruation.* The corpus luteum also begins to degenerate. The yellow margin shrinks rapidly and loses its yellow color, the lutein cells are replaced by connective tissue, and after a few weeks only the small white body, the *corpus albicans,* remains in the space which was once the location of the follicle. This cessation of the secretion of progesterone, together with the decrease of estrogen, causes a new production of pituitary gonadotropins which stimulate another crop of ovarian follicles. The ovulatory growth cycle commences anew.

If the ovum is fertilized, the corpus luteum does not degenerate. Rather, it continues to secrete progesterone which keeps the endometrium or uterine lining sensitized and ready to implant the blastocyst, a stage of development of the fertilized ovum, and to develop membranes needed for the survival of the egg.

During the very earliest days of implantation—actually, from about the middle of the first month of pregnancy—the *chorionic villi* begin to secrete a gonadotropic hormone which is excreted in the urine of the mother-to-be. The chorionic villi are small finger-like protrusions developed from the covering of the fertilized egg that form the tie between the egg and uterine wall, and which are the forerunner of the placenta. This gonadotropic hormone reaches its peak of discharge during the third month of pregnancy.[252] Its excretions then begin rapidly to decrease during the fourth and fifth months, gradually leveling off and stopping altogether by the end of pregnancy. It is this particular gonadotropic hormone, found in the urine, which makes possible a test for pregnancy, *e.g.,* the well-known frog test, during the early days after conception. This early embryonic hormone production is believed to start at about the twenty-fourth or twenty-fifth day of the menstrual cycle, because it is thought to be the hormone which causes the corpus luteum to develop, persist, and inhibit estrogen production. Without some stimulation to develop, the corpus luteum would degenerate as described earlier.

The amount of the special gonadotropic hormone secreted by the chorionic villi at the outset of its production is apparently so slight that biological tests designed to confirm pregnancy cannot reveal its presence in the urine until about ten days after the menstrual period would normally have started. For this reason, laboratories usually refuse even to run such a test for pregnancy until the menstrual period is about two weeks overdue. A more recent test for pregnancy[87] not involving the use of animals but, rather, a process of agglutination, will show a reaction to the hormone within one to fourteen days after menstruation should have commenced. The reliability of this test may be as high as 96%, depending upon the time elapsed since the missed period, and some forms of the test require only three minutes to determine pregnancy.[329] Still other recently developed pregnancy tests are purported to have a near 100% accuracy.[316]

In pregnancy, the bright yellow corpus luteum develops and grows until it may, at the peak of its production, occupy as much as one-half the ovary.[252] This endocrine tissue continues to function until about the fourth month of pregnancy, at which time the placenta takes over the necessary production of estrogen and progesterone, and maintains this production for the remainder of *gestation* (the period of pregnancy).

Progesterone stimulates the secretion capabilities of the mammary glands of the pregnant woman, thus causing an enlargement of the breasts. A proper amount of progesterone is also necessary to inhibit premature uterine contractions. In fact, progesterone hormonal therapy is often prescribed by the physician when there is a danger of spontaneous abortion, especially during the tenth to sixteenth week of pregnancy when the threat of miscarriage is greatest. In a woman who is not pregnant, improper production of progesterone may produce dysmenorrhea, premenstrual tension, and similar gynecological problems.

(It might be mentioned in connection with a discussion of progesterone that birth control pills are effective because they contain the female hormones which inhibit follicular growth and ovulation. This subject will be investigated more thoroughly in the section on birth control.)

Both male and female sex hormones are produced by both sexes— that is, a small amount of female sex hormones is to be found in the male, and a small amount of male sex hormones in the female. The source of the "opposite" hormones is not known definitely, although it is thought that gonads and adrenals are probably responsible. The urine of normal men and women will contain some of the "opposite" hormones.

In adulthood, an excessive amount of male hormones in a woman, and vice versa, can produce marked changes in secondary sexual characteristics. An imbalance in the natural hormonal state in an infant or growing child can produce deviations in primary sexual characteristics, as well as changes in the secondary characteristics. Hormonal therapy is often successful in adjusting the imbalance and, in turn, correcting or preventing associated problems.

Women who have developed cancer are often successfully treated with male hormones injected in an effort to reduce the rate of growth and spread of the malignant growth. Preliminary investigations indicate that it may be possible to reduce the death rate among men from heart attacks by as much as 50% in some instances when the female sex hormone, estrogen, is used in treatment. Estrogen hormonal treatment, however, leaves the man with a decreased potency and sex drive, together with an enlargement of the breasts.[323]

Other relationships between sex hormones and certain conditions of the body, including disease, have been detected.[307] Apparently there exists a correlation between male hormones and glaucoma, a condition in which the pressure of the fluid in the eyeball elevates, often sharply, and interferes with vision. Pregnancy has been observed to reduce this ocular pressure in women with glaucoma, while injections of male hormones increase it. Castration of male rabbits, as a further example of this relationship, lowers the pressure in their eyes. Also, light has a stimulating effect on the reproductive organs of birds, and this knowledge has been utilized to the economic advantage of farmers who augment the egg production of their hens by increasing the intensity of and length of time they are exposed to light.

The male sex hormone, *testosterone,* is produced in the testicles when the developmental processes, including proper pituitary production and function, occur. A man's testicles grow and develop rapidly as a result of the pituitary gland's secretion of the follicle stimulating hormone (FSH). The FSH hormone has an effect on a man's seminiferous tubules wherein it initiates the process of *spermatogenesis,* the formation and development of spermatozoa or sperm. This is not the complete story, however, because while the germinal cell layers of the tubules become active at the time of pubescence, mature spermatozoa do not develop without the presence of the interstitial cell-stimulating hormone (ICSH) which, it will be remembered, is the same as the luteinizing hormone (LH) in woman. Without ICSH, spermatogenesis does not go beyond the secondary spermatocyte stage (the second division and second stage of spermatogenesis).

The chief function of ICSH, however, appears to be the stimulation and maintenance of the interstitial (Leydig) cells of the testes in their production of the male gonadal (androgenic) hormone, testosterone.[201] The male hormone is responsible for development and preservation of masculine secondary sexual characteristics, including facial and body hair, change of voice, muscular and skeletal development, attraction to opposite sex, and mental attitudes, as well as the development, size, and function of male accessory sex organs (seminal vesicles, prostate, penis, and scrotum).

Testosterone is furthermore associated with certain biologic conditions:[300] (1) dryness and itching of skin, (2) retention in the body of chlorides and water, (3) effectiveness of the circulation of the peripheral blood system, (4) size and function of the kidneys, (5) reactions of the nervous system, such as irritability and apprehension, as well as effective mental functioning, (6) inhibiting the development of peptic ulcers, since this disorder is thought to be related to disturbed pituitary-gonad interaction, and (7) certain forms of heart pain and disease. For example, it has been suggested that small, daily doses of female sex hormones may be of benefit to men subject to heart attacks. Such small dosages are not likely to feminize the man and perhaps may act as some sort of counterbalance to testosterone.[312]

CHAPTER 4

The Male
Reproductive System

THE MALE gonads, the *testicles* (also called testes), develop in pairs in the abdominal cavity. As in the case of many other mammals, a man's testicles descend shortly before or just after birth into the *scrotum* (or scrotal sac), a loose pouch of skin which is an outpocket of the abdominal cavity. During the seventh month of fetal life, the testes pass through the *inguinal canal,* a passageway leading from the abdominal cavity into the scrotal pouch. After the descent, this opening is usually sealed off by a growth of connective tissue, and the body cavity and scrotum are henceforth separated. Any of a variety of factors may cause the testicles not to descend in due time into the scrotum, and endocrine or surgical assistance is sometimes required to bring about the process. It has been estimated that up to 2% of men have undescended testicles at the time of birth, and in about 7% of this group the testicles remain undescended at puberty.[141] Physicians generally agree that an undescended testicle should be dealt with by the time the boy is five or six years of age.

Occasionally the inguinal ring fails to close, or reopens because of strain, a muscular tear, or some other reason, and the result is an inguinal hernia. Sometimes a loop of the intestine may slip through the ring and into the scrotal pouch. If it is caught there, it is possible that its blood supply may be cut off and an operation become necessary.

The testicles are ovoid bodies that vary in size but in the adult are usually about one and a half inches long and about an inch in diameter.[354] They are housed in the scrotum, which is supported by special muscles and tissues *(cremaster)* acting to regulate the temperature of the gonads. Ordinarily the scrotal temperature is slightly lower than that of the body itself, and this lower temperature is necessary for the production of sperm. The supporting muscles and tissue act to contract the scrotum when the outside temperature is low, thus bringing the testicles closer to the warm body, and they relax when the temperature is high, allowing the testicles to be lowered farther from the body.

Most men have heard arguments that long hot baths, prolonged use of athletic supporters, high fever, and the like can cause infertility,

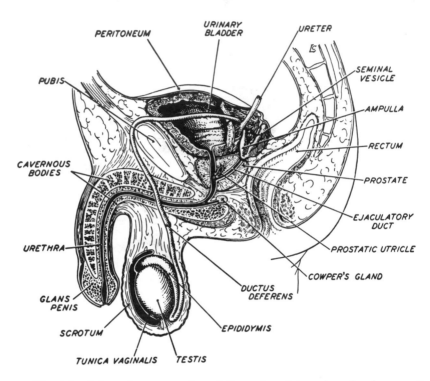

Fig. 4-1. Schematic cross section of the male pelvic region, showing organs of reproduction. From Turner: *General Endocrinology,* 4th ed. Philadelphia: W. B. Saunders Co., 1966.

especially in men with a low sperm count to start with. A two- to three-degree centigrade increase in temperature does in fact occasionally result in temporary sterility in men, but fertility returns after a short time. Also, there is little evidence of success in a man's taking prolonged hot baths by way of a contraceptive technique, which is done in some countries, although Dickinson[101] has reported that heat which is tolerable to the hand can, in a thirty-minute period, arrest the testicular manufacturing of sperm for weeks. It is well known to most men that the scrotum shrivels, bringing the testes closer to the warm body during cold showers, cold weather, and certain emotional conditions.

Each testicle has within it several hundred lobules, small divided areas which contain, in turn, several winding and tightly coiled *seminiferous* (sperm producing) *tubules* measuring from one to two feet each when uncoiled.[252] The walls of the tubules are lined with

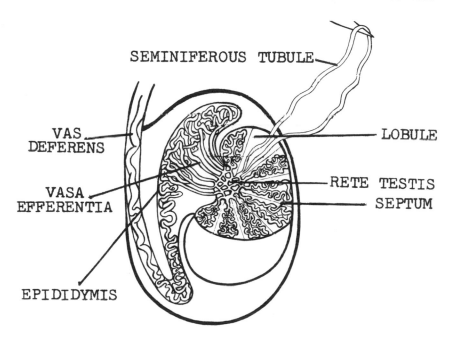

SEMINIFEROUS TUBULE

VAS DEFERENS

LOBULE

VASA EFFERENTIA

RETE TESTIS

SEPTUM

EPIDIDYMIS

Fig. 4-2. Diagrammatic cross section of a testicle.

germinal tissue, and it is here that the production of sperm by a continuing process—continuous in man, seasonal in some animals—of maturation known as *spermatogenesis* takes place.

This germinal tissue actually contains two types of cells: the *spermatogenic* cells which eventually produce the mature sperm, and the *sustentacular* cells (cells of Sertoli) which nurture the sperm at various stages of development. The space between the tubules is filled with interstitial tissue. It will be remembered that when this tissue is stimulated by the luteinizing hormone of the pituitary gland, it produces the male sex hormone, testosterone.

As a male matures, the seminiferous tubules come to contain at the inner periphery of the tubule an increasing number of cells known as *primitive spermatogonia,* which constitutes the first stage of sperma-

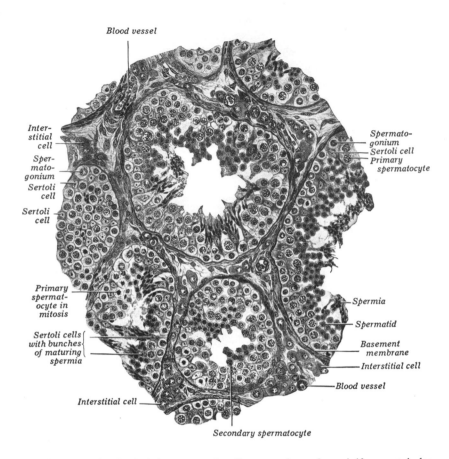

Fig. 4-3. Section of human testis. Cross section of seminiferous tubules showing various stages of spermatogenesis; interstitial cells, where male sex hormones are produced, also shown. From Bloom and Fawcett: *A Textbook of Histology,* 8th ed. Philadelphia: W. B. Saunders Co., 1962.

togenesis. *Mitosis,* or cell division, of the spermatogonia begins when a boy is about eleven, although the age varies considerably, as can be seen by the different times at which individual puberty is reached.

Through the unique process of mitosis, each spermatogonium divides by means of its chromosomes' splitting longitudinally and regrouping in such a manner as to produce two daughter cells: one is another spermatogonium, which remains at the periphery of the tubule ready to split again, thus perpetuating formation of future spermatogonia; and the second is a *primary spermatocyte,* which is the next advanced stage of spermatogenesis. The primary spermatocyte is a large cell which moves towards the center opening, or lumen, of the

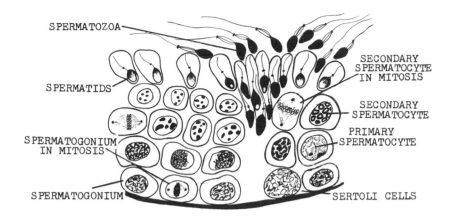

Fig. 4-4. Diagrammatic cross section of a seminiferous tubule showing the process of spermatogenesis.

tubule, and in the process splits into two smaller *secondary spermatocytes*. It is at this reduction division—primary spermatocyte to two secondary spermatocytes—that the number of chromosomes is reduced to twenty-two, plus an X in one secondary spermatocyte and a Y in the other. X and Y sperm are thus produced in equal numbers.

These secondary spermatocytes immediately cleave or split by mitotic division into the last primitive germinal cells, the *spermatids*. The process of division continues to progress from the periphery to the lumen. The spermatids begin to appear at approximately the age of twelve (the lack of ICSH hormones until this time prohibiting development beyond the secondary spermatocyte cell), and the testes grow rapidly as a result of marked enlargement of the tubules. There is an increase in intensity of the germinal activity as a boy advances to about age sixteen, at which time full spermatogenesis is usually attained. Spermatids grow, develop, and rearrange their component parts, then finally mature into *spermatozoa,* the fully formed male sperm. The total process of spermatogenesis, from spermatogonium to mature spermatozoa, takes about ten days, and is a continuing and constant process in the normal, healthy adult male.

The mature spermatozoa, or sperm—which, incidentally, were first identified under a microscope in 1677—have little motility until they mix with prostatic fluid to form the *semen.* The sperm are transported from their place of development, eventually reaching the prostate, by means of contractions and ciliary, or lash-like, movements in the walls of the tubular network that connects the testes with the prostate gland.

In very recent years noticeable differences between the Y (male) sperm and the X (female) sperm have been discovered. The Y sperm has a smaller round-headed body with a long tail, while the X sperm has a larger oval-shaped body and a short tail. It can therefore be hypothesized, and with some evidence to support it, that the sex of a child can be predetermined beyond mere chance by controlling the

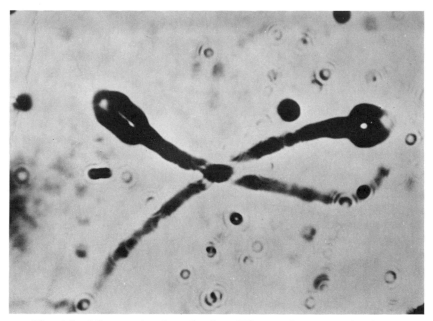

Fig. 4-5. Microscopic view showing difference between X-bearing sperm (larger, oval-shaped head) and Y-bearing sperm (smaller head, longer tail). Photograph courtesy Dr. Landrum B. Shettles.

time of sexual intercourse.[214, 351] (There is, it should be noted, hesitance on the part of some scientists to accept these reported differences in the X and Y sperms.)

Because a mature ovum is met and fertilized by a sperm in the Fallopian tube, it is reasonable to assume that the smaller-headed, longer-tailed Y sperm would be transported from vagina to ovum at a faster rate than X sperm. The first sperm contacting the ovum fertilizes it and fixes the sex of the child. If the egg is already in the tube, a Y sperm should reach it first and a male (XY) child will be produced. On the other hand, if the sperm are deposited in the vagina before the egg reaches the Fallopian tube, both X and Y sperm must wait for it. The shorter-tailed, larger-bodied X (female) sperm is apparently stronger than Y sperm, and is better able to survive longer and with proper strength to fertilize the egg when it finally arrives, thus producing a female (XX) child.[352]

Each sperm carries twenty-two similar (autosomal) chromosomes plus one chromosome—the X or Y which actually determines an infant's sex—which is different. A further postulation in support of the theory that sex can be predetermined rests on the fact that chromatin material of the Y (male) chromosome is negligible in size and weight, and is estimated to weigh about 4% less than the X chromosome. Be-

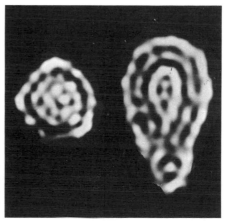

Fig. 4-6. Chromosomal arrangements of Y (male) sperm, *left;* and of X (female) sperm, *right* (original magnification × 1000). Photographs courtesy Dr. Landrum B. Shettles.

cause of its lighter weight, it is argued that the male-producing sperm can travel faster and reach the ovum quicker than the heavier female-producing sperm can.[292, 352]

A recent experiment offers still further evidence to support the hypothesis that the sex of a child can be predetermined because the X (female) sperm is larger-headed and heavier than the Y sperm. When ejaculatory fluid containing sperm was allowed to stand in a container, the lower one-third of the fluid eventually contained a much higher percentage of X sperm, while the top third of the fluid ultimately contained far more Y sperm. The middle one-third comprised equal numbers of X and Y sperm.[326] The value of this technique in producing a child of the desired sex by artificial insemination is apparent, and indeed experimentation in the control of a child's sex through artificial insemination has been successful in about 80% of the cases.[187]

Since X and Y sperm are produced in equal numbers, there is speculation why the conception ratio of males to females is, curiously, about 160 to 100.[352] The implantation ratio of male to female zygotes has been estimated at about 120 to 100, and the birth rate of boy to girl infants is approximately 105 to 100. There is substantial evidence that human sperm may live under ideal circumstances for as long as fourteen days after ejaculation. It is questionable how long they may live in the female genital tract, however, although it is generally agreed that sperm's ability to fertilize lasts for only one or two days.[354]

The seminiferous tubules, some 1000 of them, meet at the core-like structure known as *rete testis* (network of testicle vessels), located near the surface of the upper edges of the testicle. This meshwork of tubes, fibers, and vessels empties into approximately ten to fifteen efferent ducts *(vasa efferentia)* through which the sperm migrate by peristalsis (contraction) of the tubules to reach the major body of the epididymis, the chamber for maturation discussed earlier, where they, the sperm, may remain to ripen or mature for as long as six weeks. The sperm cells are nurtured by the lining of the coiled tube which makes up the epididymis. Those spermatozoa less fit to survive and endure the long journey ahead are crowded toward the center of the tube, where they are not so likely to live, and are absorbed. The epididymis thus serves also as a selection chamber.

Sperm are transported by ciliary action through the epididymis into a minute connecting duct, the *ductus deferens* or *vas deferens* (commonly called the *vas*). This tiny tube, about eighteen inches in length, originates at the small end of the epididymis where it connects to that coiled tubule and passes upward into the abdominal cavity. There it serves not only as a passageway for sperm but as a storage place as well, particularly at the upper end where the vas broadens into the ampulla as it joins the seminal vesicle at a juncture ready to pass into the prostate gland. To assess the size of a sperm, one has only to consider that it must travel 500 times its length in order to progress one inch. This is equivalent to a man's swimming almost a mile.[341]

Up to this point, the sperm have been moved by contraction and ciliary movements of the various tubes through which they pass. The *seminal vesicles*—sac-like structures of about four and a half inches when stretched—lie behind the bladder, in front of the rectum, and near the top of the prostate. The exact function of the seminal vesicle is much debated: some scientists think it is only a storage compartment for spermatozoa; others believe it is a gland specifically designed to produce a secretion that not only serves as a vehicle for the sperm, but also activates the whipping movement of their tails, thus propelling them and speeding their movements.

Even with the active lashing of their tails, however, sperm movement is greatly hastened by contractions of the uterus. These contractions are caused by ovarian hormones and by fibrillations during and subsequent to the orgasmic phase of sexual response.[36, 215, 287] Without help from the contractive action of the uterus, sperm are seldom found in the Fallopian tubes in less than ninety minutes after sexual intercourse, while with uterine contractions—as one experiment demonstrated—carbon particles, which, of course, are not self-propelled, as sperm are, may move from the vagina to the tubes in about thirty minutes.[36, 287]

Immediately below the bladder and surrounding its neck and the upper part of the urethra is the *prostate gland.* It is a firm body, weighing approximately two-thirds ounce, and is made up of partially muscular, partially glandular matter. The adult prostate is in a continual state of activity; part of its secretion is voided with the urine, and part of it makes up the greater portion of the ejaculatory fluid.

That part of the prostatic secretion discharged at the time of ejaculation is a highly alkaline, thin, milky fluid which contains many substances, including proteins, calcium, citric acid, cholesterol, and various enzymes and acids.[205] The alkalinity of the secretion apparently serves to allow the sperm to move through acid areas at a rapid pace since, for example, acid in the vaginal fluid will easily destroy them if left in contact even for a short time.

The prostate surrounds the *ejaculatory ducts,* which partially house the semen until its discharge. The *semen* or *seminal fluid* is composed of spermatozoa and secretions from the epididymis, seminal vesicles, pros-

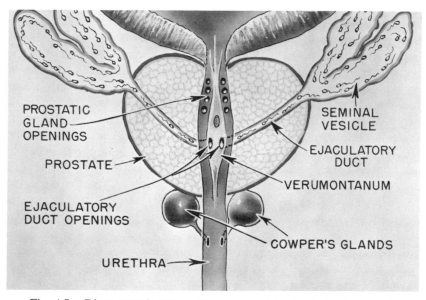

Fig. 4-7. Diagrammatic cross section of prostate gland showing ejaculatory duct openings joining the urethra. Photograph courtesy *Sexology* magazine.

tate gland, and Cowper's (bulbo-urethral) glands. It should be pointed out that the substance of seminal fluid varies from man to man, and variations in the fluid are to be expected in the same man. Frequently the fluid is thick and almost gelatin-like, while another time it will be thin and somewhat watery, the determinant being, generally, the frequency of the man's ejaculations. Semen coagulates shortly after ejaculation, but liquefies about twenty minutes later.[80]

Cowper's glands, two pea-sized structures which are situated slightly below the prostate at each side of the base of the penis, make up, along with the seminal vesicles and prostate, a man's accessory reproductive glands. During sexual excitement, the Cowper's glands secrete an alkaline fluid that lubricates and neutralizes the acidity of the urethra for easy and safe passage of the semen. This thin fluid can be observed at the opening of the glans of the penis during sexual excitement and before ejaculation. The fluid does not ordinarily contain spermatozoa, but some few sperm do occasionally make their way into the fluid, thus making it possible for a woman to be made pregnant by penetration even if the man does not actually ejaculate. Studies of precoital fluid have indicated the presence of sperm in 25% of the samples examined.

Situated just below the Cowper's glands is the base of the *penis,* a cylindrical organ composed mostly of erectile tissue. In the adult male, the length of the average penis is from three to four inches when flaccid (limp), slightly over one inch in diameter, and about three and a half inches in circumference; the size, of course, varies considerably from man to man. When in a state of tumescence (erection), the average penis extends five and a half to six and a half inches in length, and becomes one and a half inches in diameter and about four and a half inches in circumference; again, the size of the erect penis shows considerable variation from man to man. Furthermore, there is little relationship between the size of a flaccid penis and its size when erect. Neither is there as much relationship between penile and general body size as there is between the dimensions of other organs and body size.[215] The measurement of a perfectly functioning erect penis might vary from two inches in one man to ten inches in another, one being no less capable of coital performance than the other.

Men are often concerned about the dimensions of their penises because of childhood conditioning that induced them to associate an adult's larger penis with strength and masculinity. When a boy so conditioned grows up, he may well think that in order to be a man of great sexual prowess, he must have an inordinately large phallus. As will be seen later, the vagina has few nerve endings, and other than any psychological effect which might be involved, the size of the penis has little or nothing to do with the pleasure experienced by either the man or the woman, or with its impregnating ability, unless there is some hormonal dysfunction. If in a child or young boy there is a hormonal malfunctioning, the size of the external sex organs may indeed be impaired. In such instances, however, hormonal therapy may readily increase the size and functional ability of his sexual apparatus. But in a healthy and normal man, the size of the penis is fixed by heredity, and nothing can be done to make it larger.

The erect penis is somewhat triangular (inverted) in shape because the shaft is made up of three cylindrical, spongy bodies composed of erectile tissue: two larger bodies on top, and one smaller body below. The two top bodies are known as *corpus cavernosum penis,* and the single body below is called *corpus spongiosum* or *corpus cavernosum urethrae.* The lower body houses the urethra as it runs the length of the penis. These three bodies are encircled, and the lower body separated from the upper two, by *Buck's facia.* This is a band or sheet of tissue which is a continuation of the tissue joining the penis to the symphysis (connection juncture) of the pubic bone and the perineal and related muscles.

Throughout the penis, but especially at the top, both above and below Buck's facia, are heavy arteries which feed blood to its spongy erectile tissue. As the spongy structures of the penis fill with blood, it becomes erect. The erection is lost when blood leaves the penis venously faster than it flows in through the arteries.

The *glans* (Latin: acorn) is the smooth conelike head, or distal end, of the penis. It is by far the most sensitive and excitable part of a man's body insofar as sexual activity is concerned. Its surface is filled with nerve endings, especially at the *corona,* the crown-like ridge at the back edge of the glans where the glans drops down to join the shaft of the penis. The corona, particularly at the frenum, is a primary source of sexual pleasure and excitement when stimulated properly. The glans is a continuation of the corpus cavernosum urethrae; at the tip end of the glans is the *meatus,* the external opening of the urethra.

The shaft of the penis is covered by a loose skin which is continuous with that of the scrotum. This looseness of the skin allows free movement and full erection when the penis elongates and enlarges as it becomes engorged with blood. Near the tip end of the penis, the skin is no longer attached to the organ directly, but encompasses the glans, usually hanging loosely. This fold of skin which covers the glans, but which may be pulled back from it, is known as the *prepuce* or *foreskin*. It is attached to the glans on the lower surface by a thin middle-line tissue known as the *frenum*. For hygienic, functional, and in certain instances, religious reasons a portion of the prepuce

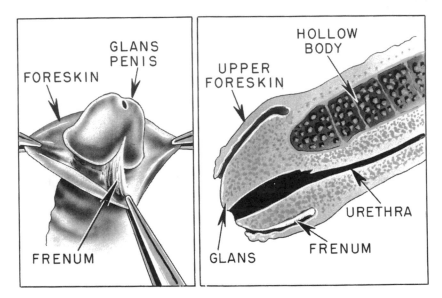

Fig. 4-8. Foreskin and glans penis showing position of frenum. Photograph courtesy *Sexology* magazine.

covering the glans is frequently removed surgically in a procedure known as circumcision, usually just after birth while the infant is still in the hospital.

Just behind the glans, under the corona and on each side of the frenum, are the *Tyson's glands*. They are modified sebaceous (suet-

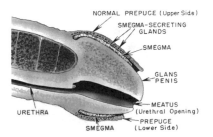

Fig. 4-9. Cross section of penis showing collection of smegma. Photograph courtesy *Sexology* magazine.

oily) glands, the secretions of which, together with cells shed from the glans and corona, form a smelly, cheese-like substance known as *smegma*. If the prepuce is tight over the glans, smegma may collect and emit a foul odor, and may act as a breeding ground for irritants and disease. Prevention of this condition is one of the main purposes of circumcision, although research showing an inverse relationship between circumcision and penile cancer makes circumcision even more important. In one investigation made, the Catholics and Protestants who comprised 67% of a general hospital's patients had 94% of the cases of penile cancer, while the Jewish 30% of the admissions had only 3%.[199] This study supports to a certain degree the belief that circumcision prevents accumulation of smegma which, in turn, encourages penile cancer.

Although the penis is ordinarily erect at the time of ejaculation, it is not necessary for it to be so. It is essential, however, for the penis to be at least partially erect for it to penetrate the vagina and thus be capable of impregnating. Of course, it is possible for a woman to become pregnant without penetration—*e.g.,* through artificial insemination—but in the present discussion only the usual method of impregnation is implied.

Erection of the penis is controlled by nerves in the spinal cord at the lower end of the *central nervous system,* and involves the synchronization of several reactions. Friction at the surface of the penis and/or surrounding areas sends impulses to a special area

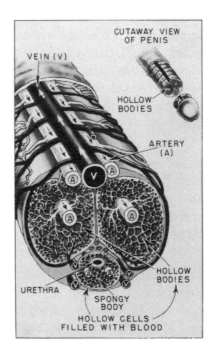

Fig. 4-10. Cross section of penis showing flow of blood. Spongy spaces fill with blood to bring about erection. Photograph courtesy *Sexology* magazine.

(sacral) of the spinal cord; sexual thoughts, dreams, erotic odors, etc., cause impulses to be sent to the spinal area from the brain; stimulation of the sexual system by sex hormones in the bloodstream; and impulses from full ejaculatory ducts—all of these work separately or together to activate the synchronized reactions.

Dilation of the arteries that feed blood to the penis results in engorgement of the spongy tissue (corpora cavernosa). This dilation is followed or accompanied by a simultaneous tonic (contractile) spasm of the muscles at the base of the penis near the anus (bulbocavernosus and ischiocavernosus), the spasm preventing the blood from escaping the spongy tissue through the veins. These reactions are brought into play by inhibition of the vasoconstrictor centers of the sympathetic nervous system (located at lumbar spinal nerves 1-2), and by the excitement of the vasodilator centers of the parasympathetic system (located in sacral spinal nerves portion 1-3). These spinal centers, while primarily operating on a reflex arc system, are in communication with the cortical, subcortical, and medulla oblongata portion of the brain.

The erection and/or ejaculatory reflex continues to exist in some men even though the connection is severed between erection centers of the lower spine and the brain.[237, 305] The action of the brain would consequently appear to serve as a modification or control of the spinal reflex center, rather than as the most essential factor in producing erections. For example, when mild electrical stimulation was applied to experimental animals at the lower spinal cord and/or to the nerves which pass between the lower spinal cord and the arteries of the penis, penile erections and ejaculations were produced.[358]

So long as there is proper and sufficient stimulation from the nerve endings of the penis, and proper and sufficient impulses from the brain, a man will maintain his erection. It should be recognized that inappropriate impulses—*e.g.,* such severe stimulation of the penis that excessive pain is the result, or disturbed emotional states such as fear, anger, guilt, anxiety, or shame—can cause an erection to collapse, or can prevent its occurring in the first place.

These emotional difficulties are the most frequent causes of loss of erection, and of impotence as well. It can be understood that a man who fails to have a satisfying erection, then worries over his "failure" and about his abilities the next time he attempts intercourse, may be establishing a vicious circle of failure within himself as far as his sexual behavior is concerned. Methods of dealing with these problems will be discussed later in Chapter 14.

Ordinarily, erection sets the stage for ejaculation. The stimulation of the glans of the penis, the presence of sex hormones in the blood, impulses from taut seminal vesicles and ejaculatory ducts, nerve responses from erotic odors, sexual thoughts: all these messages stimulate the brain to bring about and maintain an erection, as well as to build up impulses in the ejaculatory center of the lower spinal cord. Nerve impulses from the male genitals are carried by the dorsal nerves of the penis to the pudendal nerves and enter the ejaculatory center via posterior penile roots (involving sacral spinal nerves 3-4). These impulses then travel to the appropriate section of the lower spine (lumbar spinal nerves 1-2) where they, along with stimulation from the other areas mentioned, build up to a threshold where there is a sudden triggering of the process called ejaculation.

There is, first, a peristalsis (flowing contraction) of the ampulla of the vas deferens, the seminal vesicles, and the ejaculatory ducts, which moves the ejaculatory fluid (semen) containing the sperm to the membranaceous part of the urethral tract; secondly, there is an accompanying chronic (alteration of contraction and relaxation) spasm in the urogenital floor muscles, which discharges the semen by spurting it through and out the penis. This physical reaction is accompanied by a distinct and highly pleasurable sensation known as *orgasm*, to which a later chapter of this book is devoted. The strength of the ejaculatory force varies from man to man. Some ejaculate with such force that the discharged semen may go three feet or more beyond the penile meatus, while in other males, the semen may go only a few inches, or simply ooze out the urethra. The strength of the force usually depends upon such factors as general health, age, degree of sexual stimulation, and the condition of the prostate. Most men report that semen is ejaculated with little force, although men sometimes tend to correlate the subjective pleasures of orgasm with the force of ejaculation.

It is perhaps coincidental that ejaculation and orgasm occur together, since men who have had their spinal cords severed at a level higher than the ejaculatory center can still ejaculate without the accompanying pleasant sensation.[237] The neuromuscular sensation of orgasm is the result of impulses from the triggered area of the lower spinal cord reaching the brain. Erection and ejaculation may both occur without any physical stimulation, as in nocturnal emissions, which are the result primarily, if not exclusively, of erotic dreams preceded, usually, by prolonged abstinence. Furthermore, both men and women have been known to have orgasms from erotic thoughts alone or from stimulation of nongenital areas such as lips and breasts.[215]

Stimulation of the nerves of the ejaculatory center to the threshold of response does more than initiate ejaculation. Ejaculation itself causes the previously dilated arteries to narrow, so that less blood flows to the penis than is drained off through the veins. The penis is thus returned to its flaccid state shortly after ejaculation.

CHAPTER 5

The Female
Reproductive System

THE INTERNAL female genital organs consist of the ovaries, the uterine or Fallopian tubes, the uterus or womb, and the vagina.

The *ovaries,* which produce *ova* or eggs, are homologous with the testes of the male. They manufacture hormones that stimulate or activate a woman's sexual desire, and that prepare and maintain the uterus for the implantation of the fertilized ovum. Located on either side of the uterus in a recessed area of the lateral pelvic wall *(ovarian fossa),* the ovaries are held in a somewhat vertical position in an erect woman by a suspensory ligament which connects to the abdominal wall, and by the mesovarium and ovarian ligaments which connect the ovaries to the uterus. Each ovary, a pinkish grey body, is roughly the size, shape, and weight of an unshelled almond.

In each ovary of a newborn girl are some 200,000 to 400,000 follicles,[201] each housing an *oocyte,* the earliest stage of an ovum. This number decreases possibly to 10,000 by puberty. In the physically mature female, one follicle ordinarily ripens into an ovum each month, usually midway through the menstrual cycle, although the time varies. Since the average woman is fertile for approximately thirty-five years and ovulates about thirteen times per annum, it can be seen that only 400 to 500 of the many thousands of undeveloped ova are discharged. At birth, each primordial follicle of the ovaries consists of an oocyte surrounded by epithelial cells. With the body's growth, development, and subsequent hormonal secretions, the oocyte becomes a mature ovum, marking the beginning of puberty.

If one were to examine the internal structure of a typical ovary, there would be found a number of round vesicles, the *follicles* (Graafian follicles), each containing a developing ovum. The follicles are housed immediately beneath the surface, or outer layer, of the ovary (the cortex). Some are primary follicles which have not yet started growing; others are mature follicles that are approaching the time of eruption and discharge of mature ova. During the period when the follicles are very immature until the time they are fully developed, they sink deeply toward the center of the ovary (the *medulla*) where

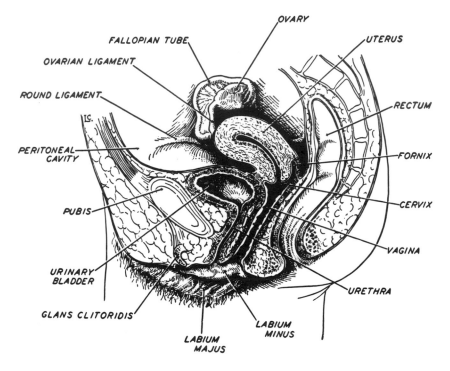

Fig. 5-1. Schematic cross section of the female pelvic region, showing organs of reproduction. From Turner: *General Endocrinology*, 4th ed. Philadelphia: W. B. Saunders Co., 1966.

they grow and mature. The medulla consists of layers of soft tissue, the *stroma*, which is abundantly supplied with blood vessels.

As the follicles grow, several layers separated by clear membrane form around the ovum, creating tiny spaces between follicular cells. These tiny spaces eventually coalesce to form one larger space (the *antrum*). The mature follicle reaches a diameter of twelve to fifteen mm and often occupies at least one-fourth of the entire volume of the ovary. The rapid increase in follicular fluid and size exerts pressure which ruptures the wall of the ovary, allowing the ovum to escape the follicular cavity in a wave of fluid.

In most cases, and in a manner that is not clearly understood,

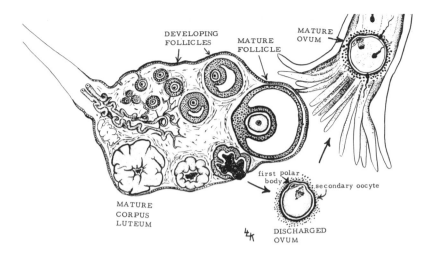

DEVELOPING FOLLICLES
MATURE FOLLICLE
MATURE OVUM
first polar body
secondary oocyte
MATURE CORPUS LUTEUM
DISCHARGED OVUM

Fig. 5-2. Diagrammatic cross section of ovary showing developing follicles, mature follicle, and corpus luteum.

the liberated ovum is deposited in the uterine tube on the same side of the body. There are exceptions to this process, as there are with most biological phenomena, in that ova have been known to enter the uterine tube on the opposite side. Just how these journeys through the peritoneal cavity come about is something of a mystery.

Physicians have recorded a large number of cases in which women who reported for surgery shortly after they had engaged in coitus had sperm in the peritoneal fluid, casting considerable doubt on the assumed necessity of the ovum's being in a Fallopian tube for fertilization to take place. Ova fertilized in these circumstances occasionally implant themselves in the abdominal wall where sections of the uterine wall structure (endometrium) have been displaced. This type of displaced or ectopic pregnancy (outside the womb) is relatively rare, and practically always requires a corrective surgical procedure, although in exceptional instances the fetus is carried full term and may survive after delivery by Caesarean section.[247]

A recent follow-up study was made on a healthy mother and child eleven years after a successful abdominal pregnancy.[41] The fetus developed outside the womb in the abdominal cavity, the placenta being attached to the left ovary and to the abdominal wall. The pregnancy was of eight months' duration, and the baby weighed five pounds four ounces at the time of its Caesarean delivery.

There are recorded in medical history a few instances of pregnancies that occurred after complete hysterectomies, all involving some misplaced endometrium tissue wherein the fertilized ovum implanted itself; none of the fetuses survived. In a recent case a fetus developed in the cul-de-sac of the vagina. The woman's ovaries and Fallopian tubes had been left untouched at the time of her hysterectomy and in some inexplicable manner, an egg became fertilized and implanted itself in the vagina.[153]

Sometimes an abdominal pregnancy is not recognized early enough, and the fetus dies. When this occurs, the dead fetus causes an irritation which accelerates the production of calcium by the mother. The consequence is a large deposit of calcium salts (bone-building material) around it that acts more or less to encase the "foreign" object and to protect the woman's body from being poisoned by the dead fetus. The whole mass becomes calcified and results in what is called a "stone baby" (lithopedion), which may not be discovered and removed for several years, if ever.

How long such phenomena have been recognized in medical history is unclear, but the first authentic case (the famous Sens, France, stone-baby) was reported in a 16th-century medical book. There is a recorded case of one woman who carried such a baby for thirty-five years without being aware of its presence.[247] Recently a forty-eight-year-old Arizona woman delivered a seven-month stone baby which she had unknowingly carried for fourteen years.[314]

After the ovum is discharged from the ovary, the empty follicle's lining grows inward and the vacated space is filled with *corpus luteum.* This new growth produces *progesterone,* the hormone that inhibits ovulation during pregnancy, aids in the implantation and maintenance of the embryo, and stimulates the mammary glands. Ovulation is generally assumed to occur alternately in each ovary, but one ovary may in fact discharge several times in succession. A single egg is usually released at the time of ovulation, but two or more ova from one or more follicles may be discharged.

In recent years the use of fertility drugs has enabled many women who were previously unable to ovulate to become fertile and have babies. Some of the drugs, however, cause several ova to mature and be discharged during the same ovulation period, resulting in a marked rise in the incidence of multiple births in many nations. In very large multiple births (seven children on several occasions, one delivery of eight, and one of nine have been reported recently), the death rate is exceptionally high.[321, 334]

One of the uterine or *Fallopian tubes* (after Gabriello Fallopius, 1523-1562) conveys the egg from the ovary to the uterus, and is also the place where fertilization of the ovum normally occurs. Each of

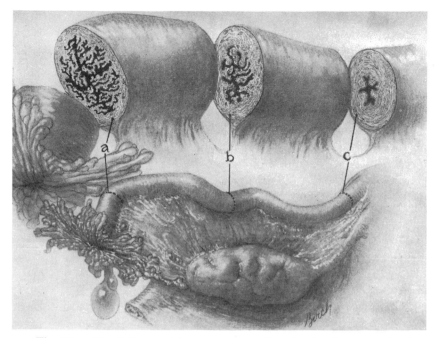

Fig. 5-3. The Fallopian tubes in cross section showing the gross structure of the epithelium in several portions: (a) infundibular; (b) ampullar; and (c) isthmic. From Eastman and Hellman: *Williams Obstetrics,* 13th ed. New York: Appleton-Century-Crofts, 1966.

the uterine tubes is about four inches long and is suspended by a ligament, allowing each tube to extend from the upper and outer part of each side of the uterus to the ovary where the flanged part of the tube connects to and slightly cups over the ovary.

The Fallopian or uterine tubes are musculomembranous structures that are usually divided into three sections: the intramural, the isthmus, and the ampulla. The ampulla is the flanged broad end of the tube which cups down over the ovary. The end *(infundibulum)* of the tube has small finger-like extensions *(fimbria),* one of which is attached to the ovary. The uterine tubes are well supplied with blood from the vessels of the ovaries and the uterus, and have many miniscule, hair-like protrusions extending inward from the wall of the tube.

The hair-like structures, cilia, extending from the interior of each Fallopian tube act in an undulating manner to sweep the ovum from the ampulla toward the uterus. Generally, fertilization occurs in the ampulla, and the fertilized egg moves along to and through the isthmus, the narrowed, wavy portion of the tube; then to the intramural or straight section of the Fallopian tube that passes through the uterine wall. The ovum then enters the uterine cavity and becomes implanted.

The *uterus* or womb is a hollow, thick-walled muscular organ shaped somewhat like a pear. In the mature woman, its size at the top measures approximately two and a half by two inches. It narrows to a diameter of about one inch at the cervix and is about three inches long. It is situated in the pelvic cavity between the bladder and rectum, and hangs slightly below and between the Fallopian tubes, as if it were suspended from them like a garment from a clothesline.

The uterus is held in position by six ligaments, two of which are broad ligaments extending from the uterus to the floor and wall of the pelvis, two more of which are the round ligaments connecting from the uterus near the openings of the Fallopian tubes laterally to the pelvic walls, and the last two of which are the uterosacral ligaments extending from the upper part of the cervix to the sacrum (the bone at the base of the vertebral column).

The shape of the uterus is slightly triangular with its apex narrowing into the cervix, which in turn opens into the rear of the vagina. The opening of the cervix into the vagina is known as the *external os,*

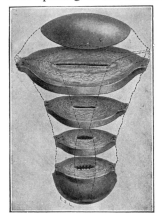

Fig. 5-4. Reconstruction of uterus showing shape of its cavity and cervical canal. From Eastman and Hellman: *Williams Obstetrics,* 13th ed. New York: Appleton-Century-Crofts, 1966.

and its opening into the uterus is known as the *internal os.* When a woman stands erect with bladder and rectum empty, the uterus lies almost horizontal, with its fundus forward, and at a right angle to the vagina.

The uterus is divided into two parts by a slight constriction near the center known as its isthmus (which is to be distinguished from the isthmus of the Fallopian tubes). The larger portion—corpus or body—of the uterus is above the second part, the *cervix.* The walls of the uterus are particularly thick at the fundus where the measurement may be one and a half cm or more. The uterine walls are made up of three layers: the outer layer or serosa *(perimetrium),* which consists of elastic fibrous tissue; the middle or muscular layer *(myometrium),* which makes up most of the uterine wall, and which consists of bundles and layers of very strong smooth muscle cells; and the inner or mucosa layer *(endometrium),* consisting of tissue that thickens as the uterus prepares for implantation of the blastocyst (one of the stages through which the fertilized ovum goes), but that otherwise will slough off, if no pregnancy occurs, at the time of menstruation.

The musculature of the uterus is complex and highly efficient. The muscle bundles combine the uterus and its tubes and ligaments into an interlacing system that produces certain contractions during the period just before ovulation when estrogen production is at its peak. It is thought that these coordinated contractions in some way move the flanged openings of the Fallopian tubes into the proper position to receive the ovum when it is discharged.

The uterine walls have longitudinal and circular muscle fibers that spiral and run through the walls in both clockwise and counter-clockwise directions. The fibers originate in each of the Fallopian tubes, and when they contract, a peristaltic wave commences at the fundus of the uterus and moves toward the cervix. The basket-like interweaving of the muscles allows the uterus both to stretch and expand to gigantic proportions during pregnancy, and to exert tremendous pressure by contracting in a downward manner at the time of labor. Contraction of these muscles also takes place at the time of a woman's orgasmic phase in her sexual response cycle.[218]

The evidence is that most present-day cultures have restrictions against, or at least distaste for, sexual intercourse during the menstrual flow. Furthermore, it has been suggested by medical authorities in the recent past that coitus during menstruation will lead to physical distress for the woman. The research of Masters and Johnson[215] has shown clearly that the fear of distress is unfounded and that, indeed, sexual activity at that time might have just the opposite effect on the woman: *i.e.,* provide relief from pain or discomfort. Of the 331 women who took part in the "orgasm during menstruation" study, only 33 objected to sexual activity on religious or esthetic grounds; 173 expressed desire for coitus, especially during the last half of the flow; and the remaining 125 had no special feelings in the matter one way or the other.

To test the effect of intercourse on menstruating women, all the subjects in a special Masters and Johnson investigation achieved orgasm in a laboratory situation through automanipulative means. During the last part of the orgasmic phase, the observers noted via a *speculum* (an instrument used to dilate the vagina) that frequently menstrual fluid spurted from the cervical os (opening) under contractile pressure that was powerful enough to expel the fluid through the vagina without touching either the speculum or the vaginal walls. The explosive force can be accounted for by a sudden contraction of uterine muscles, starting at the fundus (top) and moving towards the cervix. Perhaps the sudden clearing of menstrual fluid from the uterus and the relaxation of uterine muscles after the series of orgasmic contractions account for the reports of reduced pelvic cramping and backache from women who experience orgasm shortly after the onset of menstruation.

The cavity of the uterus is a flattened space which is little more than a slit, the total length being about two and a half inches. The flattened cavity narrows to a minute opening at the internal os, and continues through the cervix as an opening smaller than a soda straw.

The cervix is smaller than the body of the uterus; the size ratio in mature women is about one to two. In the newborn the ratio is the

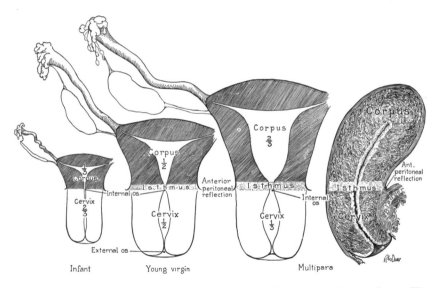

Fig. 5-5. Front and side sections of normal uterus and appendages. The comparative size of infantile, adult nonparous, and multiparous uteri. From Eastman and Hellman: *Williams Obstetrics,* 13th ed. New York: Appleton-Century-Crofts, 1966.

reverse, the cervix being about twice as large as the corpus. In young children, the ratio is about one to one, and physicians often describe women as having an infantile uterus (and frequently not capable of bearing children) when it and the cervix are nearly the same size. The body of the uterus grows proportionately larger because of hormonal secretions that commence at puberty, while the growth of the cervix merely keeps pace with the growth rate of the rest of the body.

The cervix is more fibrous than the corpus of the uterus, and its palmate (fold-like) lining contains glands that produce a mucous secretion, once erroneously thought to attract sperm cells.[215] About one-third to one-half inch of the cervix extends into the vagina, thus producing a connection for the passage of sperm into the place where they may meet the ovum. During pregnancy, the cervix is often closed by a mucous plug that serves to separate the uterus from the vagina, keeping bacteria and other undesirable matter from entering the uterus and thereby reducing the possibility of infection.

The *vagina* is a muscular tube, capable of considerable dilation, that extends from just behind the cervix—it was mentioned in the preceding paragraph that the cervix projects into the vagina by a fraction of an inch—to an external opening in the vestibule of the vulva. The vagina is about three inches long on the anterior or front wall, and about three and a half inches on the posterior or back wall. It extends upwards in an approximately vertical manner in a standing woman, roughly at right angles to the uterus. It is the organ which receives the penis during the act of sexual intercourse.

The walls of the vagina are in contact with each other under ordinary conditions, and are made up of three layers: the *fibrous coat,* which is a thin layer of elastic fibrous tissue, serving not only as an aid to contraction, but as a connective tissue to other bodily tissues as well; the *muscular coat,* which is a layer of smooth muscles, most of which run in a longitudinal direction—although there are also bundles of circular muscular fibers in the vaginal canal, *e.g.,* the sphincter muscle of striated fiber surrounding the external vaginal opening; and the *mucosa,* which contains mucous crypts and many blood vessels. The mucosa has large folds in it, giving the vagina a wrinkled appearance. The area contains an intricate network of erectile tissue which serves to help dilate and close the vaginal channel (see Chapter 11).

The mucosal coat of the vagina does not contain glands, although mucous secretions of the uterine tissue sometimes aid in moistening the vagina. Vaginal lubrication, present during sexual excitement, is brought about by the vagina itself, since it secretes a fluid through a process, similar to sweating, that is still considered something of a puzzle.[215] As sexual excitement builds and continues, little beads of "sweat" appear on the vaginal surface. Often the vaginal muscles contract suddenly, bringing the walls of the vagina together in such a manner as to force secretions out of the vagina in a spurting fashion. This secretion, along with the orgasmic platform contractions (see Chapter

11), is the foundation of the mistaken notion that women ejaculate as men do. However, the "sweat" merely serves as a lubricant to aid in the penetration of the penis, making the act of sexual intercourse easier to perform.

With the birth of children and the natural relaxation of muscles as a woman gets older, the vaginal muscles, no longer firm or strong, often sag. The result is a vagina which may be too large to allow for the partners' fullest satisfaction from coitus. This condition is especially bothersome for a man who depends largely upon friction of the vaginal wall against the glans of his penis to stimulate his erogenous nerve endings and to supply the sexual impulses that culminate in an orgasm. Similarly, this condition can also be annoying to a woman who receives little or no physiological pleasure from penile penetration—the vagina contains very few nerve endings that give sexual pleasure—but who gains some psychological pleasure from penetration.

(Although many women claim a sex act is incomplete and unsatisfying to them without penetration, empirical findings indicate that, physically speaking, an orgasm is an orgasm, whether attained by penetration, manual manipulation of the genital area, or by some other technique.[117, 122, 215] Any increase in pleasure from penetration would therefore appear to be the result of psychological or emotional factors.)

Overly relaxed vaginal muscles may be strengthened by proper exercise.[77] A woman with this condition is advised to contract the vaginal muscles in a manner similar to the contraction employed to halt urination midway. There should be a series of twenty or so alternating contractions and relaxations, to be repeated about ten times a day. After a month of these exercises, a difference in the size of the vagina should be noticeable. The exercises are not necessarily time-consuming and can be done while the woman is busy with her daily household routine. Previously, relaxed vaginas that might well have been strengthened and made smaller or tighter by exercise were operated on to produce the desired effect. Such surgery is still performed but only in extreme cases when muscle damage is severe or when other physiological difficulties exist.

The *hymen* or maidenhead is a fold of connective tissue that partially closes the external orifice of the vagina. This tissue, if still intact, is usually ruptured by the first act of sexual intercourse. More often, however, the tissue is broken by strenuous exercise, accidents to the pubic area, or experimentation. A ruptured hymen is certainly not *prima facie* evidence that a girl is not a virgin; and on the other hand, there are those rare cases in which the hymen is so flexible or pliable that coitus can take place repeatedly without rupturing the tissue.

If a woman approaches marriage with the hymen still intact, it is common practice for her physician to cut the tissue after a mild anesthetic has been applied to the area. In the case of a ring-shaped or annular hymen, the doctor may suggest inserting and rotating the fingertips or using a small dilator, either of which will stretch the tissue and permit penile penetration without pain or difficulty. Obviously, the hymenal tissue usually does not seal or close off the vagina completely, since the menstrual flow is discharged as easily from virgins as from nonvirgins. The tissue is usually annular or perforated, or it otherwise only partially closes off the opening.

Pain accompanying first sexual intercourse is frequently assumed to be a cause of frigidity. This pain is often the result of rupturing the hymen; but if the hymen has not been previously ruptured by exercise or the like, it would seem foolish to allow the tissue to be torn by forceful penile penetration when a physician can cut or remove it so easily beforehand.

The importance of an intact hymen to some women at the time of marriage is attested to by the fact that a Japanese gynecologist recently performed his ten-thousandth surgical operation whereby he creates an artificial hymen for a prospective bride.[332]

In addition to the pain of tearing the hymenal tissue, there is often pain during early, and especially first, sexual intercourse because of vaginal muscular contraction resulting from fear and ignorance of the facts of coitus. If a woman is relaxed and unafraid, there is little reason why she cannot comfortably and pleasurably accommodate a very large penis, even though she has not had sexual intercourse previously. Women under emotional stress, however, even though they might be highly experienced sexually, can have contractional spasms of the vaginal muscles (a condition known as *vaginismus*), and forced penetration is extremely painful or even impossible.

The external genital apparatus of a woman is known as the *vulva,* and is made up of the following visible parts or areas: the mons veneris (also called mons pubis), the labia majora (major or large outer lips), the labia minora (small inner lips), the clitoris, and the vestibule.

The *mons veneris* or *mons pubis* is composed of fatty tissue collected below the skin and over the pubic bone (symphysis pubis), and is covered with springy, curly hair. This area houses certain nerve endings that when stimulated by weight, pressure, or similar conditions can produce sexual excitement. From this fatty prominent mound, two longitudinal folds of skin bearing pubic hair laterally serve to form the outer borders of the vulva.

The *labia majora* are the two folds of skin described above that

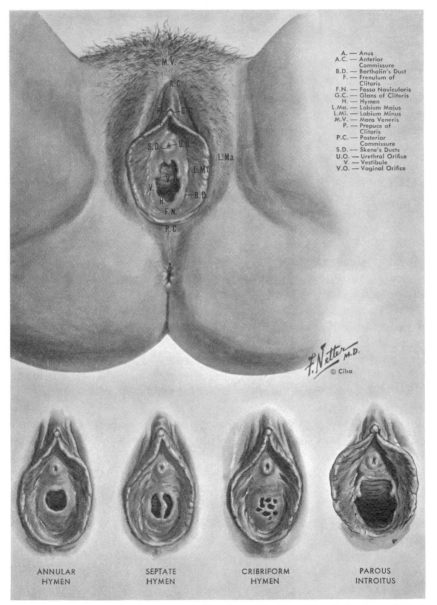

Fig. 5-6. External female genitalia. Copyright *The Ciba Collection of Medical Illustrations* by Frank H. Netter, M.D.

enclose the vulval cleft. The lips are quite fatty, and their inner sides contain sebaceous follicles and sweat glands but no hair.

The *labia minora* are also two longitudinal folds and are located within the major lips. The skin is rich in blood vessels, nerve endings, and small sebaceous glands, but contains no hair or fat cells. These small lips form the lateral and lower borders of the vestibule, and fuse at the top to form the prepuce and to enclose the clitoris. The labia minora are highly erogenous and are markedly sensitive to stimulation. While they contain no erectile tissue of the usual type, the area does change its structure somewhat during sexual excitement, apparently through some manner of trapping blood. Under the influence of such stimulation they flare or spread out, exposing the vestibule, whereas under ordinary circumstances the lips are together, more or less sealing off the inner region from view.

The *clitoris* is a small cylindrical erectile structure that is situated at the top of the vestibule and at the lower border of the pubis symphysis. Its composition consists of two *crura* (leg-like stalks) arising at the pubic bone and fusing together to form the body or shaft, terminating in the *glans,* which projects between the bifurcated branches of the labia minora. The entire clitoris, except the glans, is underneath the upper part of the labia minora where its two lips join to form the clitoral prepuce or *frenulum clitoridis.* The body of the clitoris can be felt just beneath the prepuce that covers it; unlike the penis, the clitoris does not hang free and only its glans is exposed. The body contains two corpora cavernosa, spongy erectile structures that are enclosed by a dense fibrous tissue; with stimulation, these bodies may engorge with blood and become erect. Ordinarily less than one inch in length (although there are on record striking variations in its measurements), the clitoris when sexually stimulated may enlarge considerably, especially in shaft diameter, to twice its flaccid size or more.

The glans of the clitoris has a diameter of about four to five mm.[101] Like the glans of the penis, it contains an abundance of nerve endings and is the most sexually excitable area of a woman's body. Direct contact with the glans—such as the man's pubic bone rubbing against it— and indirect stimulation through pulling and tugging of the area as the minor lips move in and out of the vagina, are coital methods of bringing a woman to orgasm. Masters and Johnson[215] have pointed out that in self-manipulation of the clitoris, women stimulate to the side of it— usually the right side if they are right-handed, and conversely—rather than stimulating the clitoris directly.

Smegma, an accumulation of genital secretions, can collect under the prepuce covering the clitoris, resulting in abrasions and cohesions between it and the glans. This causes severe pain in many cases when the clitoris enlarges during sexual excitement. Circumcision was a former remedy, but in present-day practice a probe is frequently used in order to separate the prepuce from the glans and to rid the area of the smelly ragged lumps that produce the pain. Obviously it would be difficult to enjoy sexual activity if this sort of pain accompanied it.

The *vestibule* is the cleft region enclosed by the labia minora, and it houses the openings of the vagina and the urethra. This area is also rich in nerve endings and blood vessels, and is highly responsive to proper stimulation. The urethral opening or meatus is located about halfway between the clitoris and the vagina and is, of course, the opening of the tube through which urine passes from the bladder to outside the body. The greater vestibular glands, the Bartholin's glands, are situated on each side of the vaginal orifice. Each secretes a drop or so of lubricating fluid that in the past was thought to aid in penile penetration. It has been shown by recent research that the secretion of these glands is too slight to be of significant benefit in vaginal lubrication.[215]

CHAPTER 6

Menstruation and
the Climacteric

THERE ARE two dramatic changes that take place in a woman's reproductive life: menstruation or the menarche, which commences usually in the early teens, and menopause—also called the climacteric or "change of life"—which occurs some thirty-five or so years later. Some men undergo a climacteric, but usually not until they are about fifty-five years old. When it does occur in men, it is largely psychological in its impact and may possibly result in some reduction in sexual vigor and interest because of the depressive or other negative emotional conditions it can induce.

MENSTRUATION

It has already been remarked that most girls between the ages of eleven and fifteen begin developing the physiological characteristics of puberty. Accompanying the development of breasts, reproductive organs, and secondary sexual characteristics is the *menarche,* which is that point during puberty when a monthly uterine "bleeding" called *menstruation* begins. Although this cycle can vary from twenty-one to ninety days and still be physiologically normal, the average duration is from twenty-eight to thirty days. During the thirty to thirty-five years a woman is capable of conception, she menstruates 300 to 500 times.

Although menstruation can occur without ovulation's having taken place, the general purpose of the menstrual cycle is the preparation and maintenance of the uterus for implantation of the fertilized egg. The menstrual cycle can be divided into three phases: the destructive phase, the follicular phase, and the luteal phase. In order that these phases may proceed normally, there must be a well-balanced relationship between the central nervous system and the endocrine system.

1. *Destructive phase.* Progesterone, which has prepared and maintained the walls of the uterus for implantation of the fertilized

ovum, is withdrawn when the corpus luteum regresses. This withdrawal, or even a lowered concentration of the hormone, causes the lining of the uterus to break down, slough off, and be discharged from the body in a form of bleeding. The first day of the monthly cycle is considered to be the first day of the destructive phase; this usually lasts from three to seven days, the average being four or five. The discharge consists not only of blood but of other fluids and debris from the uterine wall in the form of mucus, fragments of endometrium, and dried epithelial cells from the vagina.

The amount of discharge during the destructive phase varies widely from woman to woman, and sometimes with the same woman. On the average, however, the discharge amounts to approximately one

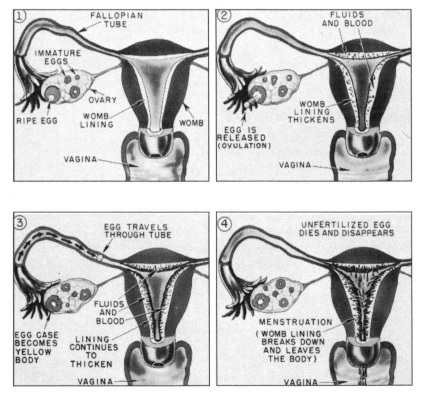

Fig. 6-1. THE MENSTRUAL CYCLE: (1) During early part of cycle, egg matures in ovary; endometrium begins to thicken. (2) About 14th day after onset of last menstruation, mature ovum is released; endometrium is thick and spongy. (3) Ovum travels through Fallopian tubes; ruptured follicle becomes corpus luteum; fluids and blood engorge uterine lining. (4) If ovum not fertilized, endometrium breaks down and sloughs off in form of bleeding (menstruation). Photograph courtesy *Sexology* magazine.

cupful (six to eight ounces), with the amount of *actual* blood loss on even the heaviest day of flow being only about one tablespoonful. Menstrual blood is entirely venous in origin, and there is usually no clotting because the essential elements for clotting—*e.g.*, fibrinogen and prothrombin—are missing.

With the onset of the destructive phase, there can be a number of organic and psychic alterations. There can be increases in frequency of urination, in the size and firmness of the breasts, and in skin disorders such as pimples. Fatigue, headaches, and marked irritability sometimes become more pronounced. The latter changes, it should be noted, may well be due to psychological factors related to certain unfortunate attitudes toward sex in general and menstruation ("the Curse") specifically, or to organic factors; perhaps both are involved. The toxic condition of the body increases as the uterine tissue dies and sloughs off. The bloodstream then picks up some of this toxic material and circulates it throughout the body. It will also be remembered that just before menstruation there is a marked decrease in the amount of progesterone hormone in the body, producing an imbalance between estrogen and progesterone. The imbalance can elicit unfortunate physical and emotional reactions in some women.

2. *Follicular phase.* After the menstrual flow stops, the uterine wall is very thin. Under the stimulation of the estrogen hormone, which is secreted by the follicles located in the ovaries, the uterus begins a process of growth which lasts about nine days. During this period there are many follicles (hence the name of this phase) containing developing ova; but the majority cease to grow, and only one usually reaches maturity during any one cycle. The mature follicle at its full growth can fill up as much as one-fourth of the ovary. Approaching the fourteenth day of the menstrual cycle, the follicle ruptures and a mature ovum is discharged; this event is called *ovulation*. After the release of the ovum, the follicle (which is now called the corpus luteum, or yellow body) seals itself off with the aid of the luteinizing and luteotropic hormones that are secreted by the pituitary gland in the process described earlier (see Chapter 3).

3. *Luteal phase.* During the follicular phase the secretion of estrogen increases gradually. There is a maximum concentration of estrogen in the blood at the moment of ovulation. Following ovulation and the development of the corpus luteum, this yellow body begins actively to secrete progesterone and the concentration of estrogen decreases. Progesterone begins preparing the uterus for the fertilized egg. The mucous membrane of the uterus becomes thicker and more vascular as small "lakes" of blood, called *lacunae,* are formed within

the endometrium (wall) of the uterus. The lacunae provide nourishment for the ovum, if it becomes fertilized and implants itself in the endometrium.

During the luteal phase, luteotropin, as well as the ovarian hormones, causes the amount of extracellular and intracellular fluid in the breasts to increase, resulting in greater size and sensitivity. There is sometimes premenstrual congestion and swelling of mucous membranes that cause an accumulation of fluid and a consequent temporary gain in weight of as much as five pounds.

There are rare instances in which extragenital bleeding occurs during the menstrual flow. This phenomenon is evoked by a sudden decrease in the size of the blood vessels (vasospasm) of the endometrium approximately forty-eight hours before the menstrual flow begins. Called "vicarious menstruation," it is usually from the nose although it has been known to occur from lungs, retina of the eye, and so forth.

There is some disagreement over the cause of this phenomenon. Some authorities relate it to *endometriosis,* an ectopic (misplaced) growth of the tissue that makes up the lining of the uterus, and others relegate its causality solely to psychological factors. In 30% of the instances of vicarious menstruation, uterine bleeding is totally displaced, while in the remaining cases the two flows occur simultaneously.[92] In light of the indirect relationship between nasal functions and sexual activity, it is relevant that the part of the body most frequently involved in vicarious menstruation is the lining of the nose. The causal relationship between acuity of smell and the production of sex hormones has already been discussed. The mucous membrane of the nose, furthermore, frequently swells during sexual excitation and may secrete more than its usual amount of mucus.[179] Moreover, oral or nasal decongestants appear to have some effect on the endometrium of the uterus during the menstrual period, reducing discomfort and the flow as well.[3] The Kinsey group pointed out the interesting similarity between a sneeze and an orgasm in physiologic buildup and explosive discharge of tensions.[179]

If conception does not occur during the menstrual cycle, the corpus luteum degenerates and the concentration both of estrogen and progesterone decreases immensely. This sudden decrease in the amounts of both hormones is believed to bring about the destructive phase of menstruation, and the entire cyclic process then starts all over again.

There is general agreement among physicians that women should not coddle themselves during the menstrual period, but should carry on their activities in the usual manner. Participating in sports during this time, for example, will cause no undue stress nor will it harm the reproductive organs.[340]

THE CLIMACTERIC OR MENOPAUSE

When the average woman reaches forty-five to fifty years, her ovaries cease to produce and liberate ova, and the uterus gradually abandons the monthly process of shedding and regenerating its lining. This cessation of the menstrual cycle is called the *climacteric* or *menopause,* and its duration does not usually exceed two years. But as long as any menstrual periods occur at all, however erratically, there is a possibility of ovulation and hence a possibility of pregnancy. If a woman has not had a menstrual period for a year, on the other hand, she can be reasonably sure that ovulation has finally ceased and that conception is impossible.

The climacteric can be quite disturbing and is sometimes beset with great emotional disquiet, even to the point of psychotic illness. Because of vastly improved techniques of hormonal therapy and other medication, however, most if not all of these distressing emotional reactions can now be avoided or alleviated. Furthermore, tranquillizers and short-term psychotherapy are presently made use of in the treatment of climacteric symptoms, and these menopausal difficulties are not so troublesome as they have been in the past.

The glandular imbalance that occurs at the change of life is the source of an instability in the vasomotor system which, in turn, effects an irregularity in the diameter of the blood vessels. This fluctuation permits more blood to flow at one time—inducing hot flashes—and less blood at another. Hot flashes last from a second or so to several minutes, and can occur several times a day. The reason for the phenomenon is unknown, but it is interesting—and perhaps encouraging—that the more hot flashes a woman experiences during menopause, the less likelihood there usually is that other troublesome conditions will develop.[274]

Other symptoms associated with menopause are fatigue, dizziness, migraine headaches, chest and neck pains, insomnia, excessive desire for sleep, and depression. The chance that the climacteric will produce any mental disturbance is about one in 50,000, and only about a quarter of menopausal women have any sort of distressful symptomatology.[274] Generally speaking, the better the mental health of the woman before the climacteric, the fewer unpleasant symptoms she will have when it occurs.[82]

The median age for the onset of menopause has advanced from

46.6 years in 1853 to 50.1 years in 1965.[167] It has been observed that women who start menstruation earlier in life than most girls will continue menstruating longer. These findings seem to hold in other spheres of individual sexual life as well;[179, 180] for instance, people who begin erotic activity at an earlier age than average appear to maintain their sexual vigor longer. Furthermore, men and women who engage in frequent sexual activity are able to continue the activity later in life than the average person.

As a man grows older, physical changes become evident which are somewhat similar to those observed in aging women. Accompanying the aging process is a diminution in certain physical responses at the time of orgasm, such as a decrease in the intensity and prolongation of the sex flush and involuntary muscular spasms.[215] There is a reduction in the size and firmness of the testicles as a man gets older. The testicular tubules that produce sperm thicken and commence a degenerative process which inhibits the production of sperm. The prostate gland becomes enlarged and its contractions are weaker. The force of ejaculation decreases, seminal fluid is thinner, and a longer time is required to effect an orgasm. Erections are less vigorous and occur on fewer and fewer occasions. There is a decline in the production of male sex hormones. Symptoms of depression or paranoia sometimes accompany the physical changes of the climacteric and can affect men and women alike.

It is widely assumed that sexual activity ceases for both men and women during the later years of their lives. The truth of the matter is that sexual interest and capacity frequently extend into old age. Almost half the men between the ages of seventy-five and ninety-two, as a point of fact, report that they engage in satisfactory sexual intercourse.[283] Scientific evidence of prolonged or permanent impotence before the age of fifty-five is rare,[82] and only about a quarter of the male population becomes impotent by the age of seventy.[180] Investigation reveals further that the average frequency of coitus for the majority of men over sixty-five is approximately four times a month, and that masturbation is a recurrent practice among 25% of them.[366] The Kinsey researchers have demonstrated that the sexual drive in a woman reaches a pinnacle in her late twenties or early thirties, and that it then remains at that plateau until she is sixty or even older.[170]

A major challenge to older men and women is finding the means to satisfy their sexual needs when the spouse has died or is no longer interested in sexual activity. Many have been counseled by experts in the field of marriage to use self-stimulative methods to gain relief from erotic tensions, and those following this advice frequently find that maintaining some form of sexual expression helps to prevent depression, frustration, and hostility.[283]

Loss of sexual vigor with age should be no greater than the loss of other physical capabilities. A man (or woman) of sixty is hardly capable of running 100 yards as quickly as he might have at twenty; but the chances are excellent that he can still run the 100 yards if he proceeds leisurely and feels no anxiety about not running so swiftly (or so often) as he did in the heyday of his youth. The loss of sexual potency before advanced age appears to be an outgrowth of psychological problems rather than of physical incapacity. Men and women frequently refrain from continuing sex relations into their late years of life, or after the death of their spouses, because, whatever other rationale they offer, they themselves regard sexual activity at their age as a little ridiculous or are frightened that they might be unable to please the partner. They therefore avoid a possible blow to their pride by shunning sexual contacts altogether.[283]

A woman's fertility ceases, and rather suddenly, some time during the menopause. As yet another instance of the assimilation by individuals of faulty notions from a society fearful and ignorant of sexual matters, many persons relate loss of fertility to loss of sexual desire.[256] This unfortunate misconception is easily refuted by clinical and experimental evidence, which confirms that men and women can engage in fairly regular and pleasurable sexual activity long after middle age.

CHAPTER 7

Fertilization, Prenatal Development, and Parturition

ALTHOUGH smaller than the period at the end of this sentence, the human ovum is a relatively large cell. It averages 0.13 mm in diameter and 0.000004 gm in weight, and is one of the largest of mammalian eggs.[107] The development of ova, a process known as *oogenesis*, has been partially described in Chapter 5. The position taken in that discussion is the most widely accepted theory concerning the origin of human ova, namely (1) that they grow within follicles which are present in the very early development of the ovaries' germinal epithelium; and (2) that they are present at the time of a girl's birth, but lie dormant until her sexual maturity, at which time they develop and become mature in a limited number, usually one by one. A second theory concerning the origin of ova is that they are not present at birth, but that they arise, fully developed, from the cells of the germinal epithelium as they are needed in the sexually mature female.

Oogenesis consists of four developmental stages: oogonium, primary oocyte, secondary oocyte, and mature ovum. In the first phase of development, the *oogonium,* or basic cell of the ovum, is enclosed in an ovarian follicle. It then develops into the second stage, the *primary oocyte,* which is somewhat larger than the original cell. Just prior to ovulation, the primary oocyte undergoes a process known as *reduction division.* The paired chromosomes within the oocyte divide, with one of each pair going to each of the two daughter cells created by the division. The number of chromosomes in each daughter cell is therefore twenty-three rather than the usual forty-six. During the stages of primary oocyte and secondary oocyte, cell division in each instance produces two daughter cells, one of which is considerably larger than the other. The smaller of the two is referred to as a *polar body,* which has little function and ultimately degenerates.

Although each daughter cell contains half the chromosomes of the primary oocyte, only one of them contributes chromosomes to the union with the male sperm. This daughter cell, called the *secondary oocyte* (the third stage of oogenesis), is much larger than the other because it retains practically all the cytoplasm (the material that maintains the life of the cell's nucleus) of the original cell. The second daughter cell is minute and contains little cytoplasm. The secondary oocyte in the process of ovulation moves from the follicle into the uterine tube where fertilization occurs, if it is to take place.

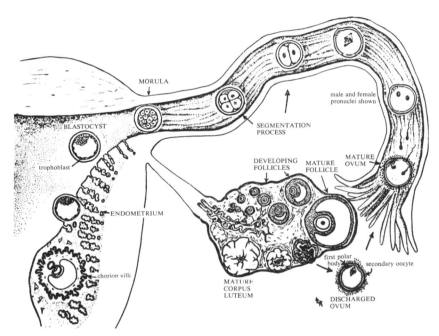

Fig. 7-1.   Ovulation, fertilization, and implantation.

FERTILIZATION

Upon penetration by the sperm—stage four of oogenesis—the ovum is considered to be mature. The entrance of the sperm into the ovum causes an immediate change in the peripheral layer of the egg, a yolk-originated membrane that prevents other sperm from penetrating it. When it enters the egg, the fertilizing sperm loses its tail, and its head and the connecting piece (neck) expand and grow into the male pronucleus and centrosome (important protoplasmic body in subsequent cell division). At this point, the female pronucleus (nucleus of the secondary oocyte) and the male pronucleus (head of the spermatozoon) approach each other, the nuclear membranes disappear, and the gene-carrying portions (chromatin) of the two nuclei join, then reform into two groups of equal number. Fertilization is now complete.

There are three general terms used to describe the fertilized ovum as it develops into the infant we know at birth. From the time of fertilization until the second week, the developing cell mass is referred to as a *zygote;* from the second to the eighth week, it is called an *embryo;* and from the eighth week until birth, a *fetus.* The appearance and initial development of all the rudimentary systems of the body mark the end of the embryonic period. The last period, the fetal stage, consists of the further growth and elaboration of existing rudimentary systems.

The process of *parthenogenesis* as described by Professor E. H. Herrick[160] might be mentioned here. Also called "virgin birth," parthenogenesis concerns the "fertilization" and development of the female's egg without any possible previous contact with spermatozoa. This phenomenon is a common occurrence in lower animals, such as the honeybee, and is the sole method of reproduction among certain other insects. Experimentation in parthenogenesis with various animals has shown that a great number of stimuli will induce the process of development as if the egg had been fertilized in the usual manner. For example, cooling the Fallopian tubes of rabbits, heating the eggs of certain moths, and even applying saliva of human males to carp eggs have sufficiently irritated the eggs to prompt their development.[160, 354] A very high percentage of the eggs of virgin turkey hens undergo parthenogenesis in experimental circumstances, although the early death rate among the hatched birds is very high.

The obvious question arises: is this phenomenon possible in human beings? There is no definite answer to the question at the present time, and there is considerable disagreement among investigators, past and present. One aspect is a certainty, however. If parthenogenesis were to occur, the offspring must invariably be female because of the way chromosomes are arranged in men and women. Since women have only one type of sex-determining chromosome (X), only the X chromosome could be passed on.

One of the leading researchers in the field of fertilization is Dr. Landrum B. Shettles. In a study of 400 human ova, he observed that the first stages of developmental processes had begun in three of the eggs, even though there could have been no contact with sperm. The logical conclusion would seem to be that if developmental processes in the human ovum can begin spontaneously, they should be able to continue to term.[160] Only further research can uncover the answer.

The phrase "virgin birth" ordinarily conveys the idea of human pregnancy and subsequent birth without a previous act of sexual intercourse followed by union of ovum and sperm. In this context, the possibility of a true virgin birth has never been scientifically established. Impregnation without penile penetration, however, is a real possibility, and it is a phenomenon that happens more often than many realize. If, for instance, a man were to have his penis near or on a woman's vulva and ejaculate during sexual play, semen could enter the vaginal opening and make its way through the vagina into the uterus. Or if a man were to ejaculate, get sperm on his hands, and soon thereafter manually manipulate the woman's genitals, especially if he inserted a finger into the vagina, he could introduce sperm into the vaginal canal. Were impregnation to result in either of these instances, and the girl's hymen was still intact, the subsequent parturition might accurately be called a "virgin birth."

The fertilized ovum produces two daughter cells by its first mitotic division. Each daughter cell receives one-half the chromosomes contained in both the sperm and ovum. The fertilized ovum in its early stage, as was stated previously, is referred to as a zygote.

The process of cell division in the zygote is known as *segmentation.* The spherical zygote undergoes mitotic divisions, forming first two cells, then four by a cleavage at right angles to the first, then into eight by yet another cleavage in a third plane. These divisions create four cells above the original cleavage and four below. The eight cells are further divided by a similar process into sixteen, then into thirty-two, and so on. The increasing number of cells develops within the fixed outer bounds of the zygote, the outer dimensions remaining the same until implantation.

Through the process of mitotic division, the fertilized ovum or zygote develops into a spherical mass of cells known as a *morula.* The morula moves slowly through the uterine tubes and into the uterus; during this process a cavity is developed within it. The cavity enlarges until there is an outer hollow sphere of cells, the *trophoblast,* from which the inner cell layer projects toward the center. At this stage the fertilized egg is referred to as a *blastocyst.*[354]

The inner ball of cells forms two layers, the *ectoderm* and the *endoderm,* in such a manner that two cavities take shape simultaneously. Later, a third cellular layer, the *mesoderm,* makes its appearance between the ectoderm and the endoderm. These three layers of primitive germ cells, which are situated between the two cavities, constitute the *embryonic disc,* from which the embryo proper develops.

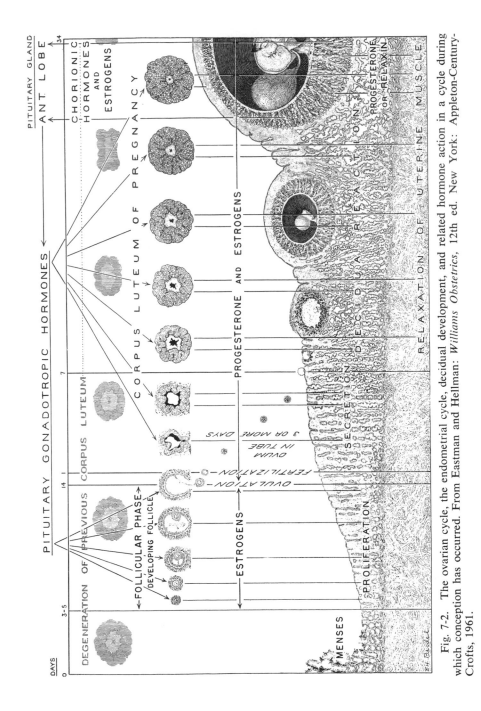

Fig. 7-2. The ovarian cycle, the endometrial cycle, decidual development, and related hormone action in a cycle during which conception has occurred. From Eastman and Hellman: *Williams Obstetrics*, 12th ed. New York: Appleton-Century-Crofts, 1961.

After the process, described in the following paragraph, whereby the embryo becomes implanted in the wall of the uterus, the three layers of primitive germ cells—the ectoderm, the endoderm, and the mesoderm—become differentiated. Eventually the nervous system, the sense organs, mouth cavity, and skin will develop from the ectoderm; from the endoderm will come the digestive and respiratory systems; and from the mesoderm, the muscular, skeletal, circulatory, excretory, and reproductive systems.[13, 354]

About the seventh or eighth day after fertilization, the blastocyst comes into direct contact with the prepared wall of the uterus, the endometrium, and adheres to it. The cells of the trophoblast apparently produce enzymes that dissolve the maternal tissue to permit entry of the blastocyst, and by the twelfth day after fertilization, the embryo has buried itself completely within the endometrium. Little finger-like protrusions, the *chorionic villi,* grow from the chorion outward into the maternal tissue. Eventually these villi limit themselves to the ultimate point of junction between embryo and uterus.

During embryonic life, peripheral membranes form and then extend beyond the region in which the embryo itself develops. They serve as a means of obtaining food and oxygen, and as an avenue for the elimination of wastes from the embryo. During the first fourteen days of gestation, the embryo has not yet developed a functioning circulatory system, and food is obtained primarily by osmosis. Since the peripheral membranes are not incorporated within the body of the embryo and are discarded at the time of birth, they are called extraembryonic or fetal membranes. These membranes—including the yolk

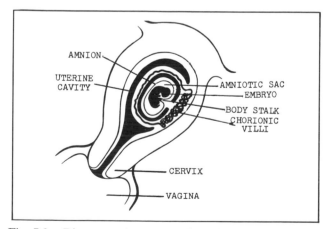

Fig. 7-3. Diagrammatic cross section of implanted embryo.

sac, chorion, amnion, body stalk, and allantois—begin developing about the second or third week of embryonic life.

Although virtually no yolk accumulates in the human ovum, a *yolk sac* is formed just as if a yolk existed. This yolk sac, which is lined with endodermal cells, is the primary material from which the primitive digestive tract is made. As the embryo develops, there is a progressive constriction of the yolk sac until it is connected to the embryo only by a thread-like structure called the *yolk stalk,* which ultimately becomes incorporated into the umbilical cord.

The *amnion* is a thin, transparent, tough membrane composed of a layer of ectodermal cells with an external covering of mesodermal cells. The amniotic cavity surrounded by this membrane appears before the body of the embryo has taken a definite shape, and is filled with a clear watery fluid called the *amniotic fluid.* The developing embryo is suspended in this fluid by its umbilical cord. The amniotic fluid has several important functions: it equalizes the pressure about the embryo, thus protecting it from jolts and mechanical injuries; it prevents the embryo from forming adhesions to the amnion that could result in malformations; it permits changes in fetal posture; and it acts as a hydrostatic wedge to facilitate childbirth by helping to dilate the neck of the uterus. In about the fifth month of pregnancy, the fetus usually begins to swallow some of the amniotic fluid. The infant's first bowel movements, consequently, are a discharge of this swallowed liquid. The baby's respiratory passages may also have to be cleared of some of the fluid after birth in order for normal respiration to begin.

The *allantois,* which ultimately constitutes part of the umbilical cord, is a tubular division of the posterior part of the yolk sac. During the development of the embryo, furthermore, it fuses with the chorion (described below) in the formation of the placenta. Functionally, the allantois of itself has no great importance except that it acts as a rudimentary umbilical cord in the early weeks of gestation.

The *chorion,* the outermost extra-embryonic membrane, completely surrounds the embryo. It is composed of two layers of epithelial cells: an outer ectoderm and an inner mesoderm. The most important role played by the chorion is in the formation of the placenta.

The *placenta* is formed by the interlocking of the *decidua basalis* (the portion of the uterine mucosa or endometrium directly underlying the chorionic vesicle) with the *chorion frondosum,* which is the external surface of the chorion that is covered with villi (finger-like projections). The placenta, comprised of uterine tissue and its interwoven villi, serves as a special organ of interchange between embryo and mother. The growth of the placenta is fairly rapid until about the fifth month of pregnancy. It has then reached its greatest relative size, which is approximately one-half of the internal surface of the uterus. The villi of the placenta are kept steeped in fresh maternal blood that enters the placental spaces about the villi by means of small blood vessels. As the blood drains back into the veins of the uterus, it is replaced by fresh blood from the uterine arteries.

From the beginning of its development, the fetal circulation of blood is a closed circuit. At no time during any stage of normal pregnancy is there any intermingling of maternal with fetal blood. The intermingling of the two systems can occur only in the case of injury to some portion of the placenta. The maternal and fetal blood both circulate within the placenta, but are kept separated by the walls of

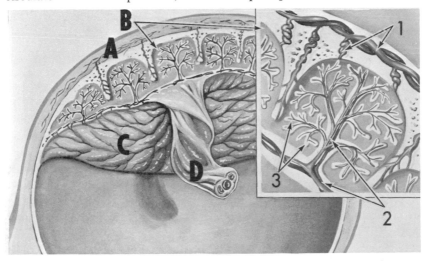

Fig. 7-4. Cross section of the placenta's attachment to the uterine wall, showing the knobby projections (B) of the placenta into the lining of the womb (A), the inside surface of the placenta (C), and the umbilical cord (D). The inset shows the interchange between the maternal blood vessels (1) and the fetal blood vessels (2) through the walls of tiny villi (3). Photograph courtesy *Sexology* magazine.

the umbilical blood vessels. All interchange between the two systems is by diffusion and absorption. A red blood cell, which is only about 1/30,000 of an inch in size, is too large to pass through the openings of the walls, yet chemicals and food bodies are small enough to penetrate the walls with no difficulty. The fetal blood absorbs food and oxygen, and it eliminates carbon dioxide and other metabolic waste products. These are taken into the mother's blood and eventually eliminated by her as waste products. Although the cellular barrier between the two blood systems generally prevents the passage of bacteria and other disease germs, some substances—antibiotics, certain viruses, and some disease germs such as the *Treponema pallidum,* which causes syphilis—are capable of crossing the barrier. The exact direction in which maternal blood flows within the placenta is not yet determined, but it is generally thought to pass through the marginal sinus and return to the uterine veins in the decidua basalis.

During the fifth week of pregnancy, the *umbilical cord* is formed. It is composed of the yolk stalk and its vitelline blood vessels, the allantois, and the umbilical blood vessels. The fully developed cord is about twenty inches long, which is also the average length of a full-term fetus.

Signs of pregnancy may be divided into three classes: the presumptive signs, which are largely subjective and are the individual experiences of each pregnant woman; the probable signs; and the positive signs. The last two classes are more objective than the first, and lie within the interpretive province of the physician and laboratory technician.[10]

The presumptive signs are the first to be noticed—cessation of the menses, morning sickness, changes in the size and fullness of the breasts, as well as the development of a dark coloration of the areolae or pigmented areas around the nipples, fatigue, frequency of urination, and discoloration of mucous membranes.

The probable signs consist of an increase in the size of the uterus; considerable softening of the cervix, commencing with the second month of pregnancy; enlargement of the abdomen at about the third month, when the distended uterus can be felt through the abdominal wall; and intermittent contractions of the uterus. Endocrine tests yield proof of pregnancy approximately three weeks after implantation, or about six weeks after the last menstrual period.

The positive signs are three in number, any one of which confirms pregnancy: the fetal heartbeats, which the examining physician can hear and count; active fetal movements, which become noticeable at the fifth month (although some fibrillating movement may be noticed earlier); and the fetal skeleton, which can be seen in X-ray films.

An interesting phenomenon known to occur in both humans and lower animals is *pseudocyesis* or false pregnancy. A woman, for example, will develop symptoms that are remarkably similar to those of true pregnancy. She may cease menstruating, be consistently nauseated, and gain an inordinate amount of weight. In some instances the condition lingers for months before the symptoms disappear or are dispelled by psychotherapy. In extreme cases she will also develop a protruding abdomen and actually go into labor, only to find that the condition exists entirely because of emotional factors. All that she "delivers" is an accumulation of air and fluids.

A related phenomenon is the practice of "couvade" among some primitive cultures, wherein the husband goes to bed during his wife's parturition, and suffers in much the same manner as she does during delivery. In more sophisticated societies the husband will sometimes (in approximately 11% of the cases) show some symptoms related to his wife's pregnancy.[310] Less frequently, expectant fathers become severely nauseated, vomit, and suffer abdominal pains, all the symptoms disappearing after the wife has delivered their infant.

Most women have their first babies between the ages of twenty and twenty-four, although there have been substantiated reports of births to a girl as young as five and to women as old as fifty-five.[79] Deliveries by still older women have been reported, but investigations fail to support their claims. Recent scientific studies offer encouragement to women past forty who wish to have children; the evidence is that they have as good a chance as younger wives of giving birth to a live infant.[264] The major difference is an increased incidence of Caesarean sections among older women (8% as compared with a general average of 3%). Furthermore, the Metropolitan Life Insurance Company reported from their study of 27,700,000 births between 1951 and 1957 that multiple births are most likely to occur in women between the ages of thirty-five and thirty-nine.

There are, as almost anyone can testify, enormous variations in family size. Childless marriages are rather commonplace; but there is also a Russian couple whose marriage was "blessed" with sixty-nine children born in twenty-seven confinements consisting of sixteen sets of twins, seven sets of triplets, and four sets of quadruplets.[142] The average number of children in an American family is 1.33, according to a preliminary census taken in 1964.

The size of babies at birth also varies considerably. The two largest on record registered thirty inches in length and weighed only slightly under twenty-four pounds, while the smallest surviving infant on record weighed only one and a half pounds. The average newborn weighs about seven and one-half pounds and is about twenty inches long.[203] Very large infants usually must be delivered by Caesarean section.

Approximately one out of ten couples is never able to have children, while pregnancy in some marriages would seem to occur with distressing frequency. When couples are purposely attempting to conceive a child, about 30% will succeed the first month, about 60% will have succeeded by the end of six months, and about 75% by the end of the first year. The age of the woman plays an important role in her ability to conceive. Gynecological opinion is that among women capable of conceiving—assuming, of course, that no contraceptive precautions are being utilized—those over thirty-two years of age should be able to do so within six months, and those between twenty-six and thirty-two, within one year. On the other hand, it can take as long as two years for women between eighteen and twenty-five years to become pregnant.[283]

There are manifold reasons why a couple are, or seem to be, unable to conceive a child, and the responsibility in numerous instances lies with the husband.[74] Many men do not wish to accept the fact that they might be the source of the couple's barrenness, believing it to be a reflection on their manliness. Men often have a low sperm count and in some cases have no active sperm at all, even though they are quite capable of having frequent and pleasurable sexual intercourse. Physicians consider a sperm count of less than 200,000,000 per ejaculation as being so small that conception would be rendered difficult.[81] The effect that frequency of ejaculation has on sperm count and fertility is obviously a matter of individual variation, but generally speaking, the optimal time interval between ejaculations to insure maximum fertility is about forty-eight hours. Too much or too little sexual activity can negatively affect a man's fertility.[64, 217]

Women may have any of several anomalies that interfere with the ability to conceive. There are congenital anatomical defects, such as imperfect Fallopian tubes or uterus. In certain cases, all or any one of these organs, as well as the vagina, may be missing altogether. Sometimes organs of reproduction become nonfunctional because of acquired obstructions; for example, douching with water under pressure can force harmful bacteria into the Fallopian tubes, producing an infection and subsequent scar-tissue that permanently closes the tubes. In some women, ova simply do not develop properly. In others (very rarely) ova cannot be released from the ovary because its covering is too tough to rupture, even though the ova are quite capable of fertilization and proper development.

(It should be recognized that women may have glandular difficulties, an abnormal endometrium, uterine tumors, and the like that will not allow them to carry the fetus to term even though conception is quite possible.)

Women sometimes develop antibodies that eventually appear in the vagina and produce an immunity to sperm, making conception impossible.[215] This immunity can be built up against the sperm of any man, and in some cases the immunity may exist against one man's sperm but not another's.[168] It is not unusual for a couple to be unable to have children together, but after remarriage, both to produce children with another partner.

An increasingly popular method of treating infertility is artificial insemination (A.I.). This is a process whereby sperm of the husband is mechanically introduced into the vagina or uterus of his wife at the time when conception is calculated as being the most likely to occur (A.I.H.); or when the sperm of a donor is inserted, rather than that of the husband (A.I.D.).

Artificial insemination has been practiced in animal husbandry for years. As far back as the 14th century, Arabic tribes supposedly used semen from an inferior breed of stallions secretly to inseminate the thoroughbred mares of their enemies.[193] Today, A.I. is regularly employed to build up the bloodlines of various species of animals. One thoroughbred bull can sire calves by many cows with a single sample of ejaculatory fluid, and the semen can easily be refrigerated and shipped.

Artificial insemination of humans has been performed in this country with some regularity since the turn of this century, especially after the appearance of the early works of the famous American physician and sexologist, R. L. Dickinson. Donor sperm produce pregnancy 80% of the time, whereas the husbands' sperm artificially introduced are only 5% successful. The disparity in these percentages is understandable when one considers that the husbands' sperm, for whatever reason, were incapable of effecting pregnancy by sexual intercourse in the first place.[193]

In 1955, the Society for the Study of Sterility passed almost unanimously a resolution approving A.I.D., with the stipulation that the procedure must be in harmony with the medical opinion of the physician and the ethics of both husband and wife. Undoubtedly this resolution contributed significantly to the subsequent increase in all A.I. pregnancies (about two-thirds of them A.I.H.) in the United States from an estimated 50,000 in 1955 to 100,000 in 1958. The figures are thought to be far higher today.[193]

The following year, 1956, Pope Pius XII stated unequivocally that the Roman Catholic Church opposed both A.I.D. and A.I.H. The Church, however, will permit "assisted insemination" whereby an instrument is used to push the sperm towards and into the cervix after the semen has been deposited during marital intercourse.

In May, 1967, the governor of Oklahoma signed into law a bill legalizing artificial insemination and declaring legitimate the children thus conceived. The most comprehensive legislation on this subject to date, it guarantees the children of A.I. the same rights as those conceived naturally.

Because of wars, irradiation from atomic energy, injuries, and illnesses, many couples are finding it expedient to take advantage of recent scientific advances which make it possible to store sperm for a considerable period of time by freezing it, along with protective chemicals, in liquid nitrogen. Healthy babies have been born from both A.I.H. and A.I.D. conceptions in which the sperm used came from a sperm bank where they had been frozen and stored for as long as two years.[303, 349]

Much has been written about the dangers of travel, exercise, sexual intercourse, and driving during pregnancy. These activities are not dangerous for the healthy woman, however, when pursued moderately and sensibly; to the contrary, they are often beneficial to the expectant mother.[169] During recent wars, pregnant women traveled by all modes of transportation, much of it uncomfortable, for hundreds of miles in order to be with their husbands; yet they had a lower miscarriage rate than those women who stayed home. The emotional satisfaction of joining their husbands, even though it entailed considerable traveling, probably contributed to the good health of these young women.

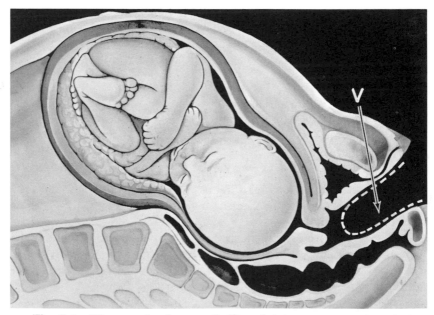

Fig. 7-5. Diagram showing practicality of intercourse even in advance stage of pregnancy; dotted line demonstrates angle at which penis may be introduced into vagina. Photograph courtesy *Sexology* magazine.

Sexual intercourse during gestation is ordinarily sanctioned and even encouraged until approximately the final six weeks.[160] Even after this time, when sexual intercourse may become impossible for the wife because of abdominal size, sexual relief for her and the husband through such means as mutual masturbation is now recognized as valuable to each partner and to the marriage. As a matter of fact, indications are that if no sexual release is otherwise available for the husband during his wife's pregnancy and shortly thereafter, this is the time he is most likely to seek extramarital outlets for his sexual needs.[215] Sensible precautions must be taken in regard to sexual as well as other activity during pregnancy. The obstetrician directing the pregnancy can offer guidance in these matters.

For generations, girls have been indoctrinated in the belief that childbirth is an event burdened with suffering and threat to life. As an unfortunate consequence, the entire sex life of many women falls under the pall of their fears of pregnancy and childbirth. Coitus, therefore, develops overtones of unpleasantness and pain and becomes something to be avoided.

Anthropologists have demonstrated that suffering during childbirth is related to the individual woman's past experiences, her expectations regarding the nature and severity of childbirth pains, and the culture in which she lives.[234] There is, to be sure, some pain to be expected from the uterine contractions and vaginal expansion involved in parturition, but extreme suffering is likely to be an outgrowth of the agents mentioned above. Understanding the birth process, confidence in the obstetrician, and security in the home and with the husband are important factors leading to an easy delivery. The art of relaxation and freedom from fear are stressed in books used in instructing women who are interested in "natural childbirth." An interesting illustration of childbirth unencumbered by anxiety was the recent account of a Michigan woman who delivered a healthy infant weighing just under eight pounds while she took an afternoon nap.[335]

A strikingly valuable contribution to maternal peace of mind and comfort has come with the introduction of anesthetics in the conduct of parturition. The art and science of anesthesia have become so refined that there is now rarely an excuse for any of the anguish traditionally ascribed to childbirth. It is curious to remember, however, that the initial reaction to the use of anesthetics in childbirth was distinct opposition from the clergy, who quoted the biblical pronouncement against women from Genesis 3:16, "In sorrow thou shalt bring forth children." Some physicians as well judged the use of anesthetics in this connection as being in opposition to nature. Most of these objections were dispelled, however, when Queen Victoria was delivered of her seventh child with the aid of anesthetics.[22]

It is surprising that many people, physicians as well as laymen, still argue that a woman will not love her child unless she experiences pain during delivery. Such nonsensical thinking is rapidly disappearing. The indications actually are that if any difference in mother love exists, it is in an increase in love for the child because the mother did *not* experience any severe pain that she might later consciously or unconsciously associate with the child.

PRENATAL DEVELOPMENT OF THE CHILD

The development of the child during the nine months before birth is more rapid than at any subsequent time during his entire life span. In the twenty years from an individual's birth to maturity, his body weight will increase approximately twenty times. By comparison, in the nine months between fertilization of the ovum and delivery of a fully developed baby, the increase in weight is about six billionfold. The most rapid period of growth for the human organism, then, is during the early part of gestation. From the time of fertilization to the end of the first month, the egg increases in weight by about a million percent (from 0.000004 to 0.04 gm). During the second month, the weight increase is 7400%, dropping to an 1100% increase during the third month, and to a comparatively insignificant increase of 30% during the final month. The increase in rate of weight gain drops even more after birth. If this were not so, the infant would weigh from 160 to 170 pounds by the end of the first year of postnatal life.[107]

There now follows a general outline[13, 107, 133] of total prenatal development from the beginning of the mother's last menstrual flow preceding pregnancy:

A. FIRST MONTH
1. First Week
    a. The destructive phase of menstruation occurs.
    b. An ovum is being prepared for ovulation.
2. Second Week
    a. The follicular phase of menstruation occurs.
    b. Ovulation occurs on approximately the thirteenth day of the menstrual cycle.

    c. The ovum is fertilized by a sperm in the ampulla of the Fallopian tube.

    d. At the instant of fertilization, all hereditary characteristics are determined through the pairing of chromosomes from ovum and sperm.

3. Third Week

    a. The fertilized ovum passes along the Fallopian tube toward the uterus for a period of three or four days.

    b. Cell divisions take place in the ovum during this journey.

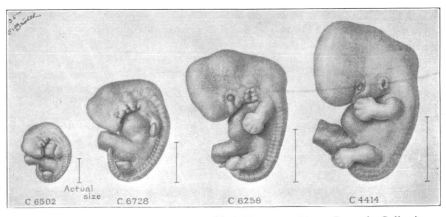

Fig. 7-6. Human embryos, magnified 2½ times. From Carnegie Collection. Ovulation ages: #6502, 28 days; #6728, 31 days; #6258, 38 days; #4414, 39 days. From Eastman and Hellman: *Williams Obstetrics,* 13th ed. New York: Appleton-Century-Crofts, 1966.

4. Fourth Week

    a. As the blastocyst comes into contact with the wall of the uterus, implantation commences.

    b. Upon completion of implantation, the fetal membranes start developing.

B. Second Month

1. Fifth Week

    a. The embryo now appears as a small bit of greyish flesh.

    b. The development of the backbone begins.

    c. The spinal canal commences to form.

    d. The embryo is about one-twelfth of an inch in length and about one-sixth of an inch in width.

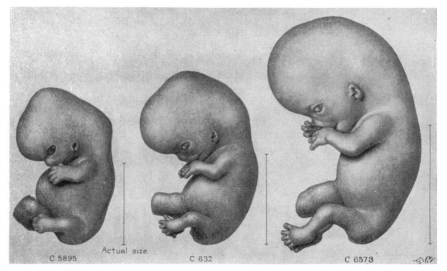

Fig. 7-7.   Human embryos, magnified 1.9 times. From Carnegie Collection. Menstrual ages: 8 to 8½ weeks. From Eastman and Hellman: *Williams Obstetrics,* 13th ed. New York: Appleton-Century-Crofts, 1966.

2. Sixth Week

    a. The head begins to form.

    b. Construction of the backbone is completed.

    c. The spinal canal is closed over.

    d. Indentations in the skin appear where the eyes will form.

    e. The tail of the embryo becomes distinct.

    f. Rudimentary arms and legs are now visible.

    g. The embryo has grown to about one-fourth an inch in length.

3. Seventh Week

    a. Formation of the chest and abdomen is completed.

    b. The eyes are more clearly differentiated.

    c. The fingers and toes are beginning to take shape.

    d. The embryo is now about one-half inch in length.

4. Eighth Week
   a. The primary facial features are forming.
   b. The ears begin to develop.
   c. The embryo is almost an inch long, and weighs about one-thirtieth of an ounce.

C. THIRD MONTH

1. Ninth Week
   a. The sympathetic ganglia and nerves have begun to form.
   b. Stubby toes and fingers are identifiable.
   c. The appendages are partially formed.
   d. The formation of the gross facial characteristics becomes complete.
   e. The liver, lungs, pancreas, kidneys, and intestines take on shape and begin to function to a limited degree.
   f. The embryo is a bit over one inch in length and weighs about one-fifteenth of an ounce.

2. Tenth Through Twelfth Week
   a. The following external bodily parts are completely formed by the end of this period: ears, arms, hands, fingers, legs, feet, and toes.
   b. The fingernails begin to form.
   c. The head remains proportionately much larger than the rest of the body.
   d. The external genitalia begin developing their characteristic structure, and an expert may be able to determine the sex of a fetus born at this time. If the fetus is still in the amniotic sac, or if placed in a warm saline solution, spontaneous movements may occur.
   e. The fetus is about three inches long and weighs about one ounce.
   f. The fetus looks like a miniature infant from this point on.

D. FOURTH MONTH

1. Thirteenth Through Fourteenth Week
   a. The sex of the fetus is easily distinguishable.

  b. Fine downlike hair covers the skin.
  c. Eyebrows and eyelashes make their first appearance.
2. Fifteenth Through Sixteenth Week
  a. Near the end of this period, fetal movements are felt and the heartbeat can be detected.
  b. The fetus is about eight and a half inches long and about six ounces in weight.

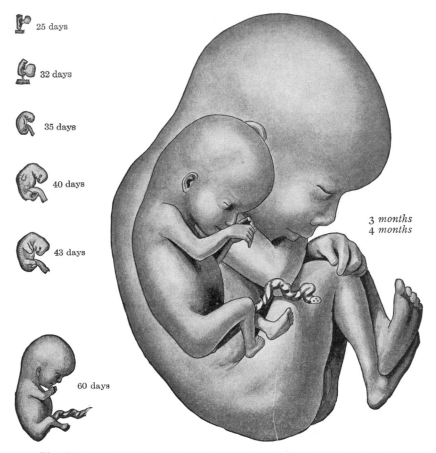

25 days

32 days

35 days

40 days

43 days

60 days

3 *months*
4 *months*

Fig. 7-8. Human embryos of twenty-five days to four months. Actual size. From Arey: *Developmental Anatomy,* 3rd ed. Philadelphia: W. B. Saunders Co., 1934.

E. FIFTH MONTH
  1. Seventeenth Through Eighteenth Week
    a. Fat begins to accumulate under the skin.

        b. Hair on the head first appears.

   2. Nineteenth Through Twentieth Week

        a. The fetus is now approximately twelve inches long and weighs one pound.

        b. Should it be born at this time, it might live for a few minutes but cannot survive.

F. SIXTH MONTH

   1. Twenty-First Through Twenty-Second Week

        a. The fetus first opens its eyes.

        b. It is now covered with a cheese-like secretion called the *vernix caseosa.*

        c. The head is fairly well-developed.

        d. The skin is wrinkled.

   2. Twenty-Third Through Twenty-Fifth Week

        a. The fetus if born at this time can live several hours or even days. In one out of ten instances, it will survive if given expert care.

        b. It is now approximately fourteen inches long and weighs two pounds.

G. SEVENTH MONTH

   1. Twenty-Sixth Through Twenty-Seventh Week

        a. The testicles descend into the scrotum of the male fetus.

        b. If the infant is born at this time, it has a 50% chance of survival.

   2. Twenty-Eighth Through Twenty-Ninth Week

        a. The fetus is about sixteen inches long and weighs just under four pounds.

        b. It is an old wives' tale that a seven-month fetus has a better chance to survive than an eight-month fetus. The notion stems from the fact that most allegedly seven-month infants are in reality full-term. The older the fetus is at birth, the better its chance for survival.

H. EIGHTH MONTH

   1. Thirtieth Through Thirty-First Week

        a. The development of almost all the organic systems is virtually complete.

b. The downlike hair that has covered the fetus commences to disappear.

2. Thirty-Second Through Thirty-Third Week

    a. If the baby is born during this time, its chance for survival is about 90%.

    b. The length is now about eighteen inches and the weight a little over five pounds.

I. NINTH MONTH

1. Thirty-Fourth Through Thirty-Fifth Week

    a. The fetus has attained full development.

    b. The skin, still covered with vernix caseosa, has a smooth and polished look.

    c. It has lost all the downlike hair that previously covered its body, except perhaps across the shoulders. The length of the hair on the head is about one inch.

    d. The eyes are a slate color, and will not assume their final coloring until some weeks after birth.

2. Thirty-Sixth Week Until Birth

    a. The fetus's final development is rapid, and its weight gain is about a pound a week.

    b. Of infants born at this time, over 99% will survive.

    c. At birth, the baby's length is usually twenty inches and his weight approximately seven pounds.

The prospective birth date of a child is usually computed by adding 280 days to the date on which the last menstruation started. This is a fairly accurate method of predicting the date of an anticipated birth, but to be more precise, one would have to know the exact date of conception. Several investigations have demonstrated that conception can take place on any day of a woman's monthly cycle, even during the menstrual flow, despite the generally accepted theory that women can become pregnant only during the thirteenth to fifteenth day of the cycle.

The period of gestation varies from birth to birth, even with the same woman, and according to the sex of the child. Women who engage in strenuous physical exercise usually have their babies twenty days earlier than less athletic women do; brunette women deliver slightly sooner than blondes do; girls are often born from five to nine days earlier than boys are; and about 3% of pregnancies last 300 days or more.[70] The death rate among babies born after an overlong period of gestation is about three times that of babies delivered at normal term, probably because of the aging and withering of the placenta in the former instance.[5] Most obstetricians will induce labor if they suspect placental shrinkage.

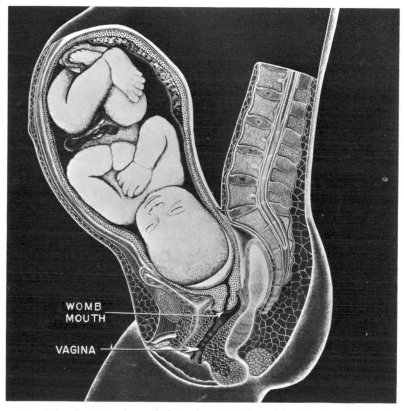

Fig. 7-9. Lateral view of fetus in woman's pelvis. Photograph *Sexology* magazine.

BIRTH POSITIONS

The manner and incidence of birth positions and presentations are as follows:

    A. *Longitudinal,* accounting for over 99% of birth positions.

        1. *Cephalic* or head presentations, which constitute 96% of longitudinal births.

            a. Head bent downward with baby's chin on breastbone.

            b. Head extended, face presenting.

            c. Head only slightly extended, brow presenting first.

2. *Breech* or buttocks presentations, accounting for 4% of longitudinal births.

   a. *Frank,* the most common form; legs bent over abdomen with toes and shoulders touching and buttocks presenting over pelvis.

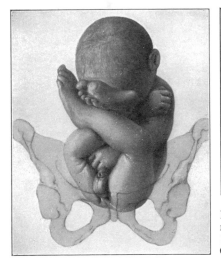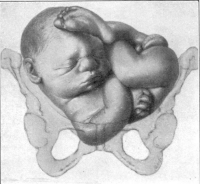

Fig. 7-10. A. Breech presentation. B. Transverse presentation. From Eastman and Hellman: *Williams Obstetrics,* 13th ed. New York: Appleton-Century-Crofts, 1966.

   b. *Footling,* with the legs, held straight in a standing position, presenting first.

   c. *Full,* the rarest of the breech presentations; baby sitting cross-legged in mother's pelvis.

B. *Transverse,* occurring once in 200 births. The fetus lies crosswise with a shoulder, arm, or hand entering the birth canal first. Either the fetus must be turned during labor, or a Caesarean section is indicated.

Great pressure is, of course, exerted on a baby during delivery. In longitudinal cephalic presentations, the infant's head may be oddly molded in the birth process, or the facial features may be bruised and swollen. The buttocks and genital area of an infant born in a breech presentation often become swollen and discolored during delivery. These conditions are understandably quite distressing to the new parents, but the irregularities correct themselves within a few days of birth and there is very rarely any permanent damage.

Although a breech presentation is rather unusual, almost 50% of infants assume this position prior to the seventh month of fetal life.

Most infants in the breech position then make a 180° turn to the cephalic position before the ninth month. A fetus that does not make

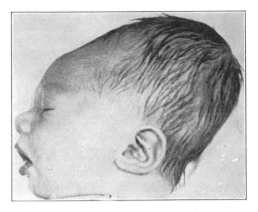

Fig. 7-11. Molding of infant's head at birth. From Eastman and Hellman: *Williams Obstetrics*, 13th ed. New York: Appleton-Century-Crofts, 1966.

the turn often can be manipulated by the obstetrician into the proper cephalic position in the later stages of pregnancy.

MULTIPLE BIRTHS

Multiple births occur about once per 80 to 89 births.[62, 107, 375] Twins occur once in 80 births, triplets once in 80 x 80 cases (6400), and quadruplets once in 80 x 80 x 80 cases (512,000). Heredity, the age of the mother, and racial factors appear to be of significance in that multiple births apparently occur more frequently in one family than in another, and to more women in their thirties than in their twenties.

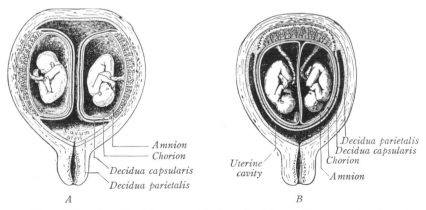

Fig. 7-12. A. Double-ovum (fraternal) twins with separate placentas. B. Single-ovum (identical) twins with a common placenta. From Arey: *Developmental Anatomy*, 3rd ed. Philadelphia: W. B. Saunders Co., 1934.

Negroes have more twins than do whites, who in turn have more twins than do oriental women.[107] Triplets are born to whites at a one to 10,200 ratio and to nonwhites at a 1 to 6200 ratio, this difference holding in both northern and southern states.[107]

Identical twins develop from a single fertilized ovum that first divides and then separates. Each part then continues the process of cell division separately. Identical twins, consequently, have identical sets of chromosomes, are always of the same sex, and have a single placenta. If the cell mass does not make a complete separation in the identical-twinning process, the result is Siamese or joined twins. Fraternal twins develop from two separate ova, both of which are usually fertilized at relatively the same time. A single follicle may expel two or more mature ova, or ova in two or more follicles may develop to maturity simultaneously.[107] Fraternal twins can be of the same or different sex, will have separate placentas, and will bear no more resemblance to one another than separately born siblings.

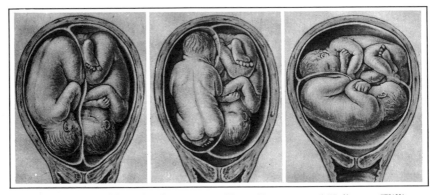

Fig. 7-13.   Position of twins *in utero*. From Eastman and Hellman: *Williams Obstetrics,* 12th ed. New York: Appleton-Century-Crofts, 1961.

The birth of most twins follows the usual pattern of parturition, although there occasionally have occurred some interesting variations in the conception and birth process. For example, most twins arrive within a few minutes to an hour of each other; however, there are infrequent cases in which considerable time elapses between their births. In one instance, the babies arrived forty-eight days apart; in another, thirty, with one infant being born in December and the other in January. Mothers have given birth to twins of two different races, fathered, it follows, by two men, the conceptions having taken place within a short time of each other. At least one birth of twins has been recorded in which the babies, obviously fathered by different men, had different blood types.[62]

Triplets may result from the fertilization of three different ova. More commonly, only two eggs are involved, one of which separates and then develops into identical twins. Quadruplets are for the most part the product of the fertilization of two ova, each of which separates and develops into a set of identical twins.

In multiple births, the percentage of males decreases with the number of children born. In one large sample study, among single births the percentage of males was 51.59; among twins, 50.85% were boys; among triplets, 49.54%; and among quadruplets, 46.48%. The explanation very likely is that from conception on, survival favors the female, and in multiple births the biological tendency observed in single births is presumably increased.[107]

Viable twin pregnancies will terminate about twenty-two days earlier than viable single pregnancies do, the average gestation period for twins being thirty-seven weeks.

Despite old wives' tales to the contrary, the future fertility of human twins, whether or not of the same sex, is no different from that of the singly born. Among lower animals, it might be noted, twins are in fact less fertile than animals born singly.[107]

PARTURITION

Parturition is the process of childbirth, and it takes place in three stages. The *first stage* of labor can be recognized by any one of the following signs:

(1) Labor pains may start to occur, usually at intervals of fifteen to twenty minutes, each pain lasting about thirty seconds. The first pains are relatively mild and rhythmic, but increase steadily in frequency, intensity, and duration. They finally occur every three to four minutes, and when they do, the fetus is well on its way. Toward the end of labor, each pain lasts a minute or more.

The pains, which are actually powerful muscular contractions, may feel as if they commence in the back and then move forward to the abdomen primarily because the fetus is being pressed toward the back, as it has not yet made the turn into the vagina. Between contractions there is complete relaxation, a condition not found in most instances of muscle cramping. The first stage of labor should produce a dilation of the cervix from its normal size (about one-eighth inch) to approximately four inches, in order to permit the emergence of the baby into and through the four- to five-inch-long vagina. Each contraction pushes the baby downward, eventually with a force equal to twenty-five or thirty pounds of pressure. When the cervix is completely dilated, the first stage of labor has ended. This stage lasts about sixteen hours for first babies, sometimes less, and about eight hours in subsequent deliveries.

(2) Another indication that labor has begun is the *expulsion of the mucous plug* from the base of the uterus. The mucus will be flecked with bright red blood. The purpose of the plug, as was pointed out previously, is to act as a barrier between the vagina and the uterus against the invasion of undesirable matter.

(3) A third indication that labor is imminent is the *rupture of the amniotic membrane,* which causes a flow of clear water-like fluid to issue from the vagina.

When any one of the three signs of parturition is present, it is time to notify the obstetrician and to proceed to the hospital with reasonable haste. The expectant mother should refrain from eating after the appearance of any of these initial signs of labor. After the patient checks in at the hospital, she may spend a few hours in her room before time for the actual birth of the baby, unless there is some sort of emergency.

Second stage: The second phase of labor—from the time the cervix is completely dilated until the fetus is expelled—lasts approximately two hours in the instance of first babies. In subsequent deliveries, the time is about one hour. In some confinements, the amniotic membrance or sac will not have ruptured in spite of other initial signs of labor. The obstetrician will then surgically rupture the membrane. The head of the fetus at this phase presses on the mother's lower vagina and bowel, the pressure producing a reflexive action of the muscles in that area that act to expel the fetus. The infant is pushed along the birth canal with each contraction until its head appears at the external opening of the vagina. The anesthetized mother is now placed on the edge of the delivery table in such a position that her knees are bent and the leg holders keep her thighs wide apart. Wrist straps secure the wrists only for the purpose of preventing movement of the hands while the patient is anesthetized. The genital area, abdomen, and inner thighs are cleansed thoroughly, and the region is covered with a sterile sheet containing an eighteen-inch opening. The patient is catheterized to be sure there will be no accidental voiding while the baby passes through the vagina. Severe pressure on a full bladder, furthermore, could be injurious to the mother.

As the head of the fetus pushes forward in the progress of labor, the tissue between vagina and rectum must stretch to an extreme degree. Frequently the opening to the vagina is not sufficiently elastic and the emergence of the baby's head forces a tear. The obstetrician therefore often performs an *episiotomy,* which is a cutting of the tissue with scissors, in order to prevent such a tear. The straight cut is simple to repair and heals rapidly.

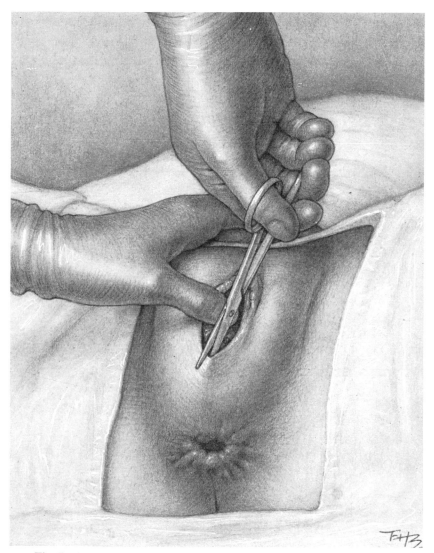

Fig. 7-14.   Scissors in position for episiotomy. From Eastman and Hellman: *Williams Obstetrics,* 13th ed. New York: Appleton-Century-Crofts, 1966.

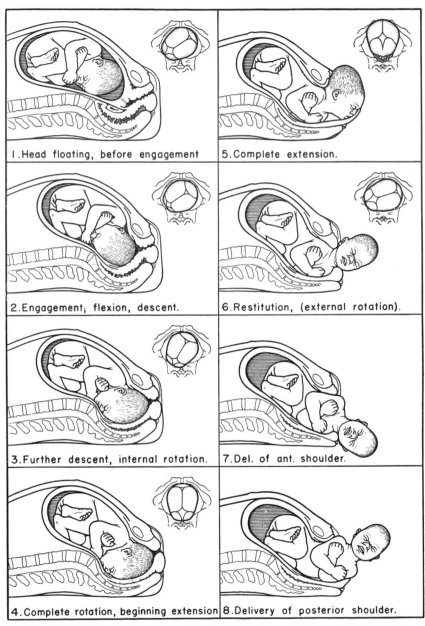

1. Head floating, before engagement
2. Engagement; flexion, descent.
3. Further descent, internal rotation.
4. Complete rotation, beginning extension
5. Complete extension.
6. Restitution, (external rotation).
7. Del. of ant. shoulder.
8. Delivery of posterior shoulder.

Fig. 7-15.   Principal movements in the procedure of labor and delivery. From Eastman and Hellman: *Williams Obstetrics,* 13th ed. New York: Appleton-Century-Crofts, 1966.

The mother is now made aware of the need for her help to force the baby into the world by contracting her abdominal muscles to create additional pressure. The obstetrician may also apply pressure on her abdomen, and sometimes it is helpful in speeding up the birth process if he applies pressure on the chin of the infant through the thin tissue of the perineum.

When the infant's head emerges from the vagina, it turns spontaneously either to the right or left, depending upon the way the shoulders are turned. The physician holds its head with both hands and gently guides it downward—never pulling, only guiding—while one shoulder emerges and then the other. After the expulsion of the head and shoulders, the rest is a simple matter because the trunk and limbs are quite small in comparison with the head and shoulders. The baby sometimes emerges with too much skin for his face and head, giving him a wrinkled appearance. This is because the bones of the head, which have not yet grown together, overlap and decrease the size of the skull in order to facilitate the birth. The head will quickly return to its normal shape and the wrinkles will fill out.

As the baby's head emerges, the obstetrician, by using a rubber bulb-type syringe, removes any blood, amniotic fluid, or watery mucus that may have accumulated in the infant's nose and mouth. To facilitate his first breath, some doctors still hold the infant upside down by his heels and slap his bottom; but most physicians do not consider this necessary, since the change in temperature and atmospheric pressure is sufficient to cause the breathing to start. With an infant's first breath, a drastic change occurs in his circulatory and respiratory processes. Nourishment and oxygen had previously been supplied by the placenta by way of the umbilical cord. The same pressure and temperature changes that force the baby to breathe also create a vacuum in the chest cavity, and this vacuum causes the blood from the ductus arteriosus to be directed into the pulmonary artery and lungs. The sphincter muscle of the ductus arteriosus contracts, but never relaxes. Blood circulates to the heart through the pulmonary veins and fills the left auricle.

There is now no further need for an opening between the auricles, and a flap of tissue therefore closes the opening. It takes a few minutes for the process to be activated and to become effective. During this time the baby is bluish in color, but as circulation is directed into its pulmonary system he becomes pink. This process seldom fails, but if it does, the result is a "blue baby." Fortunately, modern surgery can correct this abnormality.

Now that the infant is breathing the oxygen of the outside world, he no longer needs the placenta or the umbilical cord. Once the cord stops pulsating and the baby is breathing regularly, the cord is clamped and cut about three inches from the abdomen. The clamp is left in place until the stub dries up and drops off.

To eliminate any possibility of a gonorrheal or other eye infection, a weak silver nitrate solution is used in the newborn's eyes, or he is given an injection of penicillin (50,000 units).

Third stage: About fifteen minutes after the baby's birth, the placenta is delivered. Muscular contractions shrink the uterus and the area of placental attachment. This systolic action detaches the placenta from the uterus wall and expels it into the vagina within a short period—three to ten minutes. The obstetrician sometimes presses the uterus downward to facilitate expulsion. Occasionally his efforts are unavailing, and the physician must then follow the umbilical cord with gloved fingers and peel the placenta from the uterus.

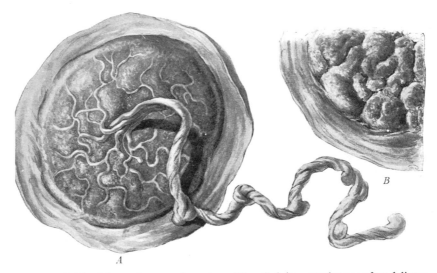

Fig. 7-16.   Mature human placenta and its adjoining membranes after delivery. A. Fetal surface.   B. Maternal surface. From Arey: *Developmental Anatomy,* 3rd ed. Philadelphia: W. B. Saunders Co., 1934.

If an episiotomy was necessary, the obstetrician repairs it with absorbable catgut. The tissue heals rapidly and without discomfort.

Parturition has now been completed. All that remains to be done is to wheel the mother to the recovery room and the baby to the nursery, while the nervous father is reassured and congratulated!

A Caesarean section is a surgical procedure whereby the baby is born through a low transverse incision in the abdominal wall and in the anterior wall of the uterus. The popular but erroneous legend that Julius Caesar was delivered surgically gives the operation its name. Probably the term "Caesarean" originated from an ancient Roman law, which was later incorporated into a legal code called Lex Caesarea. This statute, aimed at trying to save the child's life, made it mandatory that an operation be performed on a woman who died in the advanced stages of pregnancy.

In the past, the death rate among women undergoing this surgery was exceptionally high because of hemorrhage and infection. Today, however, death following a Caesarean section is extremely rare, and a woman may have two or three babies this way. The Caesarean delivery of five or six infants to the same mother is not too unusual, as a matter of fact. The scar tissue left by a Caesarean operation, however, is not as strong as normal tissue, which suggests a limitation on future pregnancies that must be terminated by a section. Physicians often suggest the tying of the woman's Fallopian tubes after her third such delivery.

LACTATION

Lactation is the process of milk secretion from the mother's breasts following childbirth. The placenta not only provides for the development of the fetus through its linkage with the mother, but also produces hormones that prepare the mammary glands for secreting milk. During pregnancy, these same hormones inhibit the pituitary gland from producing the milk-forming chemical until such time as it is needed.

Oddly enough, the milk is not needed by the baby immediately after birth. The need usually arises from two to five days later. The first secretion the baby receives from the breast is *colostrum*, a substance that is present in the breast immediately after birth. The effect of colostrum upon the newborn is not positively known, but it is of high protein content and is believed to aid in giving the child immunity to many infectious diseases during the early months of his life.[354] Some obstetricians believe that its main function is that of a laxative to aid in ridding the infant's intestines of a substance called *meconium,* fecal matter consisting of mucus, bile, and epithelial threads. Colostrum disappears two or three days after delivery and true milk replaces it.

After the placenta is expelled and its inhibiting hormones are no longer produced, the pituitary gland begins to produce *prolactin,* the lactogenic hormone that induces lactation. When lactation first begins, the breasts become swollen and congested. The ducts leading from breasts to nipples fill with milk, and the mother usually experiences an uncomfortable sensation, or even pain, for a period of a day or so.

Lactation is often accompanied by certain psychological and physiological symptoms, such as fatigue, headache, hot and painful breasts, and low-grade fever. The infant's sucking provides relief. In addition, it is the opinion of many doctors that the sucking also prompts certain muscular contractions of the uterus that help to reduce it to its normal size.

Certain substances consumed by the lactating mother, such as alcohol, strong sedatives, and vegetable cathartics, may adversely affect the infant. The concentration of alcohol is the same in the milk as it is in the mother's blood. A nursing mother should consume none of these substances unless they are approved by her physician.

The adverse effects of smoking on the human organism have been well documented and widely publicized, to the extent that the federal government now requires a caution about possible health hazards to be printed on each cigarette package. The deleterious effects of smoking on a fetus during pregnancy have not been so carefully investigated, but current research indicates some danger.[245] The facts that tobacco smoke contains over 250 chemical compounds and substances, many of which, such as nicotine and tars, are noxious, and that the smoke can be absorbed through the membrane tissues of the mouth as well as by inhalation, should be enough to deter any pregnant woman from smoking. If not, recent research findings should serve as an additional warning. When the mother smokes, the heartbeat rate of the fetus is affected, her infant is likely to be born weighing somewhat less than the baby of a nonsmoker, and the chance for a premature birth is doubled. Furthermore, the rate of death or malformation for infants of mothers who smoked during pregnancy is higher than among babies of nonsmokers.[245]

There are occasionally encountered certain physiological difficulties in nursing a baby, in which case the physician can usually offer a solution. One of the most recurrent of these problems is an inverted nipple, which is a congenital anomaly and is the result of fibrous bands that hold the nipple in rather than allowing it to protrude in the normal manner. At the time of lactation, severe pain may be experienced by the mother if the condition is not corrected. Sometimes a small suction cup may be used successfully to draw out the nipple, and in other instances nursing will serve to correct the inversion.

———◆◆◆———

A recent issue of *Medical Economics* revealed the fact that only 12% of the babies leaving the hospital in 1956 were breastfed. In 1946, the figure had been 23%, and in the not too distant past, as many as 90% of all babies were breastfed. Women reveal genuine anxiety over the shape and size of their breasts, and often feel inferior in their role as a woman and sexual being if they consider their breasts too small. Indeed, sweater and brassiere-padding enterprises have bene-fitted from this excessive concern over breast size (if, indeed, they have not deliberately encouraged it). At least one shop advertises, "We fix flats!" Plastic surgeons have devised ingenious methods for remolding breasts into desired shapes and sizes through the use of surgery, plastics, and silicone, although this means of increasing a wo-man's narcissistic image is ill-advised in the majority of cases because of certain physiological complications that sometimes develop.

It is little wonder that people consider breasts a symbol of ultimate sexuality in view of the emphasis placed on them in advertisements and clothing styles. Even toy stores pander to this mammary preoccupation by keeping their shelves well stocked with the high-bosomed dolls for which little girls clamor.

In view of the near-fetishism over the female breast, it would appear that neither men nor women realize that the appeal of the breast varies widely from culture to culture, and from era to era; or that breast size and shape have nothing to do with sexuality, except insofar as psychological factors are concerned. The erotic quality of breasts apparently has more psychological than physiological content, it would appear, since about 75% of men receive sensual excitement from the stimulation of a woman's breasts, while only slightly more than 50% of women find this sort of sex play to be sexually exciting.[299]

It cannot be denied, of course, that both male and female breasts have many nerve endings which, when properly stimulated, often afford sexual excitement and pleasure, but there are an equal number of these endings in small breasts and in large ones. Since the supply of nerve endings is the same, regardless of breast size, it is a simple matter to make the calculation that small breasts are per square inch by far and away more erogenous than larger ones, and may in fact be a dis-tinctly pleasurable advantage for both husband and wife during sex play. Furthermore, very large breasts are not necessarily an advantage in lactation, because they often contain an excessive amount of fat tissue that can interfere with the function of the milk glands.

The development of the breasts in a hormonally normal woman is largely a matter of heredity, and little can be done by way of exercise, injection of hormones, or application of creams and salves to alter nature's design. Nevertheless, many persons of questionable ethics continue to bilk the small-breasted female public with various worthless and often expensive preparations and mechanical devices, as the National Better Business Bureau can testify. Sagging of the breasts can to some degree be prevented by well-designed and properly fitted brassieres. However, a good posture, sensible nutrition, and proper hygiene remain the biggest assets to an attractive figure. A physician can offer the best advice for preventing breast-tissue breakdown during pregnancy, lactation, and weaning. If a woman finds the dimensions of her breasts unsatisfactory, the use of a padded and properly supportive brassiere is the most sensible solution.

Women who are caught up in narcissistic breast symbolism too often avoid proper physical examinations for fear that some previously undetected abnormality of the breast will be discovered which will necessitate surgery, thus destroying their femininity. This refusal to face the possibility of a breast malignancy needlessly endangers the lives of many women, and a reassessment of their system of values is certainly indicated.

It is a normal phenomenon for many of the lower mammals to have multiple breasts and a milk-line that the mammary glands follow. About 1% of human females, however, have more than the normal two, making the condition less uncommon than many would believe.[252] There is usually only one extra breast in these cases, and it is usually nonfunctional, but it can be quite normally developed and functional. Men occasionally have breast development nearly identical to that of a normal woman. Surgery will usually remedy the anomalies of extra and abnormally oversized breasts,[252] and thereby reduce or remove altogether the stresses that "being different" create.

CHAPTER 8

Birth Control and Related Topics

BIRTH CONTROL and contraception are often discussed as if they were synonymous terms, but they are not. Contraception may be defined as any means or device permitting coitus between fertile partners that prevents conception; contraception is, however, only one form of birth control. The methods of conception prevention or birth control fall into four major categories, which will be treated in the following order in this chapter: abortion, abstinence, sterilization, and contraception.

ABORTION

Abortion is the spontaneous or induced expulsion from the uterus of an embryo before it has reached a point of development sufficient for its survival, generally considered to be the twenty-eighth week of gestation.[253]

Induced abortion is a term used for expulsion of the embryo in consequence of an intentional effort to terminate a pregnancy. Because it involves a purposeful act, it is a form of birth control and is therefore germane to this discussion. *Spontaneous abortion* is medical terminology for a miscarriage that occurs prior to the third month of fetal life. It is not a form of birth control.

The subject of abortion appears throughout history in social, economic, political, and—particularly—religious contexts. The Chinese are said to possess the oldest method of abortion, the procedure having been described in a manuscript over 4000 years ago. Aristotle considered birth control the best method of population control through which an orderly community might be developed, and he regarded abortion as an acceptable alternative if other methods of birth control failed.[253]

Hippocrates rejected the concept of abortion as a means of population control. He included in his oath, still taken by physicians today, a pledge not to give a woman an abortive remedy, which he considered an interference with nature. Hippocrates was actually among the minority when he proclaimed against abortions. It is interesting to

115

speculate on what present-day attitudes toward abortion would be, had someone from the majority group written the physicians' oath.

To the Romans, abortion was simply the removal of a portion of the body, like an arm or leg. The idea that abortion is akin to murder did not occur to them. Here again, considerations of population control predominated, although abortion came to be practiced so extensively among the ruling classes that the ratio of citizens to slaves became a matter of grave political concern. Efforts were made to outlaw abortion, but they met with only partial success.

As early as 1500 B.C. (and perhaps earlier), in adherence to the biblical mandate, "a life for a life," the Jewish people assessed the death penalty against those implicated in an abortion. This severity is more understandable when one remembers that the Jews of that day were a combative people desirous of increasing, rather than decreasing, the size of their tribes. Larger tribes, quite simply, provided greater protection against their foes.

The world has seen vast evolutions in its various civilizations since the days of ancient Greece and Rome. Yet abortion remains the principal method of population control in some countries and among certain primitive tribes. Among the world's most advanced nations, on the other hand, war and famine have been paradoxically accepted as "nature's method" of reducing burgeoning populations. This is an era in which man has gained almost inconceivable control over natural forces. Surely, then, he does not have to wait passively for a tragic war or the literal starvation of large masses of people to remedy the problem of overpopulation. Indeed, many physicians, medical societies, government officials, and certain religious groups are making increasing demands that laws regarding abortion and other methods of population control be restudied and revamped in the light of today's civilizations.

Authorities differ in their views on the value, incidence, and dangers of abortion.[253] Some state that there are as many as 1,000,000 induced abortions per annum in the United States, while others set the figure at half that number. About 80% to 90% of all abortions are performed on married women, 22% of all married women having undergone at least one induced abortion.[143] There is a greater incidence of abortion in urban communities—reportedly as high as one for every five births—than in rural areas, where one abortion is performed for every nine births. In Chile, the estimate is one illegal abortion for every two and a half live births.[52]

Reports on maternal deaths resulting from both therapeutic and illegal abortions seem to indicate that abortion constitutes a high percentage (about a third, some say) of the total maternal deaths in the United States. These figures are often used by those who are attempting to defend their stand against legalizing abortion, but the totals are not strictly valid because they lump together all abortions, legal and illegal. Most authorities will readily agree that if abortions are performed under the proper and sterile conditions of an operating room, the maternal death rate is no higher than in full-term deliveries.

One report reveals only three deaths in 30,000 abortions performed by capable persons.[110] Unfortunately, too many abortions are performed under nonsterile conditions and by unskilled persons, and the death rate in these circumstances is understandably high. Despite these undesirable conditions, the number of recorded fatalities from illegal abortions in New York City dropped from 140 in 1918 to 15 in 1951, probably as a result of the discovery and use of antibiotics.[253] In addition to the physical hazards that confront a woman in an illegal abortion, there is also the psychological stress growing out of society's condemnation of her actions, which frequently has the effect of intensifying her feelings of guilt and shame.

Abortion has been attempted through a wide range of techniques. There are primitive methods, such as jumping on the abdomen; using sticks as uterine probes; using potions made from animal secretions, dung, herbs, and seawater; and having recourse to magic and mystical incantations. There are attempts at self-induced abortion through medications and violent physical exercise. And there are visits to illegal abortionists and to competent physicians.

Pills advertised to correct menstrual irregularities are frequently taken in the hope of inducing an abortion. These pills are usually extremely strong laxatives containing one or more such herbs as tansy, ergot of rye, aloes, or quinine. Strong medication of this type has been known to produce severe poisoning, leading to blindness and other permanent disabilities. Strenuous physical exertion—lifting of unusually heavy objects, jumping from high places, or violent exercise—is as ineffective in inducing an abortion as the pills just described.

When an abortion is induced by others, the method may involve drugs and spraying the uterus with chemicals. But the most common procedure is a form of dilation and curettage of the womb, which is most often done by the woman's husband or an abortionist who inserts some sort of instrument into the uterus and scrapes away the embryo.

Abortionists' fees vary according to the socioeconomic status of the patient and, supposedly, of the abortionist as well: the higher the status, the higher the cost. Single women pay a higher fee than married women, but the highest price of all is paid by widows and divorcees. Age and race are additional factors in the cost of abortion: women under thirty-one pay about 20% more than older women; Negroes pay less than white women. As would be expected, the cost of abortion increases with the cost of living; present-day fees range from $150 to $1000 or more. A staggering $350,000,000 is spent annually in the United States on abortions.

Therapeutic abortions are usually recommended when certain pathologic conditions exist, the most common being serious cardiac conditions, tuberculosis, certain malignancies, diabetes, some kidney diseases, and certain mental diseases. Less common justifications for therapeutic abortions are German measles during the first three months of pregnancy, Rh factors in certain cases, and amaurotic familial idiocy.

Therapeutic abortions are performed in several ways.[253] These are some of the most frequently used techniques:

1. *X-ray radiation* is administered, halting the development of the embryo. Spontaneous expulsion then follows within a week or two. The extent of damage to the reproductive organs by radiation cannot be predicted, and the method is seldom resorted to for this reason. X-ray used on a pregnant woman in an unsuccessful attempt at abortion, or for any other reason, is a grave hazard to the child. Research evidence indicates that there is a 50% higher death rate from cancer among children who had been X-rayed *in utero* than among those who had not.[378]

2. *Antagonists* and *antimetabolites* are used to affect or interfere with cell growth and folic acid metabolism, thus ultimately killing the fetus. There are sometimes undesirable consequences, however, such as the development of anomalies in the fetus rather than its destruction. The use of these drugs may also affect the mother's bone marrow or cause other physical difficulties for her.

3. *Laminaria* is a procedure wherein a pencil-shaped object made of seaweed is inserted into the cervix. The plug-like insert swells when it becomes moist and gradually dilates the mouth of the womb. At the same time the upper end of the plug acts as a foreign body in the corpus of the uterus, and after two or three days the uterus contracts and expels both plug and fetus. Although this method is not used in America, it is employed extensively in Europe, reportedly with success.

4. The procedure of *dilation and curettage* (*"D and C,"* as it is called in medical circles) is frequently performed if pregnancy has not progressed beyond the twelfth week. This procedure should be performed in a hospital with the patient under anesthesia. The cervix is dilated by inserting graduated sizes of instruments to stretch the

opening, the largest dilator being about the size and shape of a small cigar. Once dilation is accomplished, a spoon-like instrument, a curette,

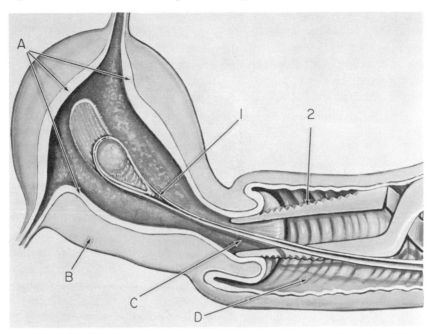

Fig. 8-1. Dilation and curettement. Dilator opens cervix through which a curette is inserted to scrape the lining of the uterus. Curette (1), dilator (2), uterine lining (A), uterus (B), cervix (C), vagina (D). Photograph courtesy *Sexology* magazine.

is used to scrape the implanted embryo or early fetus from the uterus. The embryo or fetus is usually broken up into small pieces in the process of raking out the uterine material. Care must be taken not to perforate the wall of the uterus.

5. *Hysterotomy* is a method used after pregnancy has reached twelve weeks. One technique is actually a minor Caesarean section. This surgical procedure is resorted to because the fetus is too large for usual vaginal methods of removal. Another technique entails a vaginal incision near the cervix, a slit then being made in the lower part of the uterus through which the fetus is removed.

6. In Sweden, a new method has been developed for abortion after the third month of pregnancy. A needle is used to withdraw a certain amount (usually 200 cc) of amniotic fluid through the wall of the abdomen. The fluid is then replaced with an identical amount of salt solution of a specified strength. Abortion occurs spontaneously, usually within twenty-four hours.

Legal Aspects of Abortion

Among European countries, Sweden and Denmark, as early as 1938 and 1939, respectively, passed laws permitting abortions under conditions based on humanitarian and eugenic considerations. In Sweden, a special committee of the Royal Medical Board determines eugenic indications for therapeutic abortions, which now total five for every ninety-five live births. Denmark has a special board of two physicians and one Mother's Aid Society representative to review applications and decide if a therapeutic abortion is indicated. About two-fifths of the applications are approved, and the abortions are performed in accredited hospitals. In both Denmark and Sweden, however, illegal abortions still occur.[253]

Norway's laws are similar to those of Sweden, but encompass a broader interpretation of the justifications for therapeutic abortion. Socioeconomic factors, as well as the mother's health, are taken into account.

In 1936, Russia repealed legislation enacted sixteen years earlier that had legalized abortion. Apparently there was, among other considerations, concern about the low birth rate at that particular time. In 1955, however, therapeutic abortions were once more legalized in the USSR. The present law requires hospitalization for abortion patients in special clinics established for that purpose, where they must remain for three days (longer, if there are any complications).

Japan legalized abortion in 1948. A survey was made eight years later that indicated that while legal abortions numbered 1,159,280 in a one-year period, there were nonetheless an estimated 1,000,000 illegal abortions performed. One wonders why this was so: perhaps the answer is that the doctor wished to avoid income tax by performing the operation in his offices rather than going through the formalized procedure of admitting his patient to a hospital; or perhaps the doctor was not specifically licensed to perform abortions. A physician performing an abortion after the third month of pregnancy must hand over the fetus to a mortician who sometimes charges a higher fee for his services than the abortionist.

Japan reports an increasing number of foreign women seeking abortion there, particularly American women. It is reported that American doctors refer patients to Japanese doctors, by name, for this purpose. About 8000 physicians in Japan are licensed abortionists.

Abortion laws vary considerably in the United States, although confusion, fear, and stupidity figure fairly consistently in almost all of them. The muddled and often contradictory thinking evident in present

American legislation governing abortion may well have had its inception in the efforts (which very likely emanated from his own personal problems) of one Anthony Comstock (1844-1915), who headed the New York Society for the Suppression of Vice. This man began by devoting his energies to the suppression of all forms of art not in conformance with his personal views of what was moral and what was not. His efforts, unfortunately, radiated into all areas of morality, as he succeeded remarkably well in capitalizing on the guilt and ignorance of American citizens concerning anything pertaining to sex. He induced local and state governments to enact overly severe, rigid, and unrealistic laws on contraception, abortion, and other sexually associated matters. Comstock's influence is still apparent today, although there is a growing movement on many fronts to combat antiquated and senseless laws pertaining to sex (see Chapter 17).

In the United States, punishment is leveled at the abortionist rather than at the woman seeking his services; the penalty ranges from one to fourteen years in prison. There are, however, a few states that do assess penalties against the woman who consents to abortion, although there is no record of prosecution under these laws. Death resulting from abortion is branded as murder in fourteen states and as manslaughter in fourteen others.

Under Texas law, for example, abortion is considered a crime against the pregnant woman. She is assumed to be the victim of the abortionist, whether he be her husband or a physician. Furthermore, a person who aids the abortionist by word or gesture is assumed to be guilty as a principal to the act. This legislation is not applicable, however, when medical opinion decrees abortion to be a matter of saving the mother's life. Intent and knowledge of the unlawful purpose are the crucial issues in proving a criminal act; in the case of abortion, there must also be proof of pregnancy.

Under Texas law, a wife may testify against her husband if he is charged with procuring her abortion. If convicted of participation in an abortion performed with the woman's consent, a person may serve two to five years in prison. The sentence for performing an abortion without consent of the pregnant woman can be as long as ten years. Attempted abortion is considered a misdemeanor in Texas and is punishable only by a fine.

Most states of the union punish even the intent to perform an illegal abortion, although twenty-seven states require proof of the woman's pregnancy. In those states in which legal abortions can be obtained, the grounds upon which they may be performed are extreme and unbending. The laws of nearly all states are essentially in agreement that a danger to the mother's life constitutes the only legal basis for abortion.[147]

A significant step toward acknowledging the need for more realistic abortion laws was taken by the American Medical Association at its annual meeting in June, 1967. At that time, the AMA's policy-making body revised the association's official position on the subject of abortion, which had been adopted originally in 1870 and had remained unamended since then. The new policy endorses abortion in instances of pregnancy resulting from rape or incest, when pregnancy threatens the mental or physical health of the woman, and when the infant might be born with severe mental deficiencies or physical deformities. Only a few states—notably, California, North Carolina, and Colorado—have as yet incorporated such liberalized thinking into their abortion laws. It is hoped that other legislators will now feel less skittish about seeking to inject similar realism into their states' laws (see Chapter 17).

Psychiatrists have often mistakenly blamed abortions for the eventual mental breakdowns of some of their women patients. The error here would appear to stem from the fact that psychiatrists see only those patients with severe emotional problems. They rarely have contact with any of the numerous women who not only suffer no psychological ill effects from abortion, but actually gain personal strength from the experience.[149]

Many authorities—including Dr. Alan Guttmacher, president since 1962 of an organization concerned with evolving solutions to problems of the world's population growth—voice strong opposition, in both published works and open discussions, to archaic American laws governing abortion. They advocate public education in the light of 20th-century knowledge. A reexamination of existing statutes by those legislators particularly interested in public welfare does in fact seem in order.

Society appears to have a double standard of judgment in the matter of therapeutic abortions, approval or condemnation seemingly resting on the financial condition of the woman seeking abortion. Women who can afford the charges in private wings of hospitals are able to procure many more "therapeutic" abortions than those women lying in the charity wards of the same hospitals.[151] One of the reasons for this inequity may possibly be that the poor frequently wait too long in any pregnancy to seek medical attention, thus making an abortion inadvisable. According to most authorities, however, the more probable explanation is that if a woman can pay for a "therapeutic" abortion, she very likely can procure it. Herein may also rest the explanation for the high death rate from abortion among the poor. These women cannot pay for an expensive "therapeutic" abortion, and they therefore search out illegal, but certainly less expensive—and considerably more dangerous—procedures. It has long been maintained that if a woman wants an abortion she will get it, even if she has to do so by means of a do-it-yourself kit.[375] Unfortunately, too many women must resort to quacks and untrained abortionists. The rich get richer and the poor get babies—or perhaps incur a death sentence.

———◆◆◆———

A common outcry, particularly in the popular press, is that illegitimacy is on the rise in the United States (for whatever reason ascribed). There has been, to be sure, a rather marked rise in recorded illegitimate births in the United States during recent years. However, most of the increase can doubtless be accounted for by the fact that a greater number of women at the lower socioeconomic levels now have their babies, legitimate or otherwise, in hospitals and maternity homes, where careful records are kept. In the past, women tended to have their illegitimate babies as surreptitiously as possible, and certainly not in a hospital. The increased incidence of hospital births accounts, in large part, for the jump in recorded illegitimate births among nonwhites from 46,800 in 1938 to 134,100 in 1958. Illegitimate births among whites increased from 41,200 to 74,800 during the same twenty-year period.

During this twenty-year span, the smallest increase (108%) of illegitimate births by age groups has been among the fifteen- to nineteen-year-olds. The largest increase has been in the twenty-five- to twenty-nine-year-old group (453%); next highest, among women thirty to thirty-four years old (444%); followed by those twenty to twenty-four years old (297%); then those thirty-five to thirty-nine years old (274%); and then the forty- to forty-four-year-old group, with a 200% increase.[382, 383] It is estimated that 6% of all unmarried women in the United States have been pregnant by the age of fifteen, and 25% by the age of forty.[375]

To a greater and greater extent, nonwhite women now seek hospital care during their confinements. The better care that these women receive at hospitals (in contrast to deliveries at home) accounts for the enormous increase in live births in recent years—a 70% increase in the period between 1940 and 1958, compared with an increase of only 3% among white babies born live.

ABSTINENCE

The dictionary definition of abstinence is "self-denial; an abstaining from the gratification of appetite." Obviously, sexual abstinence in marriage should be mutually agreeable; otherwise, it becomes merely "spouse-denial." Since human beings are equipped with intricate and complex mechanisms for the purpose both of experiencing and gratifying sexual appetites, abstinence would seem to be in opposition to human nature. Indeed, the practice of abstinence in marriage as a method of birth control might very well cause people to question the advisability of marriage itself.

There are those advocates of abstinence who base their arguments on Freud's theory of sublimation. They go only so far as to point out that sexual urges may be sublimated and expressed in socially acceptable and beneficial ways. They do not explain that sublimation is an unconscious process, and that, even then, total sublimation cannot be achieved. There is no empirical evidence, furthermore, that sublimation of biological drives can really be accomplished. As a matter of fact, a conscious attempt to sublimate sexual urges can result in such psychological malfunctions as frigidity, impotence, inability to concentrate, irritability, and insomnia; or in such physical problems as premature ejaculation, difficulty in achieving erection, prostatitis, ovarian and vulval congestion, and decreased sex drive.

Voluntary abstinence is less damaging to the normal functioning of the organism than is involuntary abstinence. In any event, normal sexual urges can find relatively harmless outlets, such as nocturnal emissions for men and nocturnal orgasms for women.

There are, of course, occasions when abstinence becomes a matter of consideration of one's spouse or oneself—for example, during an illness, during late pregnancy, immediately after childbirth, and to avoid contracting or spreading venereal disease. Even in these cases, the partner not physically involved may wish to have some sexual outlet, whether by engaging in such acts as oral or manual stimulation with the spouse, or by self-stimulation.

Abstinence before marriage is, in general, highly esteemed by our society. This sanction is founded in biblical proscriptions against premarital sexual relations, and on the romantic notion that it is good for marriage partners to have their first sexual experience together. Some sociological studies would seem to indicate that sexual adjustment in marriage may actually be more successful when husband or wife, or both, have had previous sexual experience, but other studies do not support these findings.

STERILIZATION

Sterilization is a surgical procedure whereby a person is rendered sterile—*i.e.,* incapable of reproduction. There are several means of achieving this end for both men and women; but the variety of methods is greater for women, as is the incidence of sterilization among them.

In the United States, it is estimated that sterilization is performed in one out of ten marriages. One study involving 245 couples revealed that the wife had been sterilized in 220 cases, the husband in 24 cases, and in one case both husband and wife had been sterilized.

In twenty-eight of the states, sterilization may be performed for eugenic reasons.[329] In other states, it may be done for therapeutic and socioeconomic considerations.

1. **Eugenic sterilization**

a. *The habitual criminal.* The rationale for sterilizing an habitual criminal is based on the theory that the "criminal mind" is inherited. A recent decision by the Supreme Court has ruled against such a measure as being cruel and unusual punishment. Furthermore, there is little scientific evidence that inheritance plays any part in criminal behavior.

b. *The moral pervert.* In most cases involving perversion, illegal enforcement of sterilization would be tantamount to punishment. In one instance, an exhibitionist submitted to castration in preference to serving a prison sentence for his deviate actions. This method of treatment is highly unlikely to benefit either exhibitionists or society, since these and many other sexual deviates are often driven to their behavior because of self-doubt regarding their masculinity. Only the sadistic or the vengeful, or the offender's unconscious desire for punishment, is served by such punitive measures.

c. *Inheritable mental disease or deficiency.* In 1927, a Supreme Court decision decreed that a third-generation imbecile may be sterilized. California law makes it mandatory that an imbecile be sterilized before he can be released from an institution. In other states, similar legislation has been expanded to include persons suffering from schizophrenic and manic-depressive psychoses, which are interpreted as inheritable mental diseases—a highly questionable assumption.

2. **Therapeutic sterilization** is sometimes performed when certain pathological conditions are present in either husband or wife: tuberculosis, cancer, cardio-renal-vascular diseases, hypertension and high blood pressure, and kidney disorders; or when certain Rh blood incompatibilities exist.[294]

3. **Socioeconomic considerations** form the basis for the majority of sterilization operations performed, and the range of motivations in requesting the operation is extensive. From a legal standpoint, the surgeon is often placed on uncertain ground. However good his intentions to help his patients, he must always be careful to guard himself against later lawsuits brought by the persons upon whom he performs the operation. Many of these people have neurotic reasons for wanting to be sterilized, in the first place, and these same neuroses or sociopathic attitudes may prompt them to bring suit against the physician who was merely trying to help them.

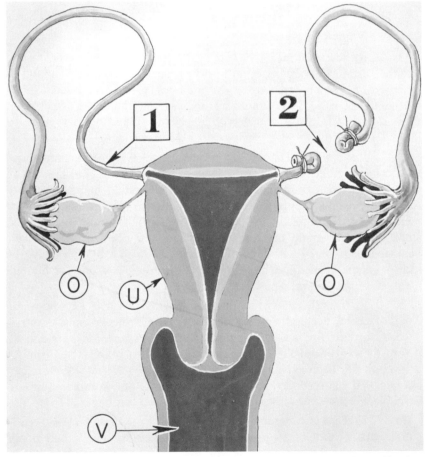

Fig. 8-2. Cutting and tying the Fallopian tubes, a form of female sterilization. Fallopian tubes (1, 2), ovaries (O), uterus (U), vagina (V). Photograph courtesy *Sexology* magazine.

Methods of Sterilization—Female

1. *Oophorectomy* is the surgical removal of both ovaries, which brings the process of ovulation permanently to a halt. Because this procedure means the removal of the source of certain hormones, it has been known to prompt certain undesirable physical changes, such as excessive weight gain, growth of facial hair, and a deepening of the voice. In addition, a woman's sexual desire frequently undergoes a change, and she may experience such discomforts as hot flashes, sweating, nervousness, and even tremor. Hormone therapy will usually correct these adverse conditions.

2. *Salpingectomy* is a straightforward but major surgical procedure, best performed during a Caesarean section. (The counterpart operation on a man, a vasectomy, is much less complicated.) The Fallopian tubes are cut, tied, and resectioned in order to prevent the two ends from thereafter meeting, thus keeping the sperm and ova from ever contacting one another.

3. *Intrauterine coagulation of the uterine tube outlet* is a method of sterilization presently used extensively in Japan, which will probably soon be performed in the United States. A specially designed instrument is inserted through the uterus to the intrauterine openings of the Fallopian tubes, where it electrically cauterizes the orifices. This process causes scar tissue to form; the tubular openings are thus blocked, and sperm and ova are prevented from coming together. The effect is permanent, for it would be almost impossible to reopen the tiny Fallopian tubes.

4. *Hysterectomy* is the surgical removal of the uterus. The process may include removal of one or both ovaries, and one or both tubes. A hysterectomy is almost never performed for the purpose of sterilization alone, but usually to remedy certain abnormalities such as a fibroid tumor. In current practice, especially in uncomplicated cases, the uterus is often removed via the vagina, thus eliminating abdominal incision and scarring.

In an investigation of 35,000 tubal sterilizations, it was found that about one in 200 of the operations failed to prevent subsequent pregnancies.[107] Women's sex drive is not likely to be impaired following sterilization; to the contrary, there may well be an increase in drive because of the sense of freedom engendered by removing the fear of pregnancy.

Methods of Sterilization—Male

1. *Vasectomy* is the surgical procedure of cutting and tying the semen-carrying ducts, the vas deferens. A small incision is made in

the scrotum, and the vas deferens is lifted out so that about an inch of the tiny tube can be cut out. The tube, or duct, is then tied at each end where the section was removed, preventing the sperm's passing from the testicles to the ejaculatory ducts. This procedure must be followed on each side of the body. The site of the incision is well

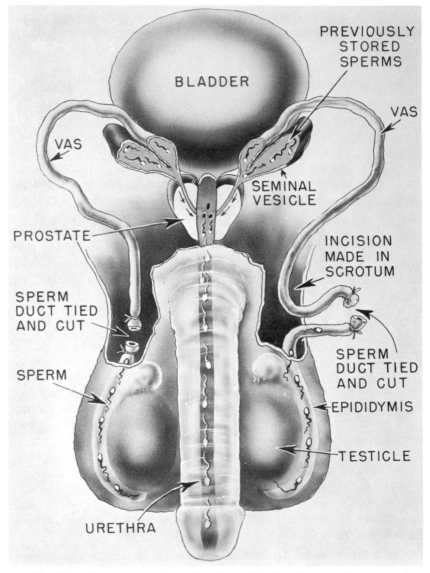

Fig. 8-3.   Vasectomy, a form of male sterilization. Photograph courtesy *Sexology* magazine.

above the testicles and in no way disturbs them or their functioning. The man remains potent but sterile, and the sperm he now produces are absorbed by his body.

A vasectomy is a simple operation and can be performed in a hospital or in a doctor's office, with either a local or general anesthetic. Afterwards, the patient should remain relatively inactive for about forty-eight hours; at least he should do no heavy work for that period of time, or longer. The doctor usually advises the use of a suspensory for several weeks in order to prevent any pulling of the testicles, and to minimize soreness during the healing process.

The patient remains in a state of fecundity (fertility) for several days following the vasectomy, because his first ejaculations after surgery will contain sperm that have been previously stored in the seminal vesicles. Sometimes sperm accumulate in a little sac at the site of the incision, causing a granuloma or lumpiness in the scrotum; the accumulation is usually harmless and dissipates in time. The effects of a vasectomy can be undone by surgery in which the ends of the tubes are rejoined. This operation is about 50% successful.[204]

The "tying of tubes" in men is much simpler, quicker, cheaper, and less dangerous than its counterpart operation performed on women, the salpingectomy. Yet many men steadfastly refuse to have the operation performed on themselves, though they willingly consent to a salpingectomy for their wives. This selfishness probably can be accounted for, in the first place, by the fact that it is women who conceive and bear children, and hence suffer any pain or difficulty associated with the birth process. Women, therefore, should be "willing to pay the price" for the operation.

Secondly, men frequently associate any cutting near the testicles with castration and are fearful of such an operation, despite the fact that they know rationally that vasectomy does not decrease sexual drive or desire, or their ability to satisfy the drive and desire. In one investigation into the impact of vasectomy on 151 men who underwent the operation, 17.9% reported an increase in sexual appetite, 74.2% showed no change, and only 7.9% reported a slight diminishing of sexual desire; these results are fairly typical of such investigations.[204] The increase in sexual drive is probably a consequence of psychological factors, such as a reduction of anxiety because the fear of impregnating the wife has been removed.

In a few cases of sterilization, there is an apparently spontaneous rejoining or recanalization of the severed vas deferens, despite the care and skill of the surgeon. In response to questionnaires sent to 1721 physicians, ninety-six reported that spontaneous recanalization had occurred among their patients.[30] The percentage of recanalization after vasectomies is not known, but is thought to be exceedingly low.

Voluntary sterilization operations are fairly common in the United States. The Association for Voluntary Sterilization estimates that there are about two million men and women in this country who have been sterilized by surgical procedures, and that about 200,000 vasectomies are performed on American men each year.[344]

2. *Castration* is a method of sterilization, known and used since ancient times, in which both testicles are surgically removed, producing sterility. If the man is an adult, castration does not necessarily mean impotence, although there is a gradual loss of sexual desire with the passage of time because of loss of male hormones produced by the testicles. Physiological changes may also result from loss of hormones, such as an increase in voice pitch, decrease in beard growth, and excess fat. The undesirable changes in secondary sexual characteristics following castration can, however, often be corrected with proper hormone therapy.

Legal Aspects of Sterilization

Sterilization for eugenic reasons is sanctioned in some states, particularly in tax-supported institutions. A doctor is free to perform sterilizing operations in these instances without concern for any legal consequences. If, however, the operation is done purely for reasons of health, the doctor's position is less safe, because he is not so well protected by state laws in these instances.

There are no uniform laws among the various states regarding sterilization. In California, malpractice suits against doctors resulting from surgery for sterilization are not usually covered by insurance companies. One study revealed[269] that 87% of the physicians sampled who had performed vasectomies had never had suit brought against them because of this surgery, 8% had faced legal action, and 5% did not reply. Written consent by the patient affords the physician some measure of safety, but is no guarantee against a subsequent suit or even prosecution in a court of criminal law. Even eugenic sterilization is prohibited in four states—Connecticut, Kansas, Utah, and Montana.[294]

Sterilization in Japan, though legal, is usually performed only upon women. In India, sterilization is limited to men, who are monetarily compensated for the time lost from work following the surgery.[30]

As may be inferred from the foregoing, sterilization procedures are frequently preceded or followed by psychological repercussions that have their roots in anxiety: will there be a reduction of sexual desire; will masculinity or femininity be diminished? These fears can usually be assuaged by the reassurance of the surgeon through his careful explanation of all the ramifications of the operation. If emotional stress should persist, however, psychotherapy will often restore stability.

CONTRACEPTION

To rephrase the definition given at the beginning of the chapter, contraception may be described as any temporary method of birth control that permits sexual intercourse between a fertile man and a fertile woman but that prevents impregnation. This definition excludes abstinence, abortion, and sterilization (including castration), which are, obviously, forms of birth control, but which are distinctly not forms of contraception.

The efficacy of a specific method of contraception is determined by comparing its incidence of success with the incidence of pregnancy in couples who use no means of contraception—the latter assessed at 60 to 100 pregnancies in 100 years of coital experience.[104] For example, if couples using condoms ("rubbers") as a contraceptive device show a pregnancy rate of 11 per 100 years (1200 months) of exposure, and if nonusers of any contraceptive methods show 100 pregnancies per 100 years of exposure, it is calculated that 89 out of 100 pregnancies were prevented by the use of the condom, and that its use as a contraceptive device is "89% effective." The following equation demonstrates the usual method of calculating the effectiveness of a particular contraceptive method.

$$\text{Pregnancy rate} = \frac{\text{number of pregnancies x 1200 months (100 years)}}{\text{patients observed x months of exposure}}$$

If, for example, 100 couples have used a particular contraceptive method for 5 years and if 50 pregnancies have occurred despite the use of the method, the equation would be as follows:

$$\text{Pregnancy rate} = \frac{50 \text{ x } 1200}{100 \text{ x } 60} = \frac{60,000}{6,000} = 10$$

When the pregnancy rating of a contraceptive method is below 10, its effectiveness is rated as high; if the rating is between 10 and 20, the effectiveness is considered to be medium; and if the rating is above 20, the effectiveness is ranked as low.[107]

Contraception serves five important purposes:

1. *To aid early sexual adjustment in marriage.* During the in-

evitable period of marital adjustment, sexual compatibility may be reached earlier and in a more satisfactory manner if fear of pregnancy is removed. It has also been shown that a wife's sexual responsiveness is directly related to the degree that both she and her husband are satisfied with their present method of contraception.[2]

2. *To space pregnancies.* Spacing the arrival of children allows a couple to give full consideration to the mother's health and to the family's economics. It has been claimed that when births are only one year apart, the death rate for babies is about 50% higher than when births are two years apart.[150]

3. *To limit family size.* Most couples prefer for many and various reasons to limit the size of their families. A primary consideration is that excessive childbearing can leave the mother with several undesirable physical conditions, such as high blood pressure, varicose veins, and relaxed vaginal tissue. Furthermore, after the birth of the second child, the chance of infant mortality increases with each additional child borne by the same mother.

Social factors also influence the number of children that individual couples want (only 10%, for instance, want more than four). Women are often reluctant to spend all their young and energetic adult lives being a mother to a baby or child. By limiting the number of children and by properly spacing them, they can frequently have their children during the first few years of marriage, leaving the latter years for a more leisurely life and, hopefully, a more meaningful one with regard to their commitment to a profession or to the community.

4. *To avoid aggravation of existing illnesses or diseases.* Many illnesses and diseases—tuberculosis, heart and kidney disease, an advanced stage of diabetes (especially when complicated by damaged blood vessels), emotional disorders, nervous afflictions, recent surgery for cancer—raise the question of the advisability of pregnancy.

5. *To prevent the perpetuation of inherited diseases.* Spread of inherited diseases, *e.g.,* Huntington's chorea, can, obviously, be best controlled by preventing the pregnancy of an afflicted woman or a woman married to an afflicted man.

A study of the growth of the American family,[139] in which 2700 white women between the childbearing ages of eighteen and thirty-nine were interviewed, revealed the following with regard to the practice of contraception:

70% of these women were practicing some form of contraception;

9% planned to do so later;

92% who had proved their fertility with the birth of at least one child, and who had been married for at least fifteen years, used contraceptives;

60% of those women who had never tried to prevent conception were relatively infertile in any event;

and with regard to religious groups:

57% of the Catholics in the study used some form of contraception, as did

75% of the Protestants, and

86% of the Jewish women.

After one child had been born, the percentages within religious groups using contraception were:

70% of the Catholic mothers,

83% of the Protestants, and

95% of the Jews.

The educational level of the couples was directly related to whether or not they used contraceptives: the higher the education received, the more likely the couples were to employ contraception. In 1955, seven in ten couples used some form of contraception, and by 1960 the number had risen to eight in ten.

Contraceptive measures currently offer a wide range of choice among medically approved devices and products.

Contraceptives Available Only with a Doctor's Prescription

1. A *diaphragm* is a thin rubber dome-shaped cup stretched over a collapsible metal ring, designed to cover the mouth of the womb (the cervix). Properly fitted and used with a contraceptive cream or jelly, the diaphragm seals off the cervix and prevents sperm from entering the womb. The cream or jelly is toxic to sperm, and provides lubrication as well. This device in no manner interferes with the conduct or pleasure of intercourse.

The diaphragm can be obtained only by prescription from a physician, and must be fitted by him the first time. Because of individual differences in women, a diaphragm of the correct size and shape is of vital importance, both for the wearer's comfort and for its effectiveness as a contraceptive. After the initial examination and insertion of the diaphragm, the physician will instruct his patient how to insert it properly herself, and how to remove it. A virgin cannot be fitted with a diaphragm until the hymen is broken. Physicians are therefore reluctant to prescribe a diaphragm for any woman until after her honeymoon.

A diaphragm may be inserted several hours before or immediately preceding coitus. It must not be removed until four to six hours after intercourse, and it may be left in place for as long as twenty-four hours. Douching (discussed more fully hereafter) is unnecessary, since the natural processes of a healthy woman keep her vaginal tract clean. If she prefers to douche, however, she must wait at least six hours following coitus in order for the spermicide cream or jelly, or the naturally acid condition of the vagina, to destroy the sperm. Dia-

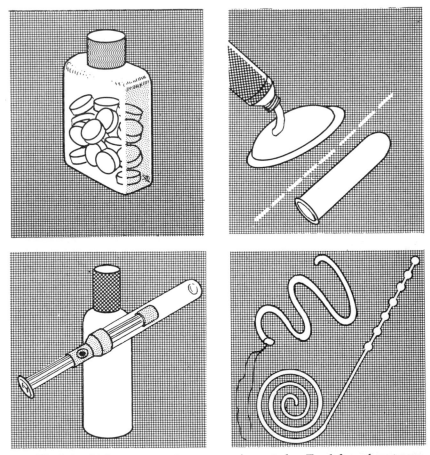

Fig. 8-4.   Major contraceptive measures in use today. Top left, oral contraceptive pills; top right, diaphragm and spermicidal jelly, and the condom; lower left, spermicidal vaginal foam; and, lower right, intrauterine contraceptive devices (loop and coil). Photograph courtesy *Sexology* magazine.

phragms are considered by many to be inconvenient, uncomfortable, and rather difficult to use.[275] For other couples, the advance preparation implies a loss of spontaneity that detracts from sexual pleasure.

With the use of this device and a contraceptive jelly, the pregnancy rate varies from 4 to 10.[275]

2. A *cervical cap* is a small deep cup usually made of plastic that fits snugly just over the cervix. Because the cervix lies so deep within the vagina, and because it is essential that the cap fit snugly, it must be fitted by a physician. Women can be trained to insert the cap, but many seem unable to learn the technique. This method of contraception is, therefore, not often used in the United States, although it is in fairly common use in Europe. Once the cap is fitted properly, the penis is not likely to dislodge it. It cannot be felt by the wearer, and it can be worn the entire time between menstrual periods. Caps made of rubber can be worn only about twenty-four hours. The cervical cap used with contraceptive cream or jelly is considered to have about the same pregnancy rate as the diaphragm used with contraceptive cream or jelly. Because the cervical cap is left in place between menstrual periods, some of the disadvantages of the diaphragm are eliminated.

3. *Oral contraceptives* (*birth control pills,* popularly called "the pill"). It was demonstrated in 1937 that the administration of the ovarian hormone progesterone would inhibit ovulation in rabbits. Since that time endocrinologists, biologists, chemists, and physicians using this and other information, and working together and separately, have developed a method of contraception for human beings that is apparently superior to any method previously employed.[1] In 1954, an oral contraceptive in the form of a pill was used in laboratory studies, then two years later in Puerto Rico and Haiti in well-controlled studies to determine its safety and effectiveness. The experiments were tremendously successful. Since that time, pharmaceutical houses have been working overtime to supply the public with the pills, and to produce even better oral contraceptives.

The birth control pill is a combination of synthetic hormones (progesterone and estrogen) that, when taken in adequate doses, prevents ovulation by mimicking the body's natural hormones produced during pregnancy. If no ovum is released, pregnancy obviously cannot occur. The pill actually does several things to prevent or to make pregnancy extremely unlikely to occur.[275] First, pituitary gonadotropin production is inhibited, which interferes with the growth and development of the ovarian follicles. In addition, the uterine mucosa is affected

in such a manner as to make implantation more difficult and early
spontaneous abortion more likely if an egg were to be fertilized. The
mucous plug of the cervix is thickened and made more formidable by
the hormonal agents, thereby helping to prevent sperm from entering
the uterus.

Counting from the first day of her monthly menstrual period, a
woman starts taking the pills on the fifth day. She must swallow one
pill daily, and preferably at the same hour, for twenty days. Menstruation will start two to five days after the last pill is taken, although
in about 3% of the cases, it fails altogether to commence. In this
latter event, a physician usually advises his patient to commence a
new round of twenty pills seven days after the last pill was taken, or
he will offer alternative suggestions.

If one pill is missed, there is a chance of pregnancy, but it is
rather remote. If taken as prescribed, however, contraceptive pills are
virtually 100% effective—and their success is unequalled by any other
means of contraception.

During the early months of taking contraceptive pills, women
seem to experience little reduction in sexual desire. The knowledge of
being well protected against an unwanted conception often removes
anxiety from both husband and wife, thereby increasing sexual desire
in both partners. Authorities have warned women, however, to expect some loss of sex drive after protracted use of the pills because of
their interference with normal hormonal production.[375] Masters and
Johnson report that a reduction in women's sex drive occurs after
their taking the pills for eighteen to thirty-six months, and they suggest that other contraceptive methods be substituted for the pill from
time to time, according to the advice of the individual woman's physician, in order that the original hormonal balance can be restored.[217]
The pill is also used to treat certain discomforts and disorders of the
menstrual cycle, such as irregularity, too copious flow of blood, and
discomfort before or during menstruation.

As contraceptive pills have been used, studied, modified, and
improved upon since their initial introduction, the negative side effects
have largely been removed. Occasional discomfort or unpleasantness
may still be experienced by some women who take them, especially
in the first months. The most common symptoms reported are mild
gastrointestinal disturbance, nausea and a bloated feeling, increase in
weight, and spotting and irregular bleeding. Other occasional negative
side effects are persistent menstrual-like cramping and painful swelling
of the breasts.[375]

A considerable amount of research is being done on a pill for men that will induce temporary sterility. To date, however, there are unfortunate side effects when men use a pill of this nature, in that sex drive is reduced and the intake of alcohol produces abnormal reactions. Much further experimentation, therefore, in this aspect of contraception is indicated.[277]

There is no evidence that serious complications, such as cancer, arise from using birth control pills, even in women who have taken them for as long as six years. Since such a pill suppresses milk production, its use is not recommended during the period just after childbirth when a mother is nursing her baby. Furthermore, there is evidence that if a mother takes birth control pills while she is nursing a boy child, the unusual combination of hormones then present in her body can work its way into the baby's bloodstream via her milk and have a feminizing effect on him.[89]

This means of contraception, as has been pointed out, is considered 100% successful when used as directed. Even when a woman occasionally misses taking one, the pill still has the excellent pregnancy rate of 3 to 7, equaling the best mechanical device. A birth control pill designed to prevent implantation of the fertilized egg is presently being studied. This pill, if taken just after sexual intercourse, would act for the next few days to prevent implantation of the fertilized egg.[304] Vaccines to immunize people against fertility for several months are also being investigated.

A pharmaceutical house has recently produced an effective oral contraceptive for dogs. The pill, administered each day for thirty days before the female's estrus period, suppresses that period without affecting the animal's capacity for producing healthy litters in the future.[319]

4. *Intrauterine contraceptive devices (IUCDs)* are small plastic or metal devices—plastic being preferred over metal because of its flexibility and the greater chance of its not being rejected by the subject's body tissue—of various sizes and shapes. They are designed to fit into the womb, and in some way they act as an irritant to prevent implantation of the fertilized ovum in the uterine wall. Technically, this method is more correctly called *contraimplantation* than contraception.

The device must be selected and fitted in the uterus by a physician. It remains permanently in place until the user wishes to become pregnant, at which time the doctor will remove it. After the birth of a child, it may be repositioned in the uterus until another pregnancy is desired. The device in no way affects the health of any children borne by the woman or her ability to conceive.

There are certain disadvantages to using IUCDs: expulsion by the uterus without the wearer's knowledge (although this can be avoided simply by checking it regularly), and, in some instances, bleeding and pain. Since the device is, of course, a foreign body, the uterus resists it for a while; but once the initial discomfort is past, the user is no longer aware of its presence. Two threads hang from the device down through the cervix into the vagina, where a frequent check should be made to determine that it has not been expelled.

Of the variety of shapes and sizes in which IUCDs are available, the best known are the spiral, loop, bow, and ring. The National Committee on Maternal Health is presently conducting a large-scale study of the devices, and it has gathered the individual case histories of almost 25,000 women who had used variously shaped IUCDs for at least a year.[374] The loop was found generally to be the most effective and comfortable, as well as having a low rate of spontaneous expulsion.

Since 1949, IUCDs have been submitted to clinical examination of their effectiveness, and the test results have been watched with interest by various planned parenthood groups. Studies indicate that IUCDs are not yet 100% effective, but that they rank among the most adequate means of contraception available. As the devices are perfected, more and more doctors are prescribing them for their patients, and their use is increasing rapidly in this country. The most successful of the IUCDs have a pregnancy rating of about 2 to 3.

Pap smears have been taken from thousands of IUCD users. They reveal no occurrence of cancer beyond its normal incidence in the female population, or evidence of other adverse effects that could be attributed to the devices.

It is interesting to observe the readiness with which the people of India have accepted this particular means of birth control—not only for themselves, but for their sacred cows as well![327] The government, realizing the many problems caused by the unrestrained productivity of the sacred animals, yet not being allowed to destroy them, even for use as food, decided to take unusual steps toward control. A special IUCD has been devised for the cows, and it is hoped that their birth rate can be thereby controlled without public outcry. Furthermore, ingenious veterinarians have developed workable IUCDs for cats and dogs—much to the delight of pet owners and pets alike!

Contraceptives Available without a Doctor's Prescription

1. *Condom.* The most widely used contraceptive device in the United States, the condom is made of strong thin rubber, or of sheep's intestine. At its open end, which is about an inch and a half in diameter,

there is a rubber ring. The closed end is usually plain, but it may have a pocket to provide space for ejaculated semen, thus lessening the possibility of its bursting. The condom usually measures seven and a half inches in length.

As a result of the U.S. Food and Drug Administration's placing condoms under its control, the product has been improved. The only drawback to its being totally effective is the possibility of breakage during use, or of its slipping off after ejaculation, with the result in either event that semen may be spilled into the vagina. The second eventuality can be avoided if there is adequate lubrication and if the condom is held onto while the penis is being withdrawn from the vagina after ejaculation. Condoms should always be inspected before use by blowing air into them, and it is advisable afterwards to fill them with water to be sure that no breakage has occurred. If a condom breaks in use, a contraceptive cream or jelly should be applied vaginally immediately. If none is available, a water douche should be used, since water is highly spermatoxic.

The efficiency in design and manufacture of the present-day rubber condom dates from about 1920, although the discovery of vulcanized rubber in the 1840s made possible the production of the condom on a large scale over a hundred years ago. Condoms made of linen or silk were used by the Italians and Chinese before the 17th century, principally as a prophylactic measure against venereal disease[374] rather than as a contraceptive device.

Prior to the development of the vulcanization process, the French and English used sheep gut or the amniotic membrane of newborn lambs[375] to fashion fairly satisfactory condoms. In recent years, manufacturers are again producing gut condoms, which, while more expensive than rubber condoms, appear to be as safe as the rubber ones, and which are aesthetically preferable because they interfere less with body warmth and other pleasurable sensations experienced during coitus.

With the exception of withdrawal (discussed in following paragraphs), the condom is probably the most frequently employed birth prevention technique, although it is used more in nonmarital than in marital coitus. About 750,000,000 condoms are produced each year in the United States. They are cheap, available in most pharmacies, simple to use, and easily disposable.

Some men object to the condom because it somewhat dulls pleasurable sensations. Also, its use may interfere with the natural progress of mounting sexual tension because sexual play must be interrupted in order to put it on. The pregnancy rate of the condom can be judged to be about 10 or 11, since estimates in individual studies range from 6 to 19. The condom is certainly the best method, after total abstinence of preventing the spread of venereal diseases.

2. *Chemical methods.*   The most effective of the chemical methods of preventing conception are creams, jellies, and vaginal foams. They are used for two reasons: they serve to block the entrance to the uterus, and they contain an ingredient that is toxic to sperm. They must be introduced about five to fifteen minutes before ejaculation occurs, and if intercourse is repeated, more cream or jelly must be used.

Another chemical method involves the use of a vaginal suppository, a small solid cone that melts at about 95° F. It is toxic to sperm, but the disadvantage in its use is that it must be inserted at least fifteen minutes before ejaculation if it is to be effective. Suppositories usually have one of three bases—cocoa butter, glycerin gelatin, or soap. Pregnancy rates vary from 5 to 27.

Vaginal tablets have the same drawbacks as suppositories. Moisture is needed to dissolve them and it may not be present in sufficient quantity. The tablets, moreover, are very unstable in damp climates. They are given a pregnancy rate of 8 to 27.

3. *Douche.*   The theory behind douching as a contraceptive measure is that semen can be flushed from the vagina before it has a chance to enter the mouth of the womb. Actually, however, sperm move so quickly that the douche often fails to reach them. Although water makes a satisfactory douching solution, strong soapsuds, three tablespoonfuls of vinegar, or a teaspoonful of alum per quart of water is probably better. Douching is not medically approved as an effective method of birth control, since it has the unsatisfactory pregnancy rate of 36. It serves better to cleanse the vagina than to prevent pregnancy.

4. *Other contraceptives.*   A sponge and foam combination is a contraceptive that is inexpensive but relatively ineffectual. The sponge is dipped in water and squeezed; the contraceptive ingredient is then added and worked into a foam. The sponge, which is inserted deep into the vagina before intercourse, will remain effective for several hours. Another sponge can be added to the first one if intercourse is repeated. The sponge must remain in place for six hours following the last act of coitus. No douche is necessary.

Another contraceptive means is a tampon containing a spermatoxic chemical, which is inserted into the vagina as close to the cervix as possible. The chemical is a contraceptive jelly that begins a foaming action upon contact with sperm. This method and the one described in the preceding paragraph have the poor pregnancy rate of 27 to 42.

A recent innovation in contraception consists of foam preparations that are inserted into the vagina by way of an aerosol spray can. These products contain effective spermicidal powders; they are easy to apply and have a pregnancy rate of from 3 to 10.

As part of their extensive research on human sexual response, Masters and Johnson investigated the effectiveness of eight commercial contraceptive products;[170] none of the methods tested—two creams and one each of a vaginal jelly, a liquid, a gel, a tablet, a foam, and a suppository—was given perfect scores in the various tests performed. Each of the women taking part in the tests had her cervix capped, used the contraceptive according to the manufacturer's instructions, and engaged in artificial coition by means of a plastic penis until she had an orgasm. At this point, fertile semen was introduced into the vagina, and samples of vaginal content were taken from various parts of the vagina, the first sample being taken within one to five seconds after semen injection, followed by samples taken after fifteen seconds, thirty seconds, sixty seconds, two minutes, and five minutes. In another series of artificial coitions, which involved the same contraceptives and which was similarly conducted to the point of orgasm, the same sampling procedure was instigated one hour after injection of semen, then three and five hours later.

Findings of the study were that the diaphragm failed in a large percentage of the cases investigated (8 of 30) because of vaginal and uterine enlargement during the sexual response cycle, and because the reinsertion of the penis after the initial insertion and withdrawal tended to dislodge the diaphragm from its snug and properly fitted position. There was evidence, furthermore, that even a highly spermatocidal chemical may not be effective if the substance containing it does not dissolve or spread properly within the vagina. A chemical may be very effective in a suitable foam, but ineffective in a jelly, cream, or foaming tablet.

Other Methods of Birth Prevention

1. *Coitus interruptus* or *withdrawal* requires the husband to withdraw his penis from his wife's vagina before he reaches a climax. There are disadvantages, however, to this form of birth control.

Sexual intercourse cannot be enjoyed in a relaxed mood by either partner if the uppermost thought is withdrawal in the nick of time. The popular misconception that prolonged reliance on this method may eventually cause premature ejaculation is not supported by evidence; neither is the contention of some physicians that withdrawal is both unreliable as a conception preventive and damaging to health. For a woman slow to reach orgasm, preejaculatory withdrawal by her husband may not allow sufficient time for her to reach orgasm. The withdrawal, in turn, causes congestion of blood in the genital organs and can result in chronic pelvic pain and other gynecological complaints. This reaction, however, may follow any sexually stimulating experience that is prolonged yet does not result in orgasm.

The first few drops of the ejaculate contain the great bulk of the male spermatozoa. Should the man be slow to withdraw, and should any of this first ejaculate enter the vagina, *coitus interruptus* can very easily be a failure as a means of birth prevention. Furthermore, the secretion in the Cowper's glands of many men contains sperm cells that frequently ooze into the vagina even if no ejaculation follows.[231]

Many couples rely upon this technique for years with both success and satisfaction, and without experiencing any of the alleged dangers to health. Certainly it is the oldest known form of contraception. It is mentioned in the Old Testament (Genesis), and anthropologists report that it has been widely used throughout the world for centuries. Probably the most distressing aspect of *coitus interruptus* is the onus on the husband to withdraw at the crucial moment. At the time of ejaculation, the typical male impulse is to drive the penis as deeply into the vagina as possible, and to hold it there. This impulse is quite inimical to the movements of withdrawal. The husband should also time coital activity so that his withdrawal and ejaculation occur after his wife's climax. In addition, he would be most unwise to reenter the vagina for a considerable period of time after ejaculation, because of the presence of residual sperm in the urethra.

Generally speaking, those couples who use *coitus interruptus* extensively do not find it particularly undesirable, while other couples despise the technique. Depending upon the care and timing of the man, the pregnancy rate is from 8 to 40.

2. *The rhythm method.*   Authorities differ on the subject, but it is a generally accepted biological postulate that an ovum lives approximately only twenty-four hours after ovulation unless it is fertilized.[102, 104] Sperm released into the uterus remain alive and are capable of fertilizing the egg for about forty-eight hours. This means that only during three days per month can a woman become pregnant. The difficulty, of course, is pinpointing the exact three days.

As a general rule, the average woman releases an ovum 14 to 16 days before her next menstrual period is due. If she menstruates every 28 days, she should ovulate midway between the two periods—about the 13th to 15th day after the first day of her period. If the cycle is 25 days, ovulation should occur between the 10th and 12th day; if it is 35 days, between the 20th and 22nd day.

Since different women menstruate on different schedules, to compute the fertile ("unsafe") and infertile ("safe") days, a written menstrual record should be kept for twelve consecutive months. To determine the fertile and "safe" days, the following formula is suggested:[375] subtract 19 from the number of days in the shortest menstrual cycle observed during the preceding twelve months to get the number of safe days during the first half of the cycle (beginning with the first day of the cycle); next, subtract 11 from the number of days of the longest cycle of the preceding year to get the number of safe days during the last half of the cycle. For example, if the shortest cycle for the preceding year was 24 days and the longest cycle was 28 days, the first calculation is made this way: $24-19=5$; this means that from the first day of the menstrual flow, the next 5 days are considered "safe." The second calculation is made this way: $28-11=17$; this means that the time from the 17th day of the cycle to the beginning of the next menstruation is considered "safe." This leaves 12 days of the menstrual cycle—the 5th to the 17th—during which conception is considered possible.

About 15% of all women have such irregular menstrual periods that they cannot safely use the rhythm method for avoiding conception. Those women who vary as much as ten days or more should have medical advice to determine their "safe" period. After childbirth, the first few menstrual cycles may be very irregular, and the rhythm method is therefore particularly unreliable at that time.

A refinement of the rhythm system, which is based on the same biological postulation concerning the time of monthly ovulation, is the *temperature method* of birth control. This technique goes further than a mere series of calendar observations of the occurrence of a woman's menses. It is founded on the additional premise that there is a distinct correlation between changes in body temperature and the process of ovulation. A woman's temperature is ordinarily relatively low during menstruation itself and for eight days thereafter—thirteen days in all. At the time of ovulation, midway in the cycle, there is a dip in temperature and then a sharp rise of $1/2°$ to $7/10°$. The elevation persists for the remainder of the cycle, then drops one or two days before the onset of the next period.

To achieve any sort of accuracy in predicting her "safe" period according to this method, a woman should record her temperature, preferably upon awakening, every morning for six to twelve months. The primary difficulty in so determining a "safe" period for intercourse is that in some women the changes in temperature are not so pronounced or so consistent, although a doctor is much more skilled in interpreting temperature charts than the layman. A further difficulty is that more than one ovum can mature during any one cycle. Furthermore, current research[51] indicates that the time interval between ovulation and the temperature rise can vary up to four days. Whichever the approach, rhythm or temperature, this technique has a pregnancy rate of 14.

CHAPTER 9

Techniques in
Sexual Arousal

IN MANY authoritative writings, much has been made of the fact that various sexual stimuli affect men and women in different ways, but this point requires clarification. In the first place, these differences arc not so cxtensive as one is often led to believe, and the Kinsey investigators have demonstrated the fact.[170, 100] For instance, in a province one takes to be strictly male—burlesque shows and stag films, among other similar erotica—the Kinsey researchers found that one-third of the women in their sample had as strong a sexual response as men to such stimuli, while a small percentage had an even stronger one.[191]

Although there are certainly some fundamental differences between men and women in particular stimuli-response patterns, there is probably considerably less such dissimilarity between the sexes than there are characterological variations in sexual response among members of the same sex.[191] Strange and interesting sexual excitants have been recorded in the erotic histories of both men and women. The Kinsey investigators report, as examples, that some women have been brought to orgasm simply by having their eyebrows stroked, by having their body or hair gently blown upon, or by having pressure applied to their teeth.[179]

Basically, the sex drive of women is as powerful as that of men; but they *do* in the main respond to different types of both psychological and physiological stimulation, and they respond in a slightly different manner. Women have been conditioned for generations, by a society muddled in its thinking on sexual matters, to inhibit, if not deny altogether, their sexuality and to stifle normal response to sexual stimuli. These culturally imposed inhibitions no doubt account for the popular misconception that women are erotically less responsive than men are.

Sexual arousal in humans, both male and female, springs from psychological as well as from physiological sources.[111, 122, 208] Such arousal usually begins with verbalization and indirect gestures.[111, 117] In time, couples usually build up their own private store of verbal endearments, which are then used advantageously to set the stage for satisfying sexual interplay. A husband can, and should, express to his wife his feelings that she is loved, exciting, and sexually desirable by calling her a pet name. The wife can, and should, convey her pleasure in her husband by responding readily with similar endearments.[111] To make the sexual partner aware that one enjoys his or her appearance, talents, intellect, strength, and the like is only half of a successful preliminary sexual interaction; the partner must also be made to know that he is enjoyed and appreciated as a lover.

To abandon oneself in an uninhibited expression of one's love and excitement, to have these manifestations eagerly accepted, to receive in turn spontaneous and equally unrestrained expressions of love and desire: these are the ingredients intrinsic to a sexual relationship in its deepest and fullest measure. Frequently the husband derives his greatest sexual pleasure not from his own orgasmic response, but from his wife's full participation in the sex act wherein she relinquishes herself completely to their lovemaking, and freely communicates to her husband that *he* is responsible for giving her such uniquely exquisite pleasure.[248] The more reckless and uninhibited the response, short of causing severe physical pain, which a wife makes at the peak of sexual excitement, the more pleased most husbands are.

On the man's shoulders, whether he likes it or not, commonly rests the burden of directing a couple's sexual activity. Furthermore, the wife ordinarily expects her husband to proceed through all aspects of their sexual life with an air of confidence. One finds it difficult to fathom just how a husband is to acquire confidence if he is inexperienced, yet has been indoctrinated with fearsome warnings against "failure in bed," as most men are in their formative years. Even though the young bride herself may be grossly inexperienced and know very little about sex, its techniques, and its stimuli-response patterns, she nonetheless is likely to expect her husband to be experienced and expert in the art of lovemaking—and often will be dismayed if he is otherwise.[59, 60, 117]

The new wife's expectation, then, of expertise and confidence on the part of her young husband in the marriage bed frequently ignores the very real possiblity that he, too, may be lacking in proper experience. Furthermore, he may, quite likely as much as his bride, be a victim of society's sexual prohibitions and unsound training in sexual matters. It is indeed unfortunate that custom has decreed fixed roles in male-female relationships, most particularly the amatory one, in which the husband is always expected to be dominant and, above all, confident. The disparity between the expectations on the one hand, and the inexperience on the other, together with the faulty sex education both husband and wife may have received, frequently lays open the way for emotional stress that eventually may be manifested in various sexual problems.

Sexually inexperienced young men (and women, too, for that matter) are therefore well advised to acquire as much dispassionate information as they can from authoritative books, lectures, teachers, and the like—and it might be pointed out that one's peer group seldom falls into this category—on the subject of sexual technique. If they enter marriage with only academic information in the matter of human sexuality, inescapably their initial sexual experiences will tend to be more mechanical than spontaneous. But they also will have more of an air of confidence than if they had no knowledge, or only knowledge dangerously based on hearsay.

Confidence and an effort at taking charge in initial sexual encounters will enhance a man's chances for success to a considerable degree. Even if he does not feel as confident as he might like, he should conduct himself as if he knows what he is doing, and as if he is in control of the relationship. His assumption of confidence will go a long way to instill confidence in his wife. It follows that once frank communication regarding their sex life is firmly established between husband and wife, helping one another in this area becomes easier and less inhibited.

MAINTAINING A GOOD SEXUAL RELATIONSHIP

As superfluous as it may appear, it is nonetheless important to mention at the outset of this discussion the fundamental significance of a clean and attractive body to successful sexual interaction. Sex appeal is most certainly not confined to the marriage bed; it exists between the partners at all times, and should be carefully nurtured. By attractiveness, facial and bodily handsomeness is not implied; rather, attractiveness means scrupulous cleanliness of body and clothing, and taking the greatest advantage possible of all the physical endowments that nature has seen fit to bestow on each of us. Not everyone can be beautiful, but there is no excuse for anyone's not being attractively neat and clean at all times.

A man who is overweight, chronically unshaven and slovenly dressed, and whose breath reeks of tobacco or alcohol, can hardly expect to be considered a desirable bed partner—even after a session with shower, toothbrush, and razor later in the evening —because his

wife's memories of his earlier unattractiveness will simply detract
from the excitement of the experience. Similarly, a woman who neglects
to make up her face, sits around home in bathrobe and curlers, allows
herself to become significantly overweight or underweight, permits
even faint urine, vaginal, or underarm odors to emanate, or does not
often shave her legs and underarms is setting the stage for a loss of
respect, admiration, and even love; sexual failure cannot then be far
behind.

Certainly before joining each other in bed, whether or not sexual
activities are anticipated, each spouse should see to it that he has at
least a clean body, fresh breath, and neat, attractive nightclothes. To
do otherwise is to deny to the marriage bed one of the basic ingredients for a happy sex life.

The sense of smell is almost as important in sexual stimulation
as the sense of sight is.[111] There is a physiological relationship between
the tissues of the nose and of the sex organs, as was described earlier.
Conditioning factors also are frequently present in the relationship
between the sense of smell and sexuality. During courtship, for example,
the faint scent of a girl's perfume or of a man's after-shave lotion may
become associated with their love and subsequent sexual arousal.
After marriage, the same pleasant scent may well serve to reestablish
the excitement that developed in the atmosphere of courtship. Conditioning quite naturally involves many sensory elements other than smell.
Almost any occurrence during the period of courtship that forms an
association with love and passion can later be woven advantageously
into the fabric of the couple's sexual interaction.

The qualities of courtesy, kindness, and sensitivity to the needs
and desires of others are fundamental to all successful human relationships; most particularly are they vital to sexual associations. Bearing in mind the differences in individual needs and desires, it is incumbent upon each person to discover what, precisely, offers the greatest
pleasure to his partner in the sexual relationship. Genuine efforts
to incorporate these discoveries into one's technique of sexual approach
must be made before one may expect complete emotional fulfillment.
For example, some partners prefer the conversation during sexual
activity to be quite earthy, even to the point that the expressions used
would be vulgar under other circumstances. Another couple might be
shocked by such utterances, preferring to speak to one another softly
in tender and loving words.

Pace, as well as style, is also a matter of individual taste. However, it is ordinarily wisest to proceed slowly and gently, with the goal
in mind of bringing gratification to the partner rather than hurrying

to satisfy one's own needs. One should not hesitate, furthermore, even to sacrifice one's own present fulfillment altogether if it means giving greater pleasure to the spouse; not only is it a generous and loving thing to do, but it will assuredly pay handsome dividends later. The best, and certainly the least stressful, way for each partner to determine the specific amatory desires of the other is to open wide the doors of candid communication. Neither partner is clairvoyant, and an inadvertently offensive gesture or clumsiness might impede the present response, and inhibit response in similar circumstances at a future time.

Variations in sexual approach and in the settings can add considerable spice to marriage. Too often sexual acts become ritualized, stale, and unimaginative, engaged in only to provide relief to physical urgency. Couples who wish to preserve delight and vigor in their sexual interaction will work as consistently on this aspect of their marriage as on any other. A husband who impulsively sweeps his wife into his arms in the middle of a happy afternoon and carries her off to the bedroom and makes wild love to her, or the couple who occasionally has sexual intercourse while taking a shower, or the wife who surprises her husband by appearing in his study wearing nothing but a smile and two cold, very dry Martinis—these couples are not likely to find sex dull, even after years of marriage. The playing of soft music, using mirrors to observe closely the intimacies of the sex act, perusing sensuous literature and art: all these can help keep boredom out of the bedroom.[122] Men and women both want variety in their sexual lives; and if this ideal is reached within their marriage, there is considerably less likelihood that either husband or wife will seek it elsewhere. Imagination and willingness to experiment, coupled with an air of confidence and consideration, will serve most marriages very well.

THE EROGENOUS ZONES

Erogenous zones are those parts of the body possessing a great concentration of nerve endings (sometimes termed "sexual nerves") that, when stimulated, cause sexual arousal. These areas are numerous, and they are basically the same in man and woman—although there are, of course, individual variations in the areas producing excitement and in the degree of arousal.

The French physician Ernest Chambard became in 1881 the first person to make a thorough scientific investigation into the erogenous areas of the human body, subsequently issuing a report of his findings. Since the time of Chambard, various studies have demonstrated that the surfaces of mucous membranes are important erogenous zones, and that many of these are capable of erection and tumescence.[200] The most sensitive erogenous areas are the genitals and the areas surrounding them: the inner and outer regions of the thighs, the buttocks, and the abdomen. The nongenital erogenous zones extend over a large portion of the body, some areas being more sensitive than others. The breasts (particularly the nipples), armpits, small of the back, shoulders, neck, earlobes, scalp, eyelids, and especially the mouth, tongue, eyes, and nose are all areas rich in nerve endings.[111, 117, 119, 179, 180, 215]

Sexual arousal takes place when messages are sent by the stimulated sexual nerve endings to the brain, and the brain then transmits them to the centers of the lower spinal column controlling sexual impulses. These centers can also receive messages directly from the genital area without the intermediary transmission and relay of the impulses by the brain.[82]

A psychological or physical block at some point can deter or even prevent sexual excitement. For example, messages of disapproval, unpleasantness, fear, pain, or injury can and often do delay or obstruct altogether the channel to sexual centers, thus preventing arousal. On the other hand, as was said before, pleasant messages such as a lovely sight, a gentle word, a soft touch, an exotic scent, or a harmonious sound, can easily evoke sexual feelings. Pleasing sensory stimuli may produce erotic thoughts, which in turn may cause penile erection; women, however, are apparently less responsive to this type of psychological stimulus than men are.[179]

The erogenous zones appear to be a matter of heredity and, in general, are common to all people. However, individual differences are wide, and are largely the result of conditioning. Present scientific data indicate that there are no abnormal erogenous regions, and those that are uncommon are so simply as the result of individual background and experience. For example, if a man were to tickle the sole of his wife's foot preceding each pleasant act of coitus, sooner or later foot-tickling would come to be associated with pleasurable intercourse, and the sole of the foot would become a conditioned erogenous zone for that particular woman. Should she later marry another person, however, the conditioned erogenous zone on the sole of the foot might well appear to be abnormal to her new husband.[388]

As with psychological factors which serve as potent erotic stimuli, mutual experimentation and frank discussion are the best ways to discover which physiological areas of stimulation are the most effective for individual sexual arousal.[58, 117] To repeat, the erogenous parts of the bodies of both men and women are, by and large, the same. There is, however, a marked degree of difference among members of the same sex, as well as between the sexes, in the method of, and time required for bringing about, sexual arousal. A man frequently becomes sexually excited with minimal tactile stimulation, while a woman very often needs loving foreplay prior to the caressing of the erogenous areas of her body.

The genitals, which are the part of the body most responsive to stimulative techniques, contain millions of nerve endings concentrated in small regions of erectile-type tissue. A man's glans or head of the penis, particularly the lower surface at the corona (ring) and frenum, is the most sensitive part of the genitalia, while the skin covering the shaft of the penis is somewhat insensitive to the touch. A woman's clitoris and its glans contain a delicate network of nerve endings in erectile-type tissue that is covered with mucous membrane. Although a woman's clitoris is the catalyst for sexual excitation and orgasm, the entire vulval region, especially the vestibule and labia minora, are rich in nerve endings and are highly responsive to stimulation. The walls of the vagina, with the exception of the upper front area where the roots of the clitoris are located, are somewhat insensitive because they contain only a few nerve endings. The cervix, furthermore, is so insensitive that it can be cauterized or surgically cut without the aid of anesthesia.[299]

The perineum of both man and woman is sensitive to manipulation. This area includes the anus and inner portion of the thighs, and extends from the anus to the lower region of the sexual organs. About a half of all men and women, in fact, report that they experience erotic reactions to some form of anal stimulation.[170] While the mouth, lips, and nose are widely recognized as highly erogenous areas, there is nonetheless considerable variation in the degree of their sensitivity, because of personal differences resulting, primarily, from conditioning and, secondarily, from differences in supplies of nerve endings, the latter condition being a matter of individual heredity. The breasts are another important erogenous zone common to both men and women. The nipples and areolae are especially responsive to several stimuli.

METHODS OF SEXUAL AROUSAL

One should be reminded occasionally that any act within the marital bed that enhances sexual pleasure, that hurts no one, and that is out of sight and sound of an unwilling observer, is permissible and should be engaged in freely.[119, 365] This reminder appears especially relevant in view of the persistent presence in bookstores of erroneous and misleading writings on human sexuality. Such books state outright, or at least imply, that petting, for instance (which includes any form of sexual foreplay and afterplay), more particularly petting to orgasm, may be harmful at the time, or may interfere with future pleasure and fulfillment in sexual intercourse. To the contrary, the evidence is that those people who enjoy petting and are capable of responding freely to it are those most capable of responding freely to sexual intercourse and of deriving much pleasure from it.[21, 117, 119, 122, 179] The only problems liable to arise from petting are unjustified feelings of guilt, and congestion of the tissue in the sexual region resulting in physical distress when the petting is protracted but does not culminate in orgasmic relief.[117, 119, 122, 179]

Wives and husbands who are reluctant to involve themselves in sex play are often simply fearful that their spouses will consider them too bold in their manner of sexual stimulation or response. The less inhibited of the two should start the amatory foreplay, and then at the appropriate time should gently but firmly put the partner's hands and lips at the spots where they are most desired.[117]

Sexual excitement is most easily heightened when a maneuver of advance and retreat is adopted.[111] Stimulation is instigated, then after a brief buildup, the stimuli are withdrawn in a slightly teasing, tantalizing manner. Stimulation is begun again, carried to a more advanced point of excitement, and once more withdrawn. Quite naturally, timing is of the essence: knowing just how long to continue advancing and retreating, recognizing when these efforts have produced an optimal level of sexual excitement, and then ceasing the teasing are the keys to success in this lovemaking strategy. To continue beyond this point may very well be interpreted as rejection by the recipient, and what started out to be a promising adventure ends in stress and unhappiness.[111]

Hands play an indispensable role in successful lovemaking.[117, 879] The hands—especially the fingers—should be used to caress, stroke, massage, squeeze, and otherwise manipulate the erogenous zones of the body to bring as great pleasure as possible to both lovers. With proper use of the hands, not only can sexual excitement be built up in one's partner, but one's own excitement can be brought to and maintained at the response level of the spouse. As an example: light stroking and caressing by the husband of his wife's body with his fingertips will build her sexual excitement faster than his own; but when he uses the palms of his hands, as well as his fingertips (along with other excitants such as darting tongue-kissing), his own excitement usually develops at about the same tempo as his wife's.[111] With this in mind, a husband may pace the development of mutual excitement to achieve a synchronized crescendo.

Initial sexual excitement is brought about by light touch—not pressure—and the more intense and prolonged the sexual buildup, the greater the orgasmic response.[111, 215] While at first the bodies of both the man and woman are stimulated with gentle, slow, generalized stroking, the caressing should gradually become more specific as sex play progresses. The general orientation of the stroking should be toward the erogenous zones, particularly the genitalia, the caresses taking place in the teasing advance-retreat-advance manner already described. It is of special importance that the genitals be stimulated lightly at first because of the sensitivity and tenderness of the area; as excitement increases, the wife may wish the pressure to be heavier.

A woman's skin is considerably more sensitive to the touch than a man's is, and care should be taken, especially during the early part of marriage, to avoid overstimulation.[111] Exceptionally gentle caressing will gradually "awaken" the nerve endings of the genital region, and will condition the bride to welcome this manner of lovemaking as something pleasant and exciting during the following years of marriage. Fingertip stroking of the abdomen and inner thighs—with general movement in the direction of the genitals—will usually prepare a woman for more direct stimulation of the genitalia.

Breast manipulation is usually thought to be one of the most effective sexual stimulants for a woman. An interesting point, however, is that only about 50% of women are sexually aroused by having their breasts stimulated, while about 75% of men who view and stimulate women's breasts become themselves sexually excited.[179] This is yet another instance of the superiority of psychological over physiological factors in sexual matters. Surprising to many is the fact that men can become as sexually excited from having their breasts stimulated as women become.[179, 231] That men enjoy this stimulation is a normal response, and the pleasure has a sound physiological basis.

In his lovemaking, a man should gently massage his wife's breasts, interspersing the manipulation with a light brushing of the nipple and an occasional tweak of its sensitive tip. Caressing with the hands can very pleasurably be alternated with soft, moist kisses and an exploring tongue. To erotic advantage, the tongue may change its tempo occasionally, and dart back and forth across the nipple in a tense, rapid-fire, impertinent manner, then resume once more the soft, moist tongue stimulation, together with manual caressing of the breasts.[58, 111, 117, 119, 122] Research evidence shows that a small percentage of women can actually achieve orgasm from breast stimulation alone.[170, 215]

The erogenous nerve endings in men's breasts are limited to the nipples and areas immediately surrounding them. When a man's breast is stimulated by gently rolling the nipple between the thumb and finger, or by the sort of oral contact described in the previous paragraph, he quite likely will experience the same sort of sexual desire and excitement that women do from the same techniques.

Kissing, like hand-fingertip caressing, should be varied in a teasing manner: open mouth, closed mouth; light lip pressure, heavy lip pressure; moist lips, dry lips; soft lips, nibbling teeth and lips; a darting, teasing tongue, a soft, sensuous tongue. The lover's face and body should be covered with kisses as the point of action varies quickly, then slowly, from the lips to the eyes, hairline, earlobes, to the mouth again, to the breast, the neck, to the abdomen, back to the lips, and all the while, the tongue should also be participating in this exploration of the lover's body. The kissing maneuver should be repeated again and again with increasing passion and delicate timing.[111, 117, 379, 380] Ordinarily, kissing of the mouth should precede kissing of other parts of the body, except perhaps the hands. In the latter instance, it should be noted that having the palms of her hands kissed is a particularly exciting and stimulating experience for a woman.[111] There is also the psychological element of its being a rather courtly and tender gesture on the part of the man.

No matter what approach the husband takes, his hands should seldom be motionless during the entire period of sex play. They should dart and slide over his wife's body—stroking, holding, caressing boldly and lightly, squeezing, and massaging—alternating strong palmar movements with light, silky stroking of the fingertips. As he brings his wife to successive levels of arousal, he must take heed of the very thin and delicate tissue of the vulva and vagina. These areas should not be manually stimulated unless the husband's fingernails are clipped and smooth, and the vulval region well moistened with either bodily secretions or with a commercial product, such as K-Y jelly. The clitoris, furthermore, is often too sensitive to accommodate direct and uninterrupted manipulation comfortably.[111] The regions to the side and around the clitoris are the sites of stimulation preferred by most women who masturbate, and this knowledge can wisely be incorporated by a husband into his love play.[215]

As mentioned earlier, sex play should be a gradual, slowly unfolding experience, especially for the woman. It has been suggested that kissing and manual stimulation of erogenous areas should be carried on for at least fifteen minutes before intercourse itself commences, although some couples prefer longer, others shorter, periods of stimulation.[065] Couples should be warned, however, that an overly protracted period of sex play can actually interfere with maximum pleasure.[111] Kinsey and his associates report that many couples prefer sexual intercourse itself as a method of stimulation.[179, 180] Communication and good timing are once more essential, and when both lovers are ready to proceed with coitus, they should let one another know.

Sexual stimulation is not a one-way street, and the wife should reciprocate with the same sort of fervor that the husband extends to her, not only because she wishes to excite and please him, but because the act of exciting one's lover should be a highly pleasurable and fulfilling experience for the bestower. There are many things a wife can do by way of lovemaking that will bring delight to her husband. She should initiate kissing or return his kisses passionately, stimulate his nipples orally and by fingertip and palmar manipulation, lightly rake her fingertips over his bare back, gently stimulate the scrotum and perineal area, and manipulate the penis with alternating light and heavy stroking (particularly at the glans and frenum). The wife, too, should remember the importance of the teasing game of advance and retreat in the art of building up sexual excitement.

In her efforts to determine what sort of lovemaking brings the greatest pleasure to her husband, the new wife should bear in mind individual differences. For example, while some men prefer a gentle stroking of the penis, others may desire heavy pressure and squeezing in such a manner that there is tugging at the scrotum and perineal area. The wife should not hesitate to use her hands, mouth, thighs, legs, toes (even eyelashes, if it comes to that) to stimulate her husband. She should employ a variety of methods of arousal, and by all means she should let it be known that she thoroughly enjoys giving, as well as receiving, such pleasurable stimulation.[111]

In attempting to discover a pleasurable means of stimulating her husband's genitalia, a bride can often obtain a helpful guideline from any masturbatory techniques he may have used prior to marriage. If, for instance, a man stimulated himself with light, slow stroking of his penis, it is quite likely that he will welcome the same sort of caressing from his wife.[191]

Women who masturbate will frequently insert their fingers into the vagina to aid their fantasy during self-stimulation. Since they are so conditioned, these women will probably find it pleasurable if their husbands arouse them in the same manner during sex play. Another method of masturbation for women, one which is far more common than many suspect, is to direct a stream of water over the genitals while bathing.[191] The running water provides a continuous pressure, with just enough variation in constancy to satisfy the physiological requirements involved in producing an orgasm. Women describe the sensation received from this method of self-arousal as being somewhat similar to (although less intense than) that received from the application of an electric vibrator.

Concerning the vibrator, couples would do well to make note of its value in heightening the pleasure of their sexual interaction. Some women apparently cannot achieve orgasm with penile penetration, nor indeed can some reach it through any of the techniques of stimulation already discussed. But direct clitoral and vulval arousal through the husband's application of a vibrator as he fondles and kisses her seldom fails to bring a woman to orgasm.[73, 117]

A few women prefer the type of vibrator that the husband attaches to the back of his hand. It allows him free movement of his fingers, to be sure, but most of the vibration is absorbed by his hand. Most women, therefore, find greater stimulation and gratification from the application of a rubber-knobbed vibrator directly on or to the side of the clitoris. Use of this vibrator meets with great success in producing single or multiple orgasms in women who might otherwise be incapable of reaching such an intense sexual response level. Furthermore, using a vibrator is much less tiring to husbands who otherwise must attempt arousal of their wives' genitals for prolonged periods of time before bringing about an orgasm, if it occurs at all. The husband also remains free to kiss, caress, and stimulate his wife in any other way he chooses. Marriage counselors frequently recommend vibrator stimulation for women who are "frigid," or who experience difficulty in reaching orgasm; and to women who are widowed, yet need sexual release.[215, 288]

Some couples find the vibrator too "mechanical" for their tastes, and others are afraid that their orgasmic response to this sort of stimulation will be so intense that other methods will be pleasurable only to a lesser degree.[288] Some husbands feel threatened by the machine, and object to using it. None of these arguments against the vibrator is strictly sound, and any such objections to it as a method of sexual arousal are psychological in nature.

Another form of sexual activity that is far more popular than many know is oral-genital stimulation. Kinsey's research shows that oral-genital contact is experienced by at least 60% of those married couples who have gone to college, by about 20% of those who have gone through high school, and by about 10% of those who have gone only through grade school.[179, 180] That the first figure is so high may come as a surprise to some people, because of the traditional taboo society has placed on this sort of sexual behavior. Many marriage counselors believe that considerably more than 60% of the higher educational-level group indulge in oral-genital sexual expression, but that they are reluctant to admit it because they fear the disapproval of others.

The prevailing negative attitude toward genital kissing is primarily an outgrowth of the fact that many people regard the genital region as "dirty." The proximity in the woman of the anus and the urethra to the genitals, and the fact that the male penis is both a seminal and a urinary outlet, are the physiological factors that have given rise to the "dirtiness" concept, but these do not constitute a logical objection to the act.[122] Certainly if one allows his body to become unclean and malodorous, especially in the anal-genital region, any type of sexual contact is likely to become objectionable. However, with the myriad supply of cosmetic and hygienic products currently on the market, there is really no excuse for an offensive odor emanating from any part of the body—including the anal-genital area.

People seldom enjoy even kissing someone when his or her breath is reeking, to say nothing of entering into more intimate physical contact with someone who needs a bath. If one has recently eaten, or suspects that the mouth might otherwise be offensive, then one is well advised to tackle the problem with toothbrush and mouthwash. The same sensible precautions should be taken with the genitals. Because the folds of skin that partially cover the surface of the genitals are natural receptacles for a collection of smegma and secretions, the region should be cleansed in such a way that there is no chance that any of the offensive material or odor lingers. In the same fashion used in cleaning the ear, a finger should move in and around the folds of the genitalia to cleanse them. If a couple give this sort of attention to keeping themselves clean and pleasant-smelling, making whatever use is indicated of "personal hygiene" and cosmetic products, the objection to oral-genital contact on the grounds of "dirtiness" is less than valid.

Oral-genital sexual behavior is considered perverted by many and is, in fact, illegal in many states, even if performed between husband and wife.[111] Nonetheless, most people of the upper educational level (*i.e.,* those who have attended college) find this act to be a normal, highly exciting, valuable means of sexual stimulation, and it constitutes a regular part of their repertoire of sexual activity.[111]

It is generally agreed by couples who engage in oral-genital contact that it is an act to be enjoyed by both husband and wife, whether giving or receiving. It is an accepted fact that the mouth and lips are erogenous zones common to nearly all people, and there is, in addition, an abundance of nerve endings in the tip of the nose. That these two areas of sensitivity universally exist no doubt accounts for mouth contact and nose-rubbing being the chief methods of "kissing" in our world, and for the fact that oral stimulation of the genitals is so pleasurable for many people.[209, 388] Furthermore, recent neurophysiological studies[204] have shown that there is a close relationship between the parts of the brain concerned with oral functions (amygdala) and those parts concerned with sexual functions (septum and rostral diencephalon). Stimulation of an area of the brain affecting oral activity will readily produce a "spillover" into areas related to genital function.

A couple may engage in mutual oral-genital contact during the early part of stimulation, but to continue the mutual act for any length of time, or to the point of climax, usually requires more acrobatic agility than most couples possess. Furthermore, simultaneous orgasms resulting from oral-genital stimulation—or even prolonged simultaneous oral-genital contact—present some of the same problems discussed under simultaneous coital orgasm: that is, neither partner can properly concentrate at the same time on himself and the spouse to the fullest satisfaction of either while receiving such intense stimulation.

The clitoris usually receives the greatest measure of the husband's attention during *cunnilingus* (Latin: *cunnus,* vulva; and *lingere,* to lick). Its sensitive glans can be stimulated in much the same manner as the nipples of the breasts are in mouth-tongue-breast contact. The tongue-stroking begins in a light, teasing manner with intermittent heavy, moist, bold tongue-stroking; the technique is varied to keep pace with the heightening sexual excitement. As the climax nears, and if the couple wishes to bring it about in this manner, the husband should put into action the findings of Masters and Johnson,[215] which demonstrate that orgasm is best produced by a steady, constant stroking of the clitoral *area;* at the height of sexual tension the clitoris withdraws under its prepuce, and direct contact can no longer be maintained in any case. Other parts of the vulva, particularly the labia minora, are also sensitive to oral stimulation. Women who have experienced oral-genital stimulation report that the method is overwhelmingly pleasurable and effective, both as sex foreplay and as the primary avenue to achieving orgasm.[191]

Kinsey has shown that women are less inclined to engage in *fellatio* (Latin: *fellare,* to suck) with their husbands than their husbands are to engage in cunnilingus with them.[179, 180] Any such reluctance is almost always based on psychological blocks. If a wife will talk over carefully the matter of fellatio with her husband, she can usually overcome this reticence, and eventually the act may become quite pleasurable for her.

The glans of the penis, especially at the frenum and contiguous areas, is highly sensitive to the wife's kisses and sucking, and to her warm, moist, now darting, now soft tongue. All the while, she should also stroke the corpus of the penis with an up and down movement, and occasionally fondle the testicles and the scrotum. This technique of lovemaking can quickly bring the husband to sexual heights that can easily terminate in orgasm. Van de Velde, who has written one of the classics among marriage manuals,[379] gives unqualified endorsement to mouth-genital stimulation as a vastly pleasurable form of sexual behavior. So also have many other authorities in the field of sex and marriage.[77, 117, 119, 122, 191, 231]

Whether climax occurs as a result of manual stimulation, oral activity, or sexual intercourse is a matter each couple must decide individually. The method that is best suited for a particular occasion should readily be adopted, with each participant expending his best efforts to bring about maximum satisfaction for his partner.[111]

Many variations of the sex act, together with special techniques for heightening pleasure during the various phases of increasing sexual response, have been proposed in marriage manuals and other writings on sexual matters.[111, 117, 119, 122, 127, 128, 179, 180, 191, 208, 215, 228, 299, 305, 375, 379, 380] However, each couple because of their individual and combined personalities and preferences must decide—through open discussion and uninhibited experimentation—just what brings them the greatest erotic pleasure. What one couple finds exciting, another might find dull or even repulsive.[111] One person, for instance, might find highly pleasurable the application of crushed ice wrapped in a cloth to the perineal area at the time the paroxysms of orgasm commence, whereas another might find it a rather ludicrous (if not chilling) experience.[111] Some couples have found that applying certain mild chemicals, such as Mentholatum, to the glans of the penis or to the vulval region (or even the use of the salve as a lubricant during coitus) enhances their sexual pleasure, while others find such a practice physically painful. Some desire anal stimulation, or the insertion of fingers or small objects into the rectum, during certain phases of the sexual response cycle; but others consider such techniques unnecessary, repugnant, or even barbaric. Whatever the sexual variation, it should be introduced spontaneously and with obvious desire by one participant, and received pleasantly and happily by the other.

Sex relations do not, or rather should not, end with orgasm.[111,] [117,379] Many couples find the interval after the sexual act to be as pleasant and emotionally fulfilling as any other part of marriage. To hold each other in a close and lingering embrace, to discuss softly the delights of the experience they have just shared, to caress the lover's body with tender, sweeping movements of the hands, to doze and relax with intertwined bodies, all serve to aid in the emotional fulfillment. Other couples are completely overcome by the release of physical and emotional tension, and are ready to drop off into a deep and restful sleep after a brief expression of love and appreciation. Partners must give as careful attention to the spouse's wishes concerning the period of resolution of sexual tensions as they do to each other's preferences in the matter of sexual foreplay.

The sum and substance of this chapter is that sex is a pleasurable, significant part of marriage, and that both husband and wife should do everything in their power to make it as joyous and satisfying as possible. Lovemaking can fulfill both the psychological and physiological needs of human beings in a way that nothing else in marriage is capable of doing. It can be approached and executed in a variety of ways, any one of which may be highly pleasurable to one couple, undesirable to a second, and simply dull to a third. Sex may be a rather grim business in a marriage, especially when it is unsatisfactory. But it can also be fun. A well-known and respected psychologist, A. H. Maslow,[208] with great perception summarized a healthy love relationship when he wrote in *Motivation and Personality:*

> It is quite characteristic of self-actualizing people that they can enjoy themselves in love and in sex. Sex very frequently becomes a kind of game in which laughter is quite as common as panting. It is not the welfare of the species, or the task of reproduction, or the future development of mankind that attracts people to each other. The sex life of healthy people, in spite of the fact that it frequently reaches great peaks of ecstasy, is nevertheless also easily compared to the games of children and puppies. It is cheerful, humorous, and playful.

CHAPTER 10

Positions in
Sexual Intercourse

No ONE POSITION of partners during sexual intercourse is more "normal" or more "acceptable" than another. There are many positions, variations of them, and variations upon the variations. Furthermore, there are valid reasons for knowing about and experimenting with different coital attitudes. Sexual instinct is a drive requiring direction, both for its pleasurable and its procreative aspects. This section is presented simply as an aid in the adaptation and fulfillment of this particular one of life's processes.

The discussion will not focus on the number of coital positions that it is possible for partners to assume; rather will it aim at a broader understanding of the reasons for, and benefits accruing from, experimentation. The four most common and basic positions in sexual intercourse (and the advantages and disadvantages of each) will be described, but variations of the four will not be. With a little imagination, a sensible attitude toward sex, and an uninhibited approach regarding experimentation, the individual should be able to work out his own adaptations—and that is the way it should be.

In any consideration of sexual behavior, no aspect presents more ramifications and difficulties than that of coital positions. Rare is the person who has observed another's sexual behavior; hence one's empirical knowledge is likely to be extremely limited. A certain amount of sound scientific information on sexual techniques exists, however, and has been available in literature for centuries.[380] Moreover, people are increasingly willing (1) to respect and examine mores different from those with which they were reared; and (2) to recognize that sexual education is often regrettably inaccurate, and that a process of reeducation may be needed.

Two persons are involved in the sexual act, and the needs of both must always be considered. The immediate situational success and the future harmonious adjustment of the partners concerned are often directly correlated to their skill in using pleasurable amatory techniques.

161

Most of the "shoulds" and "should-nots" of sexual behavior are contingent on—and only on—the mutual pleasure, comfort, and satisfaction of the two people involved.[119, 231] Each must be just as aware of the needs of his spouse as he is of his own before coition can be truly successful. Therefore, experimentation and variation in coital positions assume major importance in the effort to achieve an optimal fulfillment of the rights and desires of each partner.

Unlike lower animals, human beings have to be taught, in one way or another, how to conduct the act of sexual intercourse; extensive research into sexual behavior has disproved the popular notion that the art of love comes naturally.[155] Even the elementary facts of coitus have to be learned.

Aside from the intellectual benefits of such knowledge, distinct emotional gains accrue from varied sexual experimentation. One's self-concept is often enhanced by a certain amount of successful coital testing. Feelings of self-confidence and security must exist before one is free to give and take—without fear or guilt—in any human association, including coitus. Only with an understanding and appreciation, which must be learned, of the mechanics of sexual intercourse can a high level of mutual harmony be attained; the higher the level of comprehension of human sexuality, the more meaningful the relationship, and the greater the pleasure. Experience and confidence, combined with thoughtfulness, can make sex far more pleasurable than it would be without these factors. Stephen Vizinczey, in his book *In Praise of Older Women*,[384] makes a strong point for confidence in the following statement. "Trying to make love with someone who is as unskilled as you are seems to me about as sensible as learning to drive with a person who doesn't know the first thing about cars either. . . . Whenever I see a man reaching out for a woman with painful uncertainty—as if he had something to apologize for, as if he expected her to suffer his desire instead of sharing it—I wonder. . . ."

There are more reasons for sexual experimentation than the ones of an intellectual or emotional nature just mentioned; there are practical—situational and occasional—reasons as well. Variety in coital positions makes sexual activity more interesting and can prevent its becoming humdrum.[147] Of equal importance, however, is the fact that some positions are more pleasurable to one partner than to the other, and the preferences of each must be served. Also, the desirability of certain positions may alter from time to time, depending upon such conditions as health, weight, and pregnancy.[107, 231] It is further recognized that some coital attitudes are more conducive to conception than others.[122] Positions also vary according to whether coition is spontaneous or anticipated, takes place in a cramped or adequate space, or occurs in absolute privacy or with some danger of discovery. The experience and genital size of each spouse are also important determinants in choosing a position.

The "traditional" European and American sexual position of man atop woman is, of course, by far the most common one in our culture. The second most common position—man supine, woman atop—is used occasionally by 35% of the college-educated males, 28% of high-school-educated males, and 17% of grade-school-educated males; slightly over one-third (35%) of women born before 1900, and over half (52%) the women born after 1900 have frequently used the woman-atop position. The side position, face-to-face, has been used by 26%, 23%, and 16% of the men, depending upon whether they belong to high, middle, or low educational groups, respectively; about one-third (31%) of all women have experienced coition in this position. The rear-entry position has been tried by 11% of the college and high-school male groups, and by 8% of the grade-school-educated men; about 15% of females have had the experience of rear-entry coition.[179, 180]

There are about as many reasons for varying coital activity as there are forms of it. Most couples do their sexual experimentation during the earlier years of their marriage, and then settle down to the use of the one or two positions that best suit them.[110] If one partner has particular difficulty in becoming aroused or in reaching orgasm, it is usually helpful if the couple assume one of their preferred positions after having first experimented with other ones. Often the positions fixed upon by a couple can be more easily assumed by their first taking a quite different one and then shifting or rolling into the desired one.[122] For example, intromission can first be made in a face-to-face position, and after penetration has taken place, the couple can then shift to a side-by-side position before orgasm is reached.

Face-to-face, man-above position. It has been pointed out that this is probably the most common position for sexual intercourse in our society, so commonplace that it is often termed the "normal" one. Most women express a preference for this position, and about 70% of American males have never copulated in any other manner.[97, 180] However, the position is relatively rare in other cultures—so rare, in fact, that even considering its popularity in this country, on a universal basis it is far from being a favorite coital position.

Ordinarily, vaginal-penile contact is quite easily achieved when the woman reclines on her back with legs apart and knees bent. She can shift her pelvis or perhaps place a small pillow under her buttocks to help adjust the slant of the vagina for easy and deep penetration. It is sometimes desirable for the woman to close her legs after entry, thus constricting the vaginal opening and walls, in order to provide more

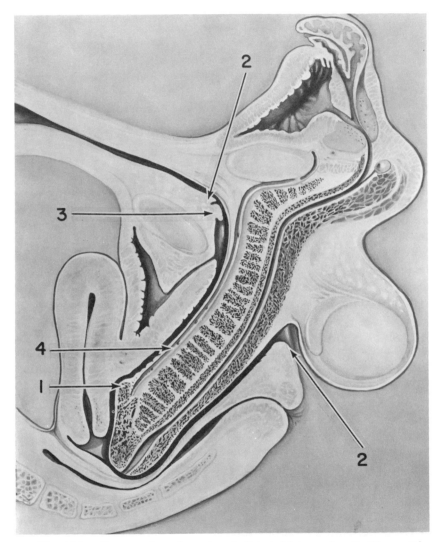

Fig. 10-1.   Cross section of erect penis inserted into vagina. 1. Glans penis. 2. Vaginal opening. 3. Clitoris. 4. Penile shaft. Photograph courtesy *Sexology* magazine.

friction against her husband's penis. This pressure against the base of the penis at full penetration helps him maintain erection.

The man partially supports himself on his elbows and knees to avoid putting his full weight on his wife. He is largely in control of the bodily rhythms, as his weight and size limit his wife to circular, up and down, and rocking pelvic movements. The husband should try to keep contact with the clitoris by putting pressure on the upper part of his wife's vulva. Pressure on her pubic bone is helpful in that it sandwiches the clitoris between it and the point of the husband's bodily contact, which is usually at his pubic bone. There are numerous variations on the man-astride position, such as the woman's pulling her knees to her shoulders, or locking her legs around her husband's body.

The advantages of the face-to-face, man-above position are many. In this posture, the woman is usually relaxed, and the man has the primary initiative; in our culture, this male-superior position appears to have certain psychological advantages. Entry is simple, and any adaptations that bring pleasure to the couple can be made easily. It is convenient for couples who enjoy the man's pelvic thrust. In addition, the husband can often maintain penetration after he has had an orgasm, and the position facilitates caressing, kissing, and affectionate intimacy between the two. It is an excellent position for impregnation, as the woman can keep her knees raised after the ejaculation, improving chances of the sperm's entering the uterus.[122, 147]

The disadvantages of the face-to-face, man-above position are the obverse of the advantages. The wife's movements and active participation may be too restricted; penetration may be too deep for her comfort. It may also be uncomfortable for a woman with an obese or awkward husband, and it may be too acrobatic for older or stouter couples. Some men have difficulty in maintaining contact with their partner's clitoris in this position, and manual stimulation of that organ is difficult during coitus. The position is often too exciting for the man, causing him to reach climax too quickly. Furthermore, it is uncomfortable and inadvisable for women in the last stages of pregnancy.[122, 147]

Face-to-face, woman above. This position is often assumed to give the woman a chance to express herself by way of a departure from her usual "passive" position. She can govern contact with her clitoris, and can, as well, control the tempo of movement and depth of penetration. The position can also be modified so that the man rests on his elbows and draws up his knees for the woman to lean back on; his arms and hands are thereby left free to clasp and caress her. Intromission is accomplished by the wife's lowering her body, usually in a sitting position with knees bent, over her supine partner and guiding his penis into her vagina. Couples may find it more pleasurable to achieve penetration in some other position, and then to turn or roll over gently, so that the penis does not slip from the vagina nor the orgasm occur in the process.

The Dutch physician Van de Velde declared[379] that coitus with the woman astride "affords the summit in excitement and response, the acme of specific physical sexual pleasure, to both man and woman." Although there is little supporting evidence, it is also his contention that the position, because it is so stimulating and vigorous, might be too exhausting for older couples and should be attempted by them only occasionally.

The advantages of the face-to-face, woman-above position are numerous and are also uniquely individual. A woman possesses maximum control and freedom to express herself sexually when she is astride her partner. The position permits fullest penetration, yet she can avoid any discomfort or pain to herself because she regulates the depth of penile entry. She controls such pleasurable movements as pelvic thrusts, which both she and her husband may find most exciting. A man may be able to delay orgasm more successfully because little physical exertion or strain is imposed on him in this position. These facts may be of significance to him if his wife is slow to reach climax, or if he tends to ejaculate prematurely or is in poor health.

There are further advantages. The husband's hands are free to caress his wife's breasts or any other part of her body. The wife can rest full-length upon her husband, and this complete bodily contact often affords pleasure and excitement to both partners. This position is especially useful when the woman is much smaller than the man; it also allows for such interaction as conversation and the observation of each other's facial expressions.

There are disadvantages, however, to the face-to-face, woman-astride position. The man's freedom of movement and pelvic thrust may be too restricted for his tastes, or the sacrifice of his "male-superior" position may cause him to lose his erection, sexual drive, or even interest. Since he is not controlling the coital movements, his penis may persistently slip out of the vagina. The woman may find that penetration is too deep in this position, causing her pain. It is not a good position for impregnation, as the sperm are likely to seep out of the vagina after ejaculation. Neither is it a comfortable position during pregnancy.[111, 122, 147, 379, 380]

Many women are not so athletically inclined that they enjoy such vigorous sexual participation. They may feel uncomfortable in such an "aggressive" role, and some men are of the persuasion that their masculinity is threatened if they assume a lower or "passive" position. Both these objections are faulty and are impressions that should be corrected. Any position which gives pleasure to both partners and causes no physical difficulties should be encouraged.

Side position, face-to-face. Coitus can often be achieved more restfully when the partners are lying on their sides facing one another. Both have an ease of motion, and either can withdraw or otherwise control the movements of intercourse. The side position has many variations. Often one partner is largely on his back with the mate resting on him.[162] The woman raises her upper leg and crosses it over the man in order to permit entry, or sometimes the side-to-side position is assumed after the partners have begun in another position, and then have rolled onto their sides. There is complete freedom to maneuver arms, hands, and legs in this position, and both partners are under little physical strain since neither is supporting the weight of the other. The couple can go to sleep after completion of the act, often with contact maintained.[111, 147, 380]

In addition to its relatively comfortable and restful nature, there are further advantages to the side-by-side position. In the interlocking attitude, maximum contact between the man's body and the woman's clitoris can be achieved. The husband can cradle his wife between his legs and hold her in close and continued contact. This position is especially helpful when conditions of fatigue, ill health, or obesity exist, or if one partner is considerably taller than the other. It is often a satisfactory position for coitus during the last months of pregnancy. Both partners—especially the man—can regulate their pelvic thrusts, and often can thereby prolong sexual activity before orgasm. Penile withdrawal and reinsertion are possible without very much change of position or adjustment, and a steady coital rhythm can easily be sustained.[122]

The primary disadvantages to the side position are the inconstancy of contact and the fact that some couples find it less comfortable than most other positions. It is not easy for some persons to achieve entry or to maintain sufficiently stimulating pressure on the vulval area in this position. Other couples, preferring more vigorous coition, find the position inadequately stimulating, since it offers little possibility for deep pelvic thrusts and penetration. Movements may be difficult in the interlocking position because of restrictions placed on certain parts of the body.

Rear-entry position. Facing his wife's back, the man can accomplish intromission in any of several manners. Both partners can be on their sides, the man entering the woman from the rear; the woman can

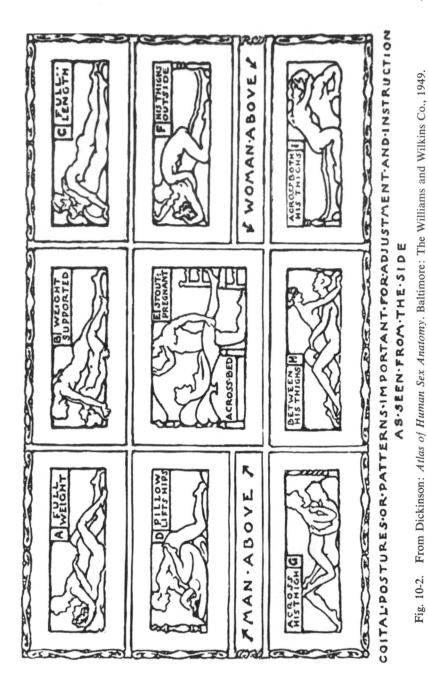

Fig. 10-2.   From Dickinson: *Atlas of Human Sex Anatomy*. Baltimore: The Williams and Wilkins Co., 1949.

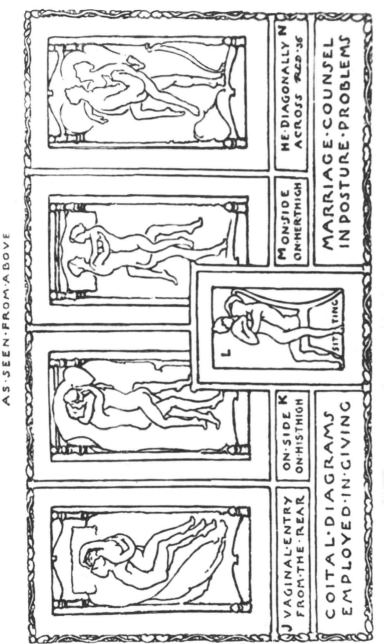

Fig. 10-3. From Dickinson: *Atlas of Human Sex Anatomy.* Baltimore: The Williams and Wilkins Co., 1949.

kneel, or lie on her stomach, as her husband enters her; or the man can sit (on bed or chair) while the woman sits on his lap with her back to him. And there are numerous other variations to rear-entry intromission.[111, 122, 380]

Entry from the rear when both partners are on their sides exacts less exertion from the woman, and places less pressure on her than other coital attitudes do; for this reason, it is a position often recommended for coition in the advanced months of pregnancy. Rear entry is also restful for a man, as he can be more relaxed than when he is astride his wife. This posture shortens a woman's vagina, which may be advantageous since less of the penile shaft is required to effect deep penetration. Because the woman's buttocks are in the way, not much of the penis can be introduced into the vagina in this position, but whatever degree of penetration is possible can be easily regulated by the husband. Often a man finds the pressure of his wife's gluteal (buttocks) area against his body to be quite exciting; furthermore, his hands are left free to encircle her body and to caress her breasts, clitoris, legs, or whatever other area pleases them both.[122]

Side-by-side rear entry is particularly relaxing to a couple when either or both are tired, debilitated, old, or convalescent, although the entry is not always easy to make or maintain. Contact is usually lost after the man's orgasm, and the position, furthermore, offers little assistance toward conception. For very stout persons, or for a man with a small penis, the side-rear position presents special difficulties.[111]

The knee-chest attitude is a more active form of rear-entry coitus, in which both partners assume a kneeling position. The woman can rest her arms and head on pillow or bed, and her husband presses his body against her buttocks to effect entry. Sexual activity is usually quite vigorous in this position, especially for the man. Knee-chest rear entry is recommended as a favorable position for conception, because the semen remains in the vagina for a longer time and closer to the opening of the uterus than in other coital positions.[111, 147]

Just as the rear-kneeling position is psychologically and physiologically exciting for some persons, so also is it objectionable to others, and for the same reasons—namely, its novel and vigorous nature. One or both partners may object to rear entry because it lacks face-to-face intimacy, or because the nature of its approach becomes associated in their minds with anal intercourse, thereby carrying with it (as it does for some people) homosexual or other repugnant overtones.

Another rear-entry coital posture is one in which the woman lies on her stomach and her partner attempts penetration while lying on top of her. It is awkward and not sufficiently pleasurable to be used by many couples.[122]

Rear-entry sitting coition involves the man's seating himself on the edge of a bed or chair, and his wife's sitting down on his penis with her back to him. This is a variation of the face-to-face sitting position so much enjoyed by many couples because of the closeness of contact and freedom of movement it allows them both.[122]

Sitting positions offer singular coital variety and novel enjoyment to some couples. However, the deep penetration that often results from these postures can also prove uncomfortable or even harmful to the woman, and should be avoided—or at least controlled—in these instances.

As was stated at the outset of this section, there are an infinite number of variations on the coital positions that have been discussed—*e.g.,* standing, sitting face-to-face, man standing between the legs of the woman whose torso is on a bed—but a detailed examination of them will not serve present purposes. As with other forms of spontaneous sexual activity, coital postures are various, and all are acceptable. The only factors to be taken into account are the tastes of the individual couple and the occasion at hand. A couple should take care, however, to avoid an exaggerated concern for the "how" of sexual intercourse while they are engaging in it. Coitus may otherwise assume artificial or mechanical overtones that can detract from the freedom and spontaneity of the relationship.

Coitus is not a gymnastic feat, an endurance contest, or an event of constant laboratory-like experimentation; it is, rather, a mutual act involving a wide range of techniques and postures. Whatever techniques of love play, sexual intercourse, and postcoital caressing that are found by a couple to bring mutual pleasure should be freely enjoyed by them.

CHAPTER 11

Orgasm

THIS TEXT has repeatedly emphasized the fact that the methods and techniques of sexual activity of individual people are many and produce varying degrees of pleasure. A method or technique is the "right" one only insofar as it is satisfactory and serves its purpose; what is "right" for one person may not be "right" for another. No matter what techniques are employed or how intense the enjoyment is, the *ultimate* goal is an orgasm.

An orgasm is a highly pleasurable, tension-relieving, seizure-like response that is the summit of physical and emotional gratification in sexual activity. The neurological and physiological structures and responses that give rise to orgasmic reactions have been discussed earlier. The particular arousal that leads to an orgasm involves a marked rise in blood pressure and pulse rate, faster and deeper breathing, engorgement of special tissues with blood, and, finally, an explosive release of muscular and nervous tension. This release is followed by a rather quick return to the normal or nonstimulated state. The subjective sensation of orgasm is centered in the pelvic region for both men and women: the penis, prostate, and seminal vesicles in men; and the clitoris, vagina, and uterus in women.[215]

The orgasm is a short-lived experience (usually about three to ten seconds) that has an intensity many find difficult to understand. However, if another body need—for example, hunger—were to be satisfied in an equally short period of time, perhaps a similar intensity of reaction would be experienced. What would the sensation be of satisfying all the tensions of a powerful hunger for food in a period of five to ten seconds, rather than in the twenty to thirty minutes that consuming a meal ordinarily takes?

The works of the two best known and most influential sex research teams—the late Alfred Kinsey and his co-workers of the Institute for Sex Research, Indiana University, and William H. Masters and Virginia Johnson of the Reproductive Biology Research Foundation, St. Louis, Missouri—have emphasized the similarities, not the differences, between male and female human sexual behavior and response.[179, 215] Both research groups conclude that there are few dissimilarities between male and female orgasm, the most noticeable difference being, of course, that male orgasm is accompanied by ejaculation.

Perhaps it should be mentioned here that a few men do, in fact, experience orgasm without ejaculation, but this is a rare and special occurrence. Some men have *retrograde ejaculation,* which means that the semen is discharged into the bladder rather than through the penis; since external evidence is lacking, it appears that the man does not ejaculate, although in reality he does. This condition is caused by some anomaly at the junction of the ejaculatory ducts and urethra within the prostate, either as a result of prostatic surgery, an accident,

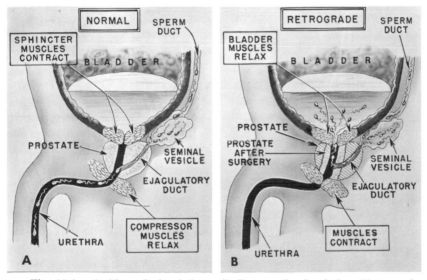

Fig. 11-1.   A. Normal ejaculation.   B. Retrograde ejaculation. Photographs courtesy *Sexology* magazine.

or some caprice of nature. Sometimes drugs, especially certain tranquilizers,[307] may inhibit the ejaculatory centers, yet not affect the erection centers of the neural network involved in orgasm. (The possible value of these drugs in treating premature ejaculation is apparent.) In other instances, diabetes will inhibit ejaculation at the time of orgasm.

Fewer women than men experience orgasmic response, although women are considerably more capable of having multiple orgasms. There are some exceptions, of course, but it is safe to state that nearly all healthy men almost always achieve orgasm once sexual stimulation progresses to a certain point. About 95% of women are capable of reaching orgasm at some point during their lifetime; only 70%, however, are able to achieve it during their first year of marriage, owing, no doubt, to the stringent sexual controls to which they have been subjected from early girlhood.[179] Because of the abundant sex nerve endings in the region of the clitoris and vulva, and because of the almost negligible number of nerve endings in the vagina, women find that masturbation (as well as other forms of similar direct stimulation), rather than coitus, brings them more orgasms and in quicker succession, and that their physical response is more intense. Most men, on the other hand, find it easier and more satisfying to achieve orgasm through coitus than through other methods.

A man usually achieves orgasm within about four minutes of intromission, while a woman requires from ten to twenty minutes of sexual intercourse before she attains an orgasmic response. However, through manual, electric vibrator, or oral-genital stimulation, usually less than four minutes is needed to bring a woman to orgasm.[179]

The debate has long raged over woman's capacity for experiencing multiple orgasms, despite the abundance of clinical evidence attesting to her capability for such sexual response. Even after the publication of their research data and clinical findings, the Kinsey researchers found themselves criticized for the "fantastic tale" of multiple orgasms in women.[261] Perhaps the findings of Masters and Johnson[215] will convince the skeptics of the validity of the Kinsey group's conclusions. It has been established through empirical and clinical evidence, and the fact should be accepted, that women are capable by natural endowment of multi-orgasm; many, in fact, are able to have six or more orgasms during a single period of sexual activity.[217] Kinsey, *et al,*[179] report that 14% of women regularly have multiple orgasms, and Masters and Johnson[215] show that if the sexual stimulation producing a woman's first orgasm is continued, a second and a third orgasm—perhaps more—will follow. Furthermore, the women in the Masters and Johnson sampling report that, subjectively, they found the second and third orgasmic responses to be more intense and more pleasurable than the first.

Although men supposedly possess a stronger sex drive, they are not nearly so capable as women of multiple orgasms. Only about 6% to 8% of men are able to have more than one orgasm during each sexual experience, and when the capacity for multiple orgasm exists, it is usually found only in very young men.[180] Furthermore, those men who have a second orgasm shortly after the first, relate that the pleasure of the first is superior to that of the second, in direct contrast to women's subjective reports.[215]

Despite their capacity for orgasm, the unfortunate fact remains that women do not, as was pointed out earlier, reach orgasm as easily as men. Psychological blocks would seem to make the difference. This explanation is understandable in the light of the training and taboos society inflicts on a girl for the first twenty years or so of her life. Many attitudes that are archaic, if not downright fallacious—*e.g.,* the "double standard," and the alleged shame and sin that many moralists impute to human sexuality—set the stage for sexual conflicts in both marriage partners, but especially in women. Another powerful inhibitor to a woman's orgasm is her fear of becoming pregnant.

Only during the past fifty years or so has the sexual gratification of women become a goal to be worked toward in sexual relationships. Surprisingly, some women are still reared with the idea that to enjoy their sexuality is immodest, animalistic, or unwomanly. It is consequently not difficult to understand why women today have problems in the sphere of sexual responsiveness on any level. These circumstances indeed contrast with the pleasure men derive from their sexual life, and the ease with which they achieve orgasm. The answer can only be that men are unencumbered by the psychological barriers that hinder women. These unhealthy conditions will not be corrected immediately, but once people can arrive at a code of ethical sexual behavior based on rationality rather than on shame and guilt, many of the sexual problems facing society today will be corrected.

In their exacting and highly significant research program on the human sexual response cycle, Masters and Johnson have described with scientific precision the physiological reactions that both men and women experience during the various phases of sexual stimulation. [211, 212, 215, 218, 219, 221–227] They have found it convenient to divide the sexual response of both sexes into four phases, which are, in order of their development and occurrence, (1) the excitement phase, (2) the plateau phase, (3) the orgasmic phase, and (4) the resolution phase. In their laboratory demonstration of what had been surmised before by some scientists, clinicians, and laymen, Masters and Johnson established that a variety of physical and psychological stimuli can produce sexual excitement; and that adverse stimuli, or a variation of stimulative techniques, can shorten, prolong, or interrupt the sexual excitement.

When effective sexual stimulation is employed, the recipient enters the *excitement phase,* which varies in length of time from a few minutes to hours, depending upon the effectiveness, intensity, and continuance of the techniques used, and upon the degree of freedom from adverse stimuli, whether physical or psychological. Generally speaking, the longer the excitement phase, the longer the resolution phase; these are the two most protracted phases of the sexual response cycle. The second phase, the *plateau phase,* is intense but of short duration; and the third or *orgasmic phase* is extremely short, lasting from three to ten seconds (sometimes longer in women). When the stimulation that was effective in evoking the excitement phase is continued, the plateau phase is reached; from this point, continuation of the same arousal techniques will culminate in the peak of the sexual cycle, the orgasmic phase. During the last or *resolution phase,* the sexual system retrogresses to its normal nonexcited state. The length of this phase is directly proportionate to the length of the excitement phase.

There is little individual diversity in the pattern of men's response during the orgasmic phase. On the other hand, women—as a group (especially) and individually—display wide diversity in their orgasmic response, both in duration and intensity. For some women, orgasm is a short-lived experience, and for others, an extended one; some experience mild orgasms, while others have such intense ones that they become unaware of their surroundings, occasionally even to the point of losing consciousness momentarily. Sexually inadequate women (who seldom or never experience orgasm) are far more likely to control their spontaneous movements towards the end of coitus than are sexually adequate women (who usually or always respond with orgasm).[2]

There is a significant variation in the response of men and women following coitus. After orgasm, the man enters the *refractory period* (a state of temporary resistance to sexual stimulation) of the resolution phase; the sexual stimulation that was previously effective and pleasurable now becomes unavailing and distasteful. Women, on the other hand, usually do not go into a refractory period. They generally are capable of returning to earlier phases of the sexual response cycle, and if the same sexual stimulation that produced the first orgasm is continued or reapplied, they may experience one or several more orgasms.

The duration of the orgasm itself is about the same whether it occurs as a result of sexual intercourse, manual or oral manipulations, or use of mechanical devices. There is, however, great personal variation in the pleasure and intensity of orgasm, depending upon the individual's preferences in the matter of sexual stimulation.

Following is a summary of identifiable human physiological responses in the order that they are experienced through the excitement, plateau, orgasmic, and resolution phases of sexual expression. This material has been presented in one form of summary or another in many publications; but for the person who is interested in studying and understanding the human sexual response cycle in greater detail, it is suggested that he read the basic two-volume work on sexual behavior by Kinsey, *et al,*[170, 180] and especially Masters and Johnson's *Human Sexual Response.*[215] Other writings by the latter authors on the same subject have appeared in various scientific publications (see Bibliography), and the following material is primarily a summary of their extensive investigation into the physiology of both men and women's sexual responses.

THE FEMALE SEXUAL RESPONSE

I. Excitement Phase

A. *The Breasts*

The most noticeable response observed in the breasts is the erection of the nipples. During the excitement phase, an increase in nipple length of 0.5 to 1.5 cm and in nipple base diameter of 0.25 to 1.0 cm may be expected, although excessively large or extremely small nipples do not enlarge as much as normal-sized ones. This erection is maintained throughout the entire cycle; there are exceptions to the erection response, notably among those women who have inverted nipples that are incapable of erection. Factors other than sexual arousal can also cause nipple erection, such as cold weather, cold baths, and removal of an excessively binding brassiere.

As sexual tension continues and increases, the pigmented area of the breast that surrounds the nipple (areola) becomes engorged and swollen, giving the false impression that the nipple-erection response has been lost, at least partially. Venous blood is trapped in the breasts during the excitement phase, and they enlarge about 20% to 25% by the end of this phase. The veins of the breast become more noticeable during the early part of this phase, because they become engorged with slow-flowing venous blood, forming the familiar "vascular tree" of the breasts.

B. *The Sex Flush*

The vascular-flush phenomenon, called the *maculopapular sex flush* by Masters and Johnson, is one of the most singular reactions to erotic stimulation. A flush of the skin, beginning at the stomach region and at the throat and neck, then spreading quickly to the breasts, appears with varying individual intensity during the excitement phase. As a rule, the intensity of the flush is in direct proportion to the intensity of the stimulation received. About 70% to 75% of sexually stimulated women exhibit the sex flush on occasion, as compared with about 25% of sexually responding men.

C. *Myotonia*

Generalized reactions during the excitement phase (and others) demonstrate that a woman responds sexually with her whole body; her reactions are not limited specifically to the pelvic zone. Increased tension (myotonia) of voluntary muscles—and to a limited extent, of some involuntary muscles—is observable during the excitement phase, especially the latter part. As the phase progresses and tension increases, the woman's movements become more restless, forceful, and swift, and there is involuntary tensing of the muscles in the abdominal region.

D. *The Rectum, Urethra, and Urinary Bladder*

There is sometimes a voluntary contraction of the rectal muscles, along with those of the buttocks, during the excitement phase, the contraction being an attempt to push sexual tension toward ultimate orgasmic response. No other reactions in these areas are noted during this phase.

E. *Cardio-Respiratory-Perspiratory Responses*

Increase in heart rate and elevations of blood pressure parallel the buildup of sexual tension during the excitement phase. There are no noticeable respiratory or perspiratory reactions.

F. *The Clitoris*

The clitoris, under magnification, undergoes a sustained tumescent reaction during the excitement phase, although tumescence can be detected by the naked eye in less than 50% of the cases. During this phase, the loose, wrinkled external skin that surrounds or covers the clitoris is filled out as the glans tissue beneath it expands through venous congestion. As sexual tension mounts, the diameter of the clitoris increases, and there is a congestive elongation of its shaft, although the latter occurrence can be visually detected in less than 10% of the cases. Clitoral tumescence persists throughout the period of sexual stimulation.

Fewer than 50% of women show clinically obvious tumescence of the clitoral glans, and it becomes observable only after sexual tension has progressed into the late part of the excitement phase. Direct manipulation of the clitoral region will produce more rapid and greater enlargement of the clitoral glans than will less direct stimulation (such as fantasy, breast manipulation, or sexual intercourse).

G. *The Vagina*

The vagina reveals its first evidence of anatomic response during the excitement phase. Within ten to thirty seconds after psychological or physiological stimulation has begun, the vagina begins to lubricate itself through the "sweating" phe-

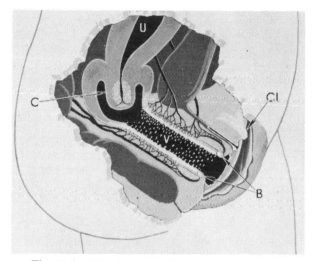

Note the enlargement of the vaginal blood vessels and the "sweating" of the vagina (V) walls during sexual arousal and climax. Bartholin glands (B), cervix (C), at the mouth of the womb (U), and clitoris (CL) are also indicated.

Fig. 11-2. Female pelvis. "Sweating" phenomenon of vagina during sexual arousal. Photograph courtesy *Sexology* magazine.

nomenon previously discussed. Little droplets of clear fluid appear on the walls of the vagina; and as sexual tension increases, the droplets coalesce to form a moist coating of the entire vaginal wall, completely lubricating the vaginal barrel. Since there is practically no glandular tissue in the vagina, it must be assumed that the lubricant is produced by vasocongestive activity in the vaginal barrel.

As the excitement phase continues, both the width and the length of the inner two-thirds of the vaginal passage increase by about 25% over their nonexcited dimensions. The entire vagina becomes dilated, but the expansion is limited to its inner two-thirds. (Under nonexcited conditions the walls of the vagina—especially of the woman who has never borne a child—are in a state of apposition; that is, the walls are touching.) The wrinkled surface of the vagina stretches and flattens, and the vaginal mucosa thins with the expansion.

The vagina also undergoes a color change during the excitement phase from its usual purple-red color to a rather patchy deep purple. The entire vaginal barrel becomes consistently darker in the subsequent phases.

H.   *The Uterus*

During the early part of the excitement phase, a fibrillation (rapid, irregular contractions) phenomenon begins in the body of the uterus. There is evidence of a developing vasocongestive reaction in the uterus during this phase; and the longer the phase lasts, the greater is the increase in the dimensions of the uterus over its unstimulated size. If a woman is sustained for an excessively prolonged period in the excitement or plateau phase, the uterus may show a twofold or threefold increase over its normal size.

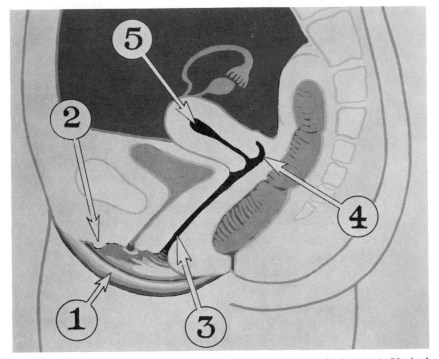

Fig. 11-3.   Female pelvis (lateral view). Normal, nonexcited state. 1. Vaginal lips. 2. Clitoris. 3. Vagina. 4. Vaginal cul-de-sac. 5. Uterus. Photograph courtesy *Sexology* magazine.

In the latter part of the excitement phase as the plateau phase nears, the entire uterus is pulled upward into the lower abdomen. The cervix is in turn lifted upward by this movement, which, along with the involuntary expansion of the vaginal walls, produces a ballooning or tenting effect in the innermost two-thirds of the vagina. (A retroverted uterus, incidentally, prevents this particular response.) Contrary to previously held notions, the cervix is in no way responsible for vaginal lubrication.

I. *The Labia Majora*

The labia majora (major lips) respond during the excitement phase in different ways, depending upon whether the woman has had no children (nullipara) or has had children (multipara). In the nullipara, the major lips thin out and become somewhat flattened; there is a slight elevation of the lips upward and outward, and they flare away from the vagina. The flattening process is not usually complete until late in the excitement phase, or until the beginning of the plateau phase.

In the multipara, the major lips become greatly engorged, often increasing in size by two or three times. There is usually a marked gaping of the lips at the meatus of the vagina so that the "anticipated mounting process" will not be impeded, even though the major lips hang in a rather loose and pendulous manner.

J. *The Labia Minora*

The labia minora (also referred to as the minor lips, inner lips, or sex-skin) commence enlarging in the excitement phase. By the end of the phase, or perhaps early in the plateau phase, they demonstrate a two to threefold increase over their normal thickness. This thickening of the inner lips adds a centimeter to the length of the vaginal barrel, perhaps more.

K. *The Bartholin's Glands*

During the excitement phase, the Bartholin's glands produce very little mucoid secretion. The secretion does not usually take place until the very end of the phase, and may not occur until the plateau phase. The amount secreted is insignificant (very seldom more than one drop for the nulliparous woman, and rarely more than two or three drops for the multiparous woman) and the discharge occurs too late in the sexual response cycle for it to be of value as a lubricant. The presumed roles, therefore, of the Bartholin's glands as a source of vaginal lubrication for easeful penetration by the penis, and as an anti-acidity agent to assist the sperm to survive longer in the vagina, can be discounted. These functions appear, rather, to be carried out by the fluid secreted in vaginal "sweating."

II. Plateau Phase

A. *The Breasts*

In a continuing response pattern that might more accurately be considered an extension of the excitement phase, the breasts reach their peak of expansion during the plateau phase. The areolae become so enlarged during this phase that they partially cover the erect nipples, giving the illusion that there is loss of nipple erection. Breasts which have never fed a baby usually show more expansive ability than those that have been suckled. Because of changes wrought by previous glandular distention and venous drainage, suckled breasts, in comparison with virgin breasts, apparently have a somewhat reduced tumescence capacity.

B. *The Sex Flush*

Of those subjects who evidence a vascular reaction to sexual stimulation by a skin flush, most of the body surface will now be involved. The rose-colored mottling spreads over the top and sides and then the undersides of the breasts. The flush may also become visible on the lower abdomen and shoulders, and as tension increases and orgasm nears, may appear on the back, buttocks, and thighs. Late in this period, the intensity of the color and the expanse of the flush reach their peak.

C. *Myotonia*

Muscular tension in the sexually stimulated woman is observable from head to toe during this phase. She frequently reacts with facial grimaces, flaring of nostrils, and marked strain of the mouth. The cords of the neck become rigid and stand erect (especially with the approach of orgasm), the back arches, and the long muscles of the thighs become very tense.

The muscles of the buttocks are often purposefully made more tense in the striving for orgasm. Late in the plateau phase, involuntary spastic contractions of hand and feet muscles develop into grasping, clawing movements *(carpopedal spasm)*. Involuntary muscle contractions lengthen the vaginal barrel.

D.   *The Rectum, Urethra, and Urinary Bladder*

The same voluntary contractions of rectal muscles noted in some women during the excitement phase frequently continue during the plateau phase.

E.   *Cardio-Respiratory-Perspiratory Responses*

As the plateau phase continues, an elevation of heart rate from the usual 80 to a rate of 110 to 175 beats per minute may be expected. During the latter part of this phase, there is also an elevation of blood pressure, with a rise in systolic pressure of 20 to 60 mm Hg over the normal 120, and a rise in diastolic pressure of 10 to 20 mm Hg over the normal 80. Hyperventilation (increase in respiratory rate) is first noticed during the plateau phase. No perspiratory responses are detectable in this phase.

F.   *The Clitoris*

The clitoris exhibits its most singular response to sexual stimulation during the plateau phase. With almost perfect consistency among all women, the body and glans of the

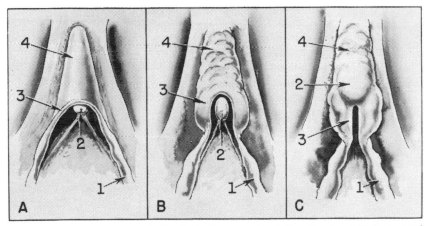

Fig. 11-4.   Response of clitoris during sexual activity, showing (A) its normal unstimulated state; (B) its response during excitement and plateau phases; and (C) its response at the end of the plateau phase and during the orgasmic phase. (1) Inner lip. Clitoris: (2) glans, (3) hood, and (4) covered shaft. After Masters and Johnson. Photograph courtesy *Sexology* magazine.

clitoris withdraw from their normal pudendal overhang position and pull back deeply beneath the foreskin or hood. At the very end of the plateau phase, just before the orgasm, the retraction is so pronounced that there is at least a 50% reduction in the total length of the clitoris. If sexual stimulation is removed during the plateau phase, the clitoris will resume its normal overhanging position; if stimulation is re-applied, the clitoris will withdraw again.

G. *The Vagina*

There is particular activity of the outer one-third of the vagina during the plateau phase, following a certain degree of dilation in this area during the excitement phase. During this second phase, marked vasocongestion within the vaginal canal occurs: the entire outer one-third, including the en-circling muscles (bulbocavernosus), becomes distended with venous blood. The central space of the outer one-third of the canal is reduced by about 33%. The distended muscles involuntarily contract, which causes the vagina to tighten around the shaft of the inserted penis during coition as the woman nears orgasm. The congested outer third of the vagina and the engorged labia minora have been given the name *orgasmic platform* by Masters and Johnson.

The depth and width of the vagina increase only very slightly during the plateau phase.

H. *The Uterus*

During this phase, the uterus elevates as fully into the lower abdomen as its supportive tissue and ligaments allow, producing an increased tenting effect in the inner portion of the vagina. The fibrillation of the corpus of the uterus inten-sifies as the response cycle progresses from early excitement to late plateau phase. Further vasocongestion of the uterus during this period produces a temporary increase in its size.

I. *The Labia Majora*

The labia majora show no further changes during the plateau phase, other than an elaboration of the changes that began in the excitement phase. Nulliparous women may develop thick, heavily engorged major lips if the stimulation is prolonged.

J. *The Labia Minora*

The color of the sex-skin (labia minora) of nulliparous women changes from ashen pink to bright rose, and toward the end of the excitement phase the color deepens further to a scarlet hue. A multiparous woman experiences greater dilation of the veins in the minor lips than the nulliparous woman does, and the sex-skin coloration of the former can therefore be expected to be deeper, ultimately darkening to a wine color during the plateau phase. There is a definite correlation between the intensity of these color changes and degree of sexual excitation; in those women who progress satisfactorily through the excitement phase, but who are unable to achieve orgasm, the labia minora become bright pink, but never a deeper color. Marked color changes are evidence of an impending orgasm.

K. *The Bartholin's Glands*

If the Bartholin's glands have not previously secreted their fluid, and if they are to produce such a secretion, they do so now. Prolonged penile thrusts during coitus may stimulate the Bartholin's glands to secrete, but frequently they do not.

III. Orgasmic Phase

A. *The Breasts*

There are no noticeable changes in the breasts at the time of orgasm, although they may appear to be heavy and pendulous because of the spasm-like reaction of the entire body when the climax occurs.

B. *The Sex Flush*

The intensity of the flush is proportionate to the intensity of the orgasm.

C. *Myotonia*

The myotonic reactions observed in the latter part of the plateau phase usually continue and intensify in the orgasmic phase. During orgasm, muscular strain may be so severe as to cause aching and soreness the following day. The woman is so extensively caught up in her orgasmic response that there is a loss of voluntary control, and she is unaware of her muscular reactions.

Orgasm produces muscular changes in the body far beyond the contractions of the orgasmic platform and the uterus. There are also involuntary contractions of the perineal area, the rectum, and the lower abdomen. Both superficial and deep muscles are involved, and the entire pelvic region is irregularly and spasmodically elevated in deviation from its usual flat positioning. Other parts of the body, such as the neck, hands, arms, feet, and legs show their own individual responses at the time of orgasm. Corded neck muscles are an easily observable reaction both just before and during orgasm, and indicate the marked and generalized muscular strain that the body undergoes at the time of orgasm.

Further changes during this phase may include flushing and slight swelling of the face, and expansion of the rib cage.

The more effective the stimulation has been, the more completely the woman's whole body becomes involved in the release of physiological and psychological tensions.

D.   *The Rectum, Urethra, and Urinary Bladder*

Involuntary contraction of the sphincter muscles of the rectum may occur during the orgasmic phase, especially if the orgasm is intense. As with the contractions in the outer third of the vagina, the rectal contractions occur at 0.8-second intervals; the rectal muscles may contract in strong orgasmic responses as many as five times. These systolic rectal reactions have been observed more frequently during automanipulation than during sexual intercourse.

Women sometimes experience an involuntary distention of the external meatus of the urethra during this phase. When it does occur, the distention disappears and the meatus returns to its normal state before the orgasmic phase is over. A woman occasionally feels an urge to urinate during or immediately after orgasm, and there possibly is a loss of urine as sexual tension mounts. Multiparous more than nulliparous women have a tendency to urinate involuntarily at this time, because their sphincter muscles are more flaccid.[78]

E.   *Cardio-Respiratory-Perspiratory Responses*

There is a further slight elevation in the heart rate beyond that reached in the plateau phase. Heart rate is usually

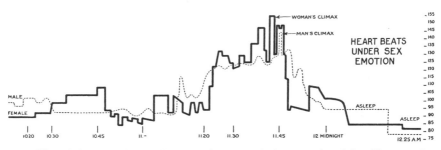

Fig. 11-5. Heartbeats of man and woman during sexual activity. Photograph courtesy *Sexology* magazine.

higher when a woman masturbates than when she engages in coition. Although the blood pressure in women continues to climb, the rise is not as great as that in men during this phase. A woman's blood pressure shows an elevation of 30 to 80 mm Hg above the normal 120, and an elevation in diastolic pressure of 20 to 40 mm Hg above the normal 80. Respiration may increase to a rate of forty breaths a minute (twenty a minute is normal) during this phase; the increase in intensity and duration of any respiratory changes is directly correlated to the intensity and duration of sexual tension. If the orgasm is mild or of short duration, there may be no increase in the respiratory rate. There are still no perspiratory reactions at this stage of the response cycle.

F. *The Clitoris*

The clitoris shows no specific reaction at the time of orgasm; that is to say, under present laboratory conditions it is not possible to observe the clitoris during this phase, since it is retracted beneath the hood of the labia minora.

G. *The Vagina*

The vagina shows a unique response during the orgasmic phase. The orgasmic platform, which is first noticeable during the plateau phase, contracts strongly in intervals of about

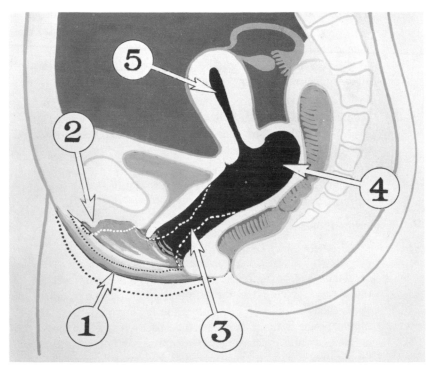

Fig. 11-6. Female pelvis. Changes in size and position of tissue and organs during increasing sexual excitement and orgasmic response. 1. Vaginal lips. 2. Clitoris. 3. Orgasmic platform. 4. Ballooning and tenting effect of inner part of vagina. 5. Uterus. Photograph courtesy *Sexology* magazine.

0.8 second. There are at least three or four such contractions, and there may be as many as fifteen. The interval between contractions lengthens after the first few responses, and the intensity also diminishes. The strength of the contractions varies from person to person, and individual contractile experiences also vary.

H. *The Uterus*

The rapid but irregular contractions noted in the corpus of the uterus during the earlier phases move into an identifiable pattern during the orgasmic phase. The contractions are somewhat similar to those of the uterus during the first stage of labor. Typically, the contractions begin at the top of the uterus (fundus) and work their way downward through the middle portion and terminate in the lower section of the cervix. It is noteworthy that the contractile reactions do not begin until two to four seconds after a woman first experiences orgasm. Current research findings indicate that uterine contractions are more severe when orgasm has been brought about by masturbatory techniques rather than by coition.

I. *The Labia Majora*

There are no observable changes in the labia majora of either the nulliparous or multiparous woman during this phase.

J. *The Labia Minora*

No reactions of the labia minora have been observed during the orgasmic phase.

K. *The Bartholin's Glands*

No reactions of the Bartholin's glands have been observed during the orgasmic phase.

IV. Resolution Phase

A. *The Breasts*

There is an almost immediate loss of the measles-like rash that has covered the breasts. There is detumescence of the areolae, giving the false impression that the nipples are again becoming erect. What actually happens is that the nipples, which have been partly obscured by the engorged areolae, remain erect longer than the areolae does; the "new" nipple erection is in fact only the "old" nipple erection once again becoming observable. The erect nipple usually undergoes *involution* (return to normal size) before the breast loses its vasocongestive reaction. The breasts are slow to return to normal size, and in a nulliparous woman, they often remain enlarged for five to ten minutes after orgasm.

B. *The Sex Flush*

The maculopapular rash disappears during this phase in the reverse order in which it developed during the excitement and plateau phases. It disappears quickly from the buttocks, arms, thighs, abdomen, and back, but is much slower to disappear from the neck, chest, breasts, face, and finally, the upper abdomen or stomach area.

C. *Myotonia*

There is a rapid decline of muscular tension during the resolution phase; if sexual stimulation is not reinstated, the tension usually disappears completely within five minutes of orgasm.

D. *The Rectum, Urethra, and Urinary Bladder*

No responses have been observed during the resolution phase.

E. *Cardio-Respiratory-Perspiratory Responses*

Heart rate, blood pressure, and respiratory rate show an early return to the normal state during the resolution phase. About one-third of all women develop a widespread film of perspiration during this phase as the skin flush resolves. Almost immediately after orgasm, a thin coating of perspiration may appear over the chest, back, and thighs. Heavy perspiration may appear on the forehead, upper lip, and the axillae (underarms) of a woman—especially if her face became mottled by a flush reaction during the earlier phases. Sometimes the entire body is coated with perspiration. Although some women quite naturally perspire from the physical exertion of coitus, the perspiratory reaction described above is apparently not related to this exertion, since the response occurs regardless of the degree of physical activity of the first three phases. The copiousness of the perspiratory response parallels the strength of the orgasm.

F. *The Clitoris*

The clitoris returns to its normal pudendal overhang position within ten seconds after the vaginal contractions cease. The time required for the return of the clitoris to its unstimulated pre-excitement phase state is roughly the same as the time required for the primary loss of penile erection after a man ejaculates. However, vasocongestion of the clitoral glans and shaft may remain for five to ten minutes after orgasm, and occasionally may persist for as long as thirty minutes.

G.   *The Vagina*

The vagina shows its first retrogressive change in its outer one-third portion. The vasocongestion that produced the vaginal orgasmic platform during the plateau phase quickly disappears, causing the diameter of the outer third of the vaginal opening to increase as the area returns to normal size. The inner two-thirds of the vagina reverts to its normal collapsed state, although this process is rather slow and irregular; first one zone, then another, relaxes. The vaginal walls regain their rough, wrinkled surface, and the deep color of the vagina fades, the retrogressive process frequently lasting for as long as ten to fifteen minutes.

H.   *The Uterus*

Early in the resolution phase, the elevated uterus rapidly returns to its normal position in the abdominal cavity. The contractile pattern that the uterus displayed during the earlier response phases ceases, vasocongestion disappears, and the organ returns to normal size. Multiparous and nulliparous experimental subjects who were sustained in an excessively prolonged plateau phase of sexual tension developed vasocongestion, together with a 50% to 100% increase in uterine size. After orgasm, an interval of ten minutes in nulliparous women, and often up to twenty minutes in multiparous women, were required before vasocongestion and exaggerated uterine size dissipated. When orgasm did not occur, the increased size of the uterus persisted for as long as sixty minutes.

Immediately after orgasmic response, there is a slight spreading apart of the external os (opening) of the cervix, and the spreading continues for the first five to ten minutes of the resolution phase. Earlier scientific opinion was that this reaction aids in the passage of sperm into the uterus, and that a sucking effect is produced at the cervix at the time of orgasm. Recent investigations demonstrate that the slight widening of the external os does not aid in the transportation of sperm, and that there is no sucking process in the uterus at the time of orgasm.

I.   *The Labia Majora*

The labia majora return to normal size faster in nulliparous women than they do in the multiparous. The labia majora of the former resume their normal thickness and flaring of the edges, and return to a midline positioning that partially covers the vaginal outlet. In the multiparous, engorgement of the major lips may persist for two to three hours before complete detumescence.

J.   *The Labia Minora*

The labia minora quickly (usually in ten to fifteen seconds) return to the light pink color of the pre-excitement phase; even when the lips had become bright scarlet or burgundy during the plateau phase, the color fades to light pink within two minutes or less. There is an unevenness of hue during the process of returning to normal, but the total resolution of the sex-skin color usually occurs within five minutes after orgasm.

The physiological return to normalcy during the resolution phase occurs in the reverse order of the changes as they took place in the excitement and plateau phases. In this final phase, the minor lips first lose their discoloration and then their vascular tension, the latter effecting a reduction to normal size and a resumption of midline positioning.

K.   *The Bartholin's Glands*

There are no observable changes of the Bartholin's glands during this phase.

———◆◆◆———

It will be noted that the description of the female sexual response cycle contains no mention of any reactions by the ovaries and Fallopian tubes. No direct observations have been made of these organs during the cycle, and their reactions are therefore not known. Some response possibly takes place, but until more satisfactory techniques of investigation are developed, little can be said about the activity of these organs throughout the cycle.

THE MALE SEXUAL RESPONSE

I. Excitement Phase

A.   *The Breasts*

About 60% of all men experience nipple erection during the sexual response cycle; when this erection does occur, it usually takes place late in the excitement phase and continues throughout the other phases. Nipple erection may be brought about by direct stimulation, although it ordinarily occurs spontaneously.

B. *The Sex Flush*

The measles-like maculopapular sex flush appears on about 25% of sexually responding men (as compared with 75% of sexually responding women), and develops in much the same fashion as it does in women. The flush may appear late in the excitement phase, but it does not usually make an observable appearance until well after the plateau phase is under way. When it occurs, the flush customarily begins over the stomach region, then spreads to the chest and later to the neck and face; in a few cases, the rash extends to the shoulders, arms, and thighs of a man.

C. *Myotonia*

Muscular tension or myotonia becomes clinically observable in the latter part of the excitement phase, although the reaction is more pronounced during the plateau phase. Muscular contractions at this point, which primarily involve the voluntary muscles, are evidenced by both restless and purposeful movements. Involuntary muscular movements are more likely to occur during the late part of this phase, at which time some elevation of both testes toward the perineum takes place, along with tension in the long muscles of both legs and arms and in the abdominal musculature.

D. *The Rectum*

There are no noticeable rectal reactions during the excitement phase. However, *direct* stimulation of the region at this time may produce irregular contractions of the external rectal sphincter.

E. *Cardio-Respiratory-Perspiratory Reactions*

As sexual tension increases, there is a corresponding increase in heart rate and blood pressure; there are no observable changes in breathing rate or in perspiratory reaction.

F. *The Penis*

Effective sexual stimulation will produce erection of the penis, as the three spongy cylindrical bodies of erectile tissue forming it become engorged with blood. Depending upon the type and intensity of sexual stimulation, the excitement phase may continue for a long period and erection may be partially lost and regained many times. During the excitement phase, erection of the penis may be impaired by adverse stimuli, such as sudden loud noises, noticeable changes in lighting or temperature, fear, and anxiety. With penile erection, the urethra, of course, also lengthens. As the excitement phase progresses, the penile urethral passage increases twofold in

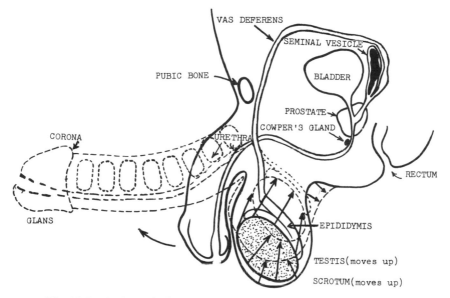

Fig. 11-7. Male genitalia. In pre-excitement phase; dotted lines represent positions in excitement and plateau phases. After Masters and Johnson.

diameter, and the urethral opening (meatus) widens. No other penile changes occur during the next two phases (plateau and orgasmic).

G. *The Scrotum*

Sexual tension causes contraction of the smooth muscles and vasocongestion of the tissue of the scrotum. Because the tissue thickens, and because there is a constriction and elevation of the scrotal sac, testicular movement is now restricted primarily to a perpendicular plane.

H. *The Testes*

With excitement-phase tension comes a shortening of the spermatic cord (contraction of cremasteric musculature), which causes an elevation of both testes. There is also a slight rotation of the axis of the testes. A prolonged excitement phase (more than five to ten minutes) may make the scrotal sac and cremasteric musculature relax, returning the testes to their original suspended position.

I. *The Secondary Organs*
    (Prostate, Vas Deferens, Seminal Vesicles)
    There are no noticeable changes in these organs during the excitement phase, other than a shortening of the vas deferens as the testes are pulled toward the body.

J. *The Cowper's Glands*
    There are no noticeable reactions in these glands during this phase.

II. Plateau Phase

A. *The Breasts*
    Nipple erection, if it is to occur and did not take place in the previous phase, will take place now and will be maintained through the plateau phase.

B. *The Sex Flush*
    If the flush is to occur and has not made its appearance during the earlier phase, it will become noticeable during the plateau phase, especially in the latter part. A man is not so likely as a woman to exhibit this response. The sex flush is a sporadic occurrence in a man, if it ever happens at all, in that it may appear prominently during one sexual experience, yet be totally absent during another. Psychological factors (such as extreme anticipation) and temperature factors (such as a heated rather than a cool room) may influence the appearance of the sex flush.

C. *Myotonia*
    There is an increase in both voluntary and involuntary muscular tensions during the plateau phase. There may be strong contraction in the muscles of the neck, face (especially around the mouth), and abdomen; if a man is in the supine position during coition, he may also show carpopedal spasm (marked contraction of the striated muscles of the hands and feet), indicating a high level of sexual excitement. As the tension mounts and as orgasm nears, clutching, clawing, and grasping contractions of the hands, if they are not otherwise occupied, may take place. The human male is more likely to display carpopedal reactions during masturbation than during sexual intercourse.

D. *The Rectum*
    Rectal response in this phase is similar to that of the excitement phase.

E.   *Cardio-Respiratory-Perspiratory Reactions*

Increased sexual tension produces hyperventilation, commonly during the latter part of the plateau phase. The heart rate increases from the usual 70 beats per minute to a range of 100 to 175 beats per minute. Blood pressure elevates; systolic pressure may increase above normal by 20 to 80 mm Hg, and diastolic pressure by 10 to 40 mm Hg. The elevation in some instances may be even higher. There are no noticeable changes in perspiratory reaction during this phase.

F.   *The Penis*

Only minor changes are noted in the penis during the plateau phase. Late in this phase the corona of the glans becomes more tumescent, and there may be a deepening of the mottled reddish-purple color of the glans and the area just below the corona. The base of the urethra (the urethral bulb) increases to three times its normal size. Late in the phase there is additional distention of the urethral bulb, although the amount of distention varies considerably from person to person; this distention is indicative of impending orgasm.

G.   *The Scrotum*

There are no noticeable reactions or changes in the scrotum during the plateau phase.

H.   *The Testes*

The testes must undergo at least partial elevation before the human male can experience a full ejaculatory sequence. Once the testes become positioned next to the perineum, the orgasmic phase will inevitably follow if effective sexual stimulation is maintained. In nearly all men, one testicle hangs slightly lower than the other does. The lower testicle, which in about 85% of all men is the left one, through muscular contractions may move up and down in the scrotum throughout the first two sexual phases. In many instances, the testicle of shorter suspension becomes elevated early in the plateau phase. There is also a vasocongestive reaction in the testes that increases their size over their unstimulated, noncongested state by approximately 50%; the increase may be as much as 100% in some men. Generally speaking, the more protracted the plateau phase of sexual tension is, the more severe the vasocongestion and the more marked the increase in testicular size will be.

I. *The Secondary Organs*
    (Prostate, Vas Deferens, Seminal Vesicles)

    There are no observable changes during this phase, other than the inevitable movement of the vas deferens following the movements of the testicles.

J. *The Cowper's Glands.*

    These two glands secrete two or three drops of pre-ejaculatory mucoid fluid during this phase.

III. Orgasmic Phase

A. *The Breasts*

    There are no noticeable reactions of the breasts during this phase.

B. *The Sex Flush*

    The flush, when present, persists during this phase. The degree of the flush usually parallels the intensity of the orgasm.

C. *Myotonia*

    During the orgasmic phase, there is loss of voluntary control, and there is also severe involuntary-muscle tension throughout the body. The male orgasmic response is one that, to a large degree, is based on vasocongestion and myotonia involving the total body. The involuntary reactions that cause a man's ejaculation have been described in some detail in Chapter 4.

D. *The Rectum*

    The sphincter muscles of the rectum commence involuntary contractions at approximately 0.8-second intervals, although the number of such contractions is usually only two to four.

E. *Cardio-Respiratory-Perspiratory Reactions*

    Hyperventilation continues into the orgasmic phase, the respiratory rate frequently rising to 40 breaths per minute. The recorded rates of heart beat range from 110 to 180 beats (or more) per minute; the lower the number of heart beats per minute during a resting, nonstimulated state, the smaller the rise in heart rate is in a sexually active and sexually stimulated state. Blood pressure during this phase goes even higher than it does during the plateau phase. The systolic pressure rises from 40 to 100 mm Hg, and the diastolic pressure from 20 to 50 mm Hg above normal.

    Only occasionally does a man experience a perspiratory

response during this phase; if it is to occur, it usually takes place early in the resolution phase. If there is a perspiratory reaction during this period, it occurs with the final ejaculatory contractions.

F. *The Penis*

A rapid distention of the urethral bulb is a signal of an imminent orgasmic response. The distention occurs simultaneously with the collection of seminal fluid in the urethra at the prostate gland, at about the time the response cycle

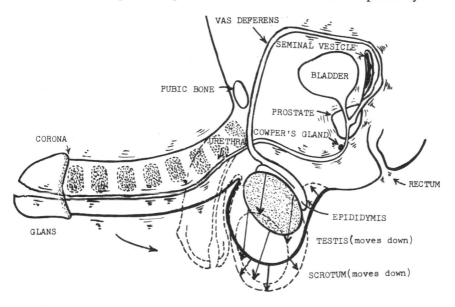

Fig. 11-8. Male genitalia. In orgasmic phase; dotted lines represent positions in resolution phase. After Masters and Johnson.

advances from the plateau to the orgasmic phase. The bulb's distention is so great that it can be seen with the naked eye.

Regularly recurring contractions of the urethra and of the muscles at the base of the penis and around the anus produce the penile ejaculatory reaction during the orgasmic phase. The intervals between contractions are roughly the same as those between orgasmic vaginal contractions—0.8 second between the first three or four major responses, followed by a lengthening of intervals between contractions. (There is also a diminution in contractile force after the first few contractions.) The urethra continues to contract slightly and irregularly for several seconds after the initial expulsive responses, the interval between the final contractions lasting perhaps several seconds.

G. *The Scrotum*

There are no observable reactions of the scrotum during the orgasmic phase.

H. *The Testes*

There are no observable reactions of the testes during this phase. Many researchers believe, however, that there may well be some response for which adequate observation and recording techniques have not yet been developed.

I. *The Secondary Organs*
(Prostate, Vas Deferens, Seminal Vesicles)

The entire ejaculatory process involves these organs. Contractions of the secondary organs produce the sensation that ejaculation is imminent; the contractions then trigger ejaculation. Apparently, contractions of the secondary organs begin with the vasa efferentia (the tubes leading from testicle to epididymis) of the testes, continue through the epididymis, the vas deferens, and, finally, the seminal vesicles. The systolic action of the prostate, which forces the seminal fluid through and out the urethra, is easily observable and measurable.

J. *The Cowper's Glands*

These glands respond in no observable fashion during this phase.

IV. Resolution Phase

A. *The Breasts*

If nipple erection occurred during the excitement phase, up to an hour after ejaculation is needed before they resume their normal size.

B. *The Sex Flush*

As in a woman, the man's maculopapular sex flush disappears rapidly during the resolution phase. The fading of the flush is in reverse order of its appearance in the excitement phase.

C. *Myotonia*

If there is no further sexual stimulation, the muscular tension that built up during the first three sexual response phases almost always dissipates during the first five minutes of the resolution phase.

D. *The Rectum*

The sphincter muscles that contracted during the orgasmic phase relax by the time the expulsive contractions of the urethra terminate. No other reactions are noticeable.

E. *Cardio-Respiratory-Perspiratory Reactions*

Hyperventilation, which reaches its peak during the orgasmic phase, resolves in the refractory period of the resolution phase, immediately after orgasm. Heart beat rate and blood pressure return to normal.

About one-third of all men show a perspiratory reaction immediately after ejaculation. As in women, the perspiration may appear over the entire body; but it is usually confined in men to the soles of the feet and palms of the hands. This response may occur whether or not there was strong physical exertion during coition or an accompanying sex flush.

F. *The Penis*

Detumescence occurs in two stages. The primary loss of erection occurs in the early refractory period, at which time the penis reduces from the dimensions of full erection to a size 50% larger than its usual flaccid state. This early loss in size is rapid; the secondary stage of detumescence persists for a much longer time, especially when there is residual sexual stimulation.

The time involved in the return of the penis after orgasm to its normal unstimulated size depends upon the form and duration of stimulation received during the excitement and plateau phases. For example, a prolonged period of vaginal penetration may produce marked penile vasocongestion that often prolongs the primary stage of penile detumescence, and hence delays the secondary stage of erection loss. On the other hand, penile involution may be speeded up by sufficiently intense external asexual stimuli. During the resolution phase, if a man removes his penis from the vagina shortly after orgasm, and, more particularly, if he does something sexually unrelated, such as walking about, urinating, reading, or smoking a cigar, detumescence will occur rapidly in both its primary and secondary stages.

The urethra, as well as the broadened urethral meatus, reverts to its customary dimensions shortly after ejaculation.

G. *The Scrotum*

The involution of the scrotal skin occurs in either of two quite different patterns during the resolution phase, a given pattern appearing fairly consistently in each individual. About 25% of all men experience a slow return of the scrotum to its normal nonstimulated state; the remaining 75% experience a rapid loss of congestion accompanied by an equally rapid retrogression of the scrotum to its relaxed, loosely wrinkled pre-arousal appearance.

H. *The Testes*

In the resolution phase, the testes undergo a loss of vasocongestion and a reduction in size. The involutional pattern is about the same as that of the scrotal sac, and similarly can be a swift or a protracted process. Generally speaking, the longer the plateau phase persists, the longer it takes for the testicles to decrease in size during the resolution phase.

I. *The Secondary Organs*
(Prostate, Vas Deferens, Seminal Vesicles)

No changes have been observed in these organs during the resolution phase.

J. *The Cowper's Glands*

No changes in these glands have been noted during this phase.

———◆●◆———

Despite the foregoing physiologic detailing of human orgasmic response, the conclusion must not be drawn that for a happy marriage and sexual competency, orgasm must accompany each sexual experience. This simply does not hold true for either men or women. Sexual response to the point of orgasm is highly desirable because of the great physical and emotional pleasure and release involved. It is, however, by no means crucial to a happy and fulfilled life; and overemphasizing orgasm can lead to conflicts that are damaging to the enjoyment of coition and the emotional relationship between husband and wife.[25]

The eminent psychologist L. M. Terman conducted a classic investigation into the sexual behavior of sexually adequate women (those who report that they usually or always experience orgasm) and sexually inadequate women (those who sometimes or never experience orgasm), together with their husbands, in regard to a number of factors—including their happiness and sexual adjustment in marriage. According to the results of Terman's research, the wife's capacity for orgasm is surprisingly not highly related to her overall happiness, and her ability to achieve orgasm is even less important to her husband's happiness.[369]

Marital happiness and sexual adjustment (the latter being a healthy attitude toward sexual activity, even in the absence of responsiveness) bear a high degree of relationship to one another, although marital happiness shows little correlation with overall sexual responsiveness (the latter meaning pleasure and satisfaction in sexual activity). If most other aspects of her marriage are satisfactory—*e.g.,* shared interests, spontaneity, naturalness, lack of defensiveness, mutual respect, the desire to please, and open lines of communication—a wife may be happy even though she is sexually unresponsive.[2]

The desirability of simultaneous orgasms for husband and wife has long been the subject of speculation.[122] Naturally, if both husband and wife prefer orgasms at the same time—and many couples do, claiming that it affords them the greatest enjoyment and satisfaction—then they should strive for this goal. However, some aspects of sexual response should be considered prior to embarking upon the uneven struggle toward simultaneous orgasm, or before accepting the premise that it offers the ultimate in amatory achievement.

Essential to rewarding sexual activity is the effort to give one's partner the fullest measure of concern and satisfaction. If either person is primarily concerned with gratifying himself, or is caught up in his own impending orgasm, he cannot give full attention to his partner. Similarly, if overmuch attention is being devoted to the partner's sexual gratification, appropriate concentration on one's own response and pleasure is impossible.

Furthermore, men and women react quite differently in bodily movements at the time of orgasm. The man's tendency, as has been said, is to plunge into the vagina as deeply as possible at the moment of orgasm and to hold this position for a length of time, to be followed perhaps by one or two deep, deliberate thrusts. The woman's tendency, on the other hand, is to have the same stroking, plunging movements of the excitement and plateau phases continued during the orgasmic reaction, with perhaps an acceleration of the thrusts and an increase of pressure in the vulval area. These two highly pleasurable patterns of movement are obviously incompatible; since they cannot both be executed at the same time, whichever pattern is carried out during simultaneous orgasm must perforce detract from the full pleasure of one of the partners.

The arguments, therefore, would appear to be stronger against than for simultaneous orgasm. It is easier for a man to achieve orgasm, but he is usually capable of only one. The sensible conduct of coition would seem to be that the husband delay his own pleasure until his wife is fully satisfied: both partners can devote full attention to giving the wife as many orgasmic responses as she wishes, and then both can concentrate wholly on providing the husband with as satisfying an orgasm as possible.

Conclusion

As has been pointed out, orgasmic responses vary for the same woman, and the variation is even greater among women as a group.[25] Sensible efforts should be expended by a husband to give his wife as strong and pleasurable a sexual response as possible—just as a wife, it might be mentioned once more, should strive to gratify her husband sexually. There should be no great anxiety, however, if the wife does not respond as intensely as either partner had hoped. Considerable sexual satisfaction may be derived by the wife from petting, coitus, or other methods of stimulation, even when these activities do not culminate in orgasm of either great or mild intensity. If feelings of desperation are kept out of the relationship, it may well retain its areas of satisfaction, and these couples can perhaps aspire to more intense levels of fulfillment.

Because of their premarital or extramarital involvement with women of profound sexual desire and response, some men are led to believe that their wives should respond to them with the same frequency and intensity. What these men fail to realize is that the very strength of the sexual drive in some women impels them into non-marital involvements, whereas their wives may simply not possess such strong sexual needs. The inference cannot be drawn that one partner, because of his or her less intense sexual drive, is any the less loving of the spouse or any the less concerned for the welfare of their marriage.

The fact that the material in this chapter has focused on the physiological considerations of human sexuality does not mean that the emotional aspects of sexuality are of less importance. A close human relationship and deep emotional involvement—love, if you wish—are of paramount importance to a complete and fulfilling sexual experience. Physiological sexual needs can be relieved without love, closeness, or even understanding; but no one can really attain complete emotional, physical, and sexual satisfaction, in all its beauty, without the intermingling of those elements. Ask any person who has had sexual intercourse in both circumstances.

CHAPTER 12

Sexual Attitudes and
Sexual Behavior

"Our sexual behavior is essentially the result of our attitudes towards sex; and these attitudes, in turn, are a product of how we have been brought up."[140] And, as pointed out earlier in this text, sex education begins with the first intimate mother-infant contacts.[54] Instruction in sexual matters, however, involves infinitely more than the interrelations between parents and child; significant roles are played by many other influences. There are not only the general demands and expectations of the specific culture in which the person lives, but also the special differences in sexual ethics within that culture—differences based on such variables as the individual's, as well as the teacher's, type of religious affiliation and depth of involvement, sex, age, educational level, and socioeconomic stratum.

SEXUAL ATTITUDES

Much has been said and written in recent years about the sexual revolution that is allegedly taking place. While research findings and clinical judgments are not wholly consistent, the general consensus is that there has been no revolution of any significance since the 1920s when those women born around the turn of the century came of age and set new sexual standards.[125, 179, 280] There may be no revolution at the present time, but there is more and more evidence that revolt looms on the horizon. One can hardly have escaped noticing a change in sexual attitudes in recent years, as evidenced by the growing freedom with which sexual topics are discussed in the various communication media, schools, churches, and governmental circles—as well as at cocktail parties and by the man on the street.

But *attitudes* (and the ease of discussing them) are not to be confused with *behavior*. Even those to whom a decision in the matter of a sexual ethic is most pertinent—today's college students—are bewildered and bedeviled by the dichotomy between prevailing sexual attitudes and sexual behavior. For example, although 75% of college girls express the belief that their classmates are "sleeping around" (attitude), surveys and research studies consistently point out that, actually, only 20% of all college girls experience premarital intercourse (behavior).[333]

It should probably be underlined at the outset of any discussion of this nature that significant changes in human mores, behavior, laws, and social institutions occur only gradually. Especially slow are changes in culturally acceptable sexual behavior, because the orientation and experiences of childhood place strong limitations on the frequency, form, and freedom of such behavior in adulthood.[125, 280]

Cultural differences, as one might expect, produce as wide a variety of attitudes toward sexual matters as they do in other areas of human interaction. It comes as a surprise to many Americans to learn that their condemnatory views on premarital and postmarital sexual activity are not shared by the majority of the world's cultures.[26, 250] For example, of 158 societies investigated in one study, 70% do not condemn premarital sexual intercourse (although this permissiveness toward premarital coitus does not imply sanction of adulterous relationships).[109]

Anthropological investigations have consistently revealed that cultures which encourage women to be completely free in their sexual expression produce sexually responsive women whose amatory reactions are as uninhibited and as vigorous as those of their men. Cultures that approve of women's having orgasms produce women who have orgasms; those cultures that do not so approve, produce women who are incapable of orgasm.[191]

With unfortunate ease, sexual attitudes can fall under the pall of such cultural maladies as misinformation and prudery. For example, women of emancipated modern societies frequently are troubled with menstrual difficulties of one sort or another. Yet Margaret Mead's anthropological studies of the women of Samoa[233] show that when they were questioned, only one woman of the entire population even understood what was meant by pain or emotional imbalance during menstruation, and that particular girl was in the employ of the island's white missionary family.

All people to a degree, but Americans most particularly (it would appear), are inclined to cling to their traditional ways of thinking and conducting themselves, whether in political, religious, or sexual matters. They are reluctant to accept change or to be swayed by outside influences, however rational or beneficial. This rather blind adherence to tradition is found not only in major cultures, but within specific subcultures as well.

Probably the greatest social change to occur in recent years has been the emergence of women into a position of equality in American society. The freedom and parity that women demanded and now enjoy in the United States have had a profound effect upon prevailing sexual attitudes. The traditional American attitude toward women's sexuality was an outgrowth of the Victorian ethic. Men and women were presumed to have characteristically different sexual needs and drives; and a woman, having little amatory interest in sex, participated in copulatory activity only for the purpose of procreation or to please her husband. Most women today are unwilling to accept the notion that each sex is subject to different standards in the matter of sexual desire and conduct. They expect the pleasures received from sexual activities as well as the restrictions governing them, to be equally applicable to both sexes.[26, 258]

An interesting side effect of this struggle for equality is that the sexual attitudes of American women are often considerably healthier than those of American men. Chroniclers of sexual histories, whether researchers or clinicians, have found that women are far more open and honest in supplying their personal data than men are. Men frequently become embroiled in the question of self-esteem, and may attempt to compensate for what they feel is a threat to their self-image by boasting, with the consequence that the data they provide are often unreliable.[206]

Despite the recent liberalizing evolution in the realm of women's rights, certain differences between the sexual attitudes of the two sexes continue to be forged by such factors as childhood rearing, the expectations of society, and certain physiological agents. Premarital chastity, particularly for girls, is still considered an "ideal," even though, as Thomas Poffenberger says, "society no longer takes the pious position that all premarital coitus is evil and the offender should be punished."[26, 258] The most significant deterrents to premarital sexual activity are religious and moral codes that condemn it, family training, various fears, a desire to wait until marriage, the lack of opportunity, and the lack of desire.[50, 109, 179, 180] Fear of pregnancy was a strong deterrent in the past, but it is no longer regarded as a prime factor in premarital continence.[46, 109, 179]

Other changes in sexual attitudes have their basis in the protracted period of adolescence that shifts in the American social structure have imposed on its youth. The imposition of additional educational and vocational requirements has made necessary an extended adolescence, on the one hand, yet the age of a youngster's physical maturation comes considerably earlier than it did in previous generations. Because of these two considerations, the period of social adolescence is now approximately twice as long as it was 100 years ago.[26, 172] During this prolonged period of youth, the two sexes begin to develop different attitudes toward premarital sexual activity. The natural feelings of insecurity which adolescence breeds and the increase in physical drives (especially in boys) make the adolescent particularly susceptible to the hawkings of Madison Avenue when it extols the supreme value of sex appeal in striving toward popularity, success, admiration, security, and the like. Boys are propagandized through the various mass communication media to believe that their masculinity (*i.e.,* success as a *man*) depends upon their success in seduction: the farther they go with girls sexually, the more masculine they are in their own eyes and from the viewpoint of their peer group.

Girls, on the other hand, are indoctrinated in the importance of being "sexy." They are exhorted to purchase an often ludicrous and useless conglomerate of products that, according to the advertisements, are guaranteed to increase sexual attractiveness. A young girl is indeed in a delicate position. She must appear and act "sexy" in order to attract as many boys and to have as many dates as possible, because these are the symbols in her all-important peer group of popularity and social success. At the same time, however, she must hold the line of propriety, because otherwise she risks losing her "good girl" status with a consequent loss of prestige. Girls too often are favorably evaluated by their peer group only in correlation with their popularity in dating (and the number of boys whom they cause to make open affectionate commitments), coupled with their ability to remain free of sexual involvements.[26, 386]

As boys and girls grow older, they come to adopt a more permissive sexual code of behavior. This doubtless is due in part to the fact that the younger teen-agers submit uncritically to the traditional sexual ethic of their parents; but as they grow older and think more and more independently of their parents, they come to a progressively greater extent under the influence of outside values, particularly those of their peer groups.[26, 271] Even with recent relaxations in sexual codes, however, changes in teen-age sexual behavior have been in the direction of increased petting rather than of increased coition.[270]

Slightly over half of teen-age girls admit to guilt feelings if they go "too far" in petting with their dates, while only one-fourth of the boys express similar guilt. These views stand in curious contrast to statements made by the other members of the same groups (one-third of the girls and three-fourths of the boys) who are more conservative in their sexual conduct, yet indicate that they desire greater sexual intimacy on dates. Boys appear interested in petting and sexual intercourse, while their girl friends are willing to neck (mild embracing and kissing limited to face and lips), but wish to hold the line there.[28] As the relationship becomes more serious—from dating, to going steady, to engagement—sexual behavior becomes more intimate, and guilt over sexual endearments becomes less for both sexes.[28, 62, 66]

Clinical observations and the results of empirical research have frequently underlined the marked discrepancy between what parents have themselves experienced (or are experiencing) by way of sexual activity, and the code of sexual ethics they profess to their children. Psychotherapists have long detected more regret among women who were virgins at marriage for *not* having experienced premarital coitus than among those women who did experience it. The clinical observations of therapists have been upheld by the results of several investigations into the attitudes of married women toward various aspects of sexual expression.[26, 50, 179] These studies show that those women who have had premarital sexual intercourse are not sorry, and maintain they would repeat their behavior if they had it to do over again; however, they expect their daughters to conform to a more conservative ethic.[50, 179] Essentially the same findings have been reported in yet another investigation, in this instance of highly educated, influential upper middle-class men and women.[66]

The question naturally arises: why do these mothers behave in one way—feeling no regret about their premarital coitus, together with an assertion that they would repeat the behavior if they could turn back the clock—yet expect their daughters to behave in a contrary manner? The dynamics are rather complex, but the explanation lies primarily in the significant differences between men and women in their interpretation of the interrelationship between sexual attraction and emotional commitment.[108] Studies indicate that for a man, love follows a sexual attraction, while for a woman, sexual involvement follows romantic attachment.[53, 108, 109, 191] (As a rule, a girl must have a strong emotional attachment before she allows herself to become sexually involved; she must be convinced that it is she, a person, who is important to the relationship, not simply her sexual potentials.)[382] A recent investigation, for instance, demonstrated that girls enter a university with conservative sexual attitudes, then shift later in their academic life to more liberal ones, but *only* if they become engaged.[20] The liberalizing of their attitudes would appear an outgrowth of their emotional commitment, to which the engagement bears witness.

A mother, then, in her own premarital sexual experiences may have had strong feelings regarding the significance of emotional involvement as a precedent to sexual contact, but cannot accept the fact that her daughter also recognizes the import of this sequence. Furthermore, the mother, through having defied the sexual prohibitions of her own rearing by engaging in premarital coitus, may now carry a residual of repressed guilt. This guilt can break through and be projected onto her maturing daughter in the form of disapproval of any premarital sexual experience on the part of the girl. In addition, the mother cannot identify sufficiently with the daughter to appreciate the strength of the girl's feelings when she becomes emotionally attached to a young man. Neither can she accept the fact that her daughter has perhaps evolved a liberal sexual ethic of her own because of this commitment.

The disparity between a woman's past behavior and her present preachments tends to become perpetuated. The sexually restrictive admonishments through which she attempts to indoctrinate her daughter quite likely will be no more effective than they were in her generation. But the unfortunate consequence will be the same—generation after generation of women who tend to follow their emotional and sexual inclinations, but with concomitant guilt and shame, because they have violated the sexual ethic with which they were reared.

A further example of the often curious difference between attitude and behavior lies in the fact that many people in our culture, especially men, have difficulty entering into a warm, close, loving interchange with others. Little boys are often taught that to be tender and compassionate is to show characteristics of being a "sissy"; little girls are admonished that it is "forward" to be warmly responsive. To grow up in an environment that restricts positive emotional responses makes it likely that the individual will learn to express only negative emotions, such as anger and hostility. All the same, these people grow into adulthood with the abstract knowledge that some warm emotional exchanges are vital and expected in successful sexual interaction. But since they learned in their formative years to express only negative emotional responses, these people will actually instigate quarrels or fights with their sexual partner in order to express the only type of emotionality they understand. Men who have never learned how to express tenderness, or who are afraid to do so, will often ignore the woman with whom they are sexually involved, or make belittling remarks to her. These men *want* to demonstrate their commitment, but not knowing how to use the appropriate positive emotions, they use the only emotional expressions they are familiar with—the negative ones.

An adolescent form of the "princess-prostitute" syndrome, described in the section of this text dealing with sexual aberrations, is the "good girls don't, bad girls do" attitude of some youths. This attitude impels them toward intercourse with girls whom they do not care for, since they consider girls whom they respect "too good" to become involved in sexual activity.[271] However, because of their fondness for the "good girls" and their developing emotional closeness to them, the boys may become sexually aroused. As a more intimate relationship grows, sexual behavior may well progress in some cases to sexual intercourse. As a result, the young boy often loses respect for the "good girl" who in his eyes now has turned "bad," and he may quite likely terminate the relationship; or he may develop strong guilt feelings for seducing a "good girl."[271]

Patterns in feelings of guilt undergo a change over a period of time in both sexes, especially among the older unmarried groups. Clinicians have presented convincing arguments that many men are beset with considerably more guilt over sexual matters than women are. Their premise is that women, in nonmarital sex relationships especially, usually and understandably want reassurance that they are desired and respected for more than their sexual performance. Women also want assurance that their men will not "kiss and tell," and that they will maintain the same level of regard for them after coitus as before. A man, on the other hand, feels that as the instigator of the sex act, he is the "seducer," and that the responsibility for the girl's participation rests squarely upon his shoulders. To placate his own guilt or anxiety, therefore, he must feel either that there is love in the relationship, or that the girl is "bad." Furthermore, since he feels guilty about his "seduction" of the girl, he comes to regard her as the instigator of his guilt. He is then impelled to express his hostility and anger by quarreling or fighting with her, speaking to her in a degrading manner, or otherwise manifesting his rejection of her—the very girl who thought enough of him to share with him the most intimate of human experiences.

Women often accuse their husbands of showing affection toward them only when they have intercourse in mind; husbands deny this. What often happens is that the husband commences simply to show affection to his wife with no ulterior motive in mind. However, in the process of expressing affection, especially if his wife responds warmly, the husband may well become sexually excited. The wife then judges only in terms of the final outcome and not the initial intent of her husband.

Fortunately, both men and women can be taught to allow themselves the joy of experiencing close, warm, and loving relationships. If they have not acquired this knowledge through normal maturational processes, or through experience and observation, psychotherapy can help them gain insight into the immense value of manifestations of affection. When men and women recognize that free expression of affection is certainly nothing to fear, nor a barometer of weakness or effeminacy, all their human relationships, including the sexual one, will be much fuller and happier.

Men are considerably more upset by the extramarital affairs of their wives than women are by similar transgressions by their husbands; only 27% of all women would consider their husband's adultery sufficient grounds for seeking a divorce, while 51% of all men would regard infidelity on the part of their wives as being totally destructive of the marriage. Furthermore, women are less likely to demand virginity of their husbands at the time of marriage than men are to expect their brides to be virgins (23% of the former as compared with 40% of the latter).[179] The more highly educated man is less disturbed today than in the past if his bride is nonvirginal, although he is likely still to prefer that she be without previous sexual experience. Because both men and women tend to regard sexual conquests and experience as indications (however stereotyped) of masculinity in a man, many women prefer that the man be nonvirginal at marriage.[50]

Girls in their mid-teens begin to recognize that, in our society, the male is supposed to be strong and confident, and to offer security to his female. Not having the insight, tutelage, or experience to evaluate what constitutes genuine strength on the part of boy or man and, furthermore, feeling inadequate herself, the girl actually does not know what to look for by way of indicators of masculine strength, and may come to accept certain warped manifestations as qualities of manliness. These are the girls who are often impressed by the "tough guys"—the hellraiser who is defiant of rules and of the society that makes them; the leather-jacketed thug on his motorcycle; the school drop-out committed to tobacco, alcohol, and profanity, and to little else in life; the dragster who is as reckless of human life as he is of human sensibilities. These girls have no way of assessing such behavioral patterns as being attempts by the boys to mask the marked feelings of inferiority that overwhelm and threaten them. The very things, therefore, that a young girl wishes to avoid—inadequacy and weakness in a man—are what she is unwittingly courting when she looks to the "tough guy" as an ideal. An unfortunate by-product of this twisted set of values is that the "nice" boy who attempts to treat such a girl with kindness and honesty, but who has no need to prove his adequacy by the unacceptable acting-out behavior described above, is too often ignored, if not regarded with downright contempt by her.

Other factors enter into the emotional complexities of these girls. As mentioned earlier, they are crossing the threshold into physical maturity and feel inadequate to cope with the social and sexual problems it poses. Since many girls evaluate themselves as rather worthless and insufficient beings, the boys who behave decently and compassionately toward them cannot, they reason, have very good judgment; or if the boys offer their friendship so unselfishly, they must not be of much value themselves. It follows, according to these girls' rationale, that the boys who callously ignore or mistreat them are exhibiting good judgment, and are therefore the obviously strong masculine ones, the social or sexual worthies. Furthermore, these girls have normal sexual desires and wishes, but frequently feel guilty about them; and it ensues in their thinking that, in our society, guilt demands punishment. Therefore, by selecting one of the "tough guys," such a girl is able not only to satisfy her sexual desires but at the same time to assure her punishment because, unconsciously or otherwise, she realizes that, sooner or later, she will be mistreated or rejected by this unsavory boy. It is, incidentally, a widely recognized phenomenon among psychotherapists and marriage counselors that many women marry "problem" men— for example, alcoholics—because they have an unconscious need to be punished.

As mentioned earlier, sexual attitudes and behavior differ from one culture to another and within the same culture, the determinants being such factors as religious affiliation, educational levels, socio-economic strata, and decade of birth. One cultural or subcultural group may be so removed from another that the sexual attitudes and behavior of one may well seem perverted or absurd to the other. For example, college-educated men employed to take sex histories of men with very limited education may be overpowered at first by some of the sexual experiences of the latter—for example, one man's claim of having pre-marital coitus with 1000 women. On the other hand, men with grade-school education may view the oral-genital sexual behavior of the college-educated couple as being perverted and deserving of condemnation. As holds in most other cases of differences in both attitudes and behavior—whether religious, sexual, or racial—misunderstanding often could be removed and differences made more comprehensible if each group would trouble itself to become acquainted with individuals in the other group and their backgrounds.[180]

SEXUAL BEHAVIOR

Human sexuality ordinarily expresses itself in six ways: masturbation, nocturnal orgasms, heterosexual petting, homosexual relations, sexual contact with animals, and heterosexual intercourse.[170, 180]

Throughout this section, frequent reference is made to men and women according to their levels of educational achievement. For the sake of clarity, these distinctions are intended:

Grade school (low educational group)—eight years of schooling or less

High school (middle educational group)—nine to twelve years of schooling

College (high educational group)—thirteen or more years of schooling

MASTURBATION

The term *masturbation* is applied to any type of self-stimulation that produces erotic arousal.[180] It is a common sexual practice among both males and females in premarital, marital, and postmarital states. Boys and girls begin the practice at an early age, 13% of both sexes having masturbated by their tenth birthday.[179, 207]

Males. The incidence of masturbation to the point of orgasm among men (whether once or 1000 times) is generally fixed at about 95% of the total male population. The college group have the highest percentage (96%) of incidence; those who have only attended high school, second highest (95%); and those who only attended grade school, the lowest (89%).[26, 180] Slightly over two-thirds of all boys experience their first ejaculation through masturbation; about three-fourths learn how to masturbate from verbal or printed sources.[179]

On the average, adolescent boys masturbate about two and a half times a week, although a certain number (17%) masturbate from four to seven (or more) times a week. The incidence of masturbation in men progressively declines in postadolescent years, although it frequently continues on a sporadic basis throughout adult life.[137] About 70% of married American men who have graduated from college will masturbate occasionally (for 9% of their total sexual outlet), although the incidence is considerably lower in the married male grade-school group (29%) and in the married high-school group (42%). Approximately 25% of the married men above the age of 60 who are capable of satisfactory coitus also masturbate.[180, 285]

Genital manipulation is by far the most common technique of masturbation among men (95%). In 72% of the cases, fantasy always accompanies masturbation; in another 17%, fantasy is only occasionally coupled with it.[179]

Masturbation among men occurs most frequently among religiously inactive Protestants, and least among orthodox Jews and devout Roman Catholics.[180]

Females. Masturbation ranks second only to heterosexual petting among the erotic activities of unmarried young women (37% to 85% of total sexual outlet, depending upon the subcultural group), and second after coition among married women (constituting about 10% of their total sexual outlet). Among previously married women, masturbation accounts for 13% to 44% of total outlet, depending once more upon the subcultural group. Of all types of sexual activity among women, however, masturbation ranks first as the most successful method of reaching orgasm—in 95% of its incidence, a climax is reached. Furthermore, women reach orgasm more quickly through masturbation than through any other sexual technique (75% in under four minutes).[179]

From 50% to 80% of all women masturbate at one time or another, the variance in figures resulting from differences in the results of several investigations into the subject. The Kinsey group reported that 34% of the women who never went past grade school, 59% of the women who had attended high school but not college, and 63% of the female college graduates masturbate. Their range of frequency is from once or twice a lifetime to 100 orgasms an hour. Of those women who masturbate to the point of orgasm, however, there is a striking similarity in frequency, regardless of age or marital status: once every two to four weeks.[170]

Most women (57%) accidentally discover how to masturbate by exploring their own genitals. Another 40% learn techniques of autoeroticism through verbal or printed sources.[179]

In contrast to men, who show a decline in the frequency of masturbation after their teens, the active incidence of self-stimulation to orgasm among women increases up to middle age, after which time its frequency becomes fairly constant.[179] Of unmarried women between fifty and seventy years of age, 59% admit to autoeroticism as compared with 30% of married women in this same age group.[331]

The large majority of women (84%) who stimulate themselves use genital manipulation as the technique, while a few others employ thigh pressure (10%), muscular tension (5%), or simply fantasy unattended by physical stimulation (2%). Fantasy is an invariable accompaniment to masturbation for half the women who stimulate themselves, but only an occasional one for a few others (14%).[179]

Among those women who had never masturbated to orgasm before marriage, about one-third (31% to 37%) failed to reach orgasm during coitus the first year of marriage, while of those who had masturbated to orgasm, only 13% to 16% failed to have coital orgasm the first year.[179]

Religious background influences the frequency of masturbation. The more devout the religious commitment, the lower the incidence of autoeroticism is.[179]

NOCTURNAL ORGASMS

It has long been recognized that men have nocturnal emissions or "wet dreams." And while women obviously cannot have nocturnal emissions, it is nonetheless true that they too have erotic dreams, frequently culminating in orgasm, although, curiously, this type of sexual outlet is persistently ignored in studies of female sexuality. (For both men and women, however, sexual dreams often have a distressing way of stopping just short of orgasm.)[179]

Males. Almost 100% of men have erotic dreams, and almost 85% of them have had dreams that culminate in orgasm. Erotic dreams occur most frequently to young men in their teens and twenties, but approximately 50% of all married men continue to have nocturnal emissions. This type of sexual expression constitutes 5% to 12% of the total sexual outlet for single men, 3% to 5% of the total outlet for married men, and from 4% to 6% for the previously married. Because married men of all ages have a much greater opportunity for release of sexual tension than single men do, the frequency of nocturnal emission among the married is only about two-thirds that of single men.[179, 180]

The incidence of nocturnal emission is considerably higher among college youths than among less educated groups, probably because college men do more petting that is not followed by orgasm, and their sexual tensions are therefore more often at a high pitch at bedtime. Over 99% of college men have sexual dreams to orgasm at some time during their lives; but only 85% of those who merely attended high school, and 75% whose education ended at grade school have nocturnal emissions.[179] This form of sexual outlet is unique in that it is beyond the individual's conscious control. A man's religious convictions, therefore, bear little relationship to the incidence of his experiencing nocturnal emission.

Females. As many as 70% of all women have had dreams of sexual content, although only about half this group have had dreams that culminated in orgasm.[179] Because there is no physical evidence afterwards, in contrast to men, that an orgasm has occurred, there is some question concerning the accuracy of data showing that 37% of all women actually dream to orgasm. However, there is no doubt in the minds of the women who have the dreams that orgasm has occurred.

The incidence of sexual dreams to orgasm reaches a peak when a woman is in her forties. There is an average of three or four such dreams a year for women, married or single, in all age groups. Over one-fourth of married women (28%) and more than one-third of those previously married (38%) have dreams to orgasm. These dreams constitute 2% to 4% of the total release from sexual tension for single girls, 1% to 3% for married women, and among the previously married, 4% to 14%.[179]

There is no correlation between frequency of nocturnal dreams to orgasm and a woman's religious or educational background, although fewer women of devout religious convictions than those of less serious commitment to a religion ever have such dreams.[179]

HETEROSEXUAL PETTING

The sexual outlet termed *heterosexual petting* involves conscious, sexually oriented physical contact between persons of opposite sex that does not involve actual coitus.[179] In the context of the present discussion, the significance of petting as a means of sexual expression will be limited to premarital petting, since petting in marriage is assumed to be a foreplay to sexual intercourse, or an outlet chosen by the partners in preference to coition as a means of achieving orgasm.

Petting is by no means limited to human beings, since many lower animals employ varying forms of it both before and after copulation. The significance of petting in relation to coitus for both man and lower animals is widely recognized. Petting is frequently practiced, and has a distinct value: it is useful not only as an arousal technique, but as a means of achieving orgasm, especially during the years before marriage.

Males. There is some increase in the incidence of petting among men born after 1910 as compared with those born before then, but the increase is slight in contrast to the sharp rise in its occurrence among women.

By the age of fifteen, 57% of all boys have done some petting; by eighteen, 84% have petted, and by twenty-five, 89%. Almost all of these incidents involve erotic arousal, but only about a third of these youths ever become involved in petting to orgasm.[179, 180]

The often significant differences in the percentages of men who engage in a particular petting practice are directly related to the social, economic, and educational backgrounds of the boys and men sampled. There also exists a distinct correlation between the frequency of petting and educational attainments. Those men with the lowest education pet the least; men of the middle group are next; and the men of the high educational group pet most of all. The frequency with which men pet to orgasm can be as high as seven times (or more) a week, but the average incidence is three to five times a year. About a quarter of all men have five or fewer petting partners during their lifetimes, while 37% have twenty-one or more partners.[26, 179, 180]

The range of petting practices is wide. Of the total male population, almost 100% engage in simple kissing; 55% to 87% engage in deep kissing; 78% to 99% in manual manipulation of the girl's breast; mouth-breast contact, 36% to 93%; manual manipulation of the girl's genitalia, 79% to 92%; and 9% to 18% of unmarried youths, in contrast to 4% to 60% of married men, orally stimulate their partner's genitalia. The two figures cited in each instance refer to men at the two extremes of educational levels.[179, 180]

Educational achievement correlates significantly with the occurrence of men's petting to orgasm. According to the levels of schooling reached, the lowest educational group achieve a climax through petting only 16% of the time, while the second group do so 32% of the time, and 61% of the petting in the college-level group culminates in orgasm.[26, 179, 180]

Females. Almost 100% of all women have had some sort of petting experience prior to their marriages, and 90% of the entire female population, whether or not they ever marry, engage in petting at one time or another. By the age of thirty-five, 80% of those women born before 1900 had had petting experience; of those born between 1900 and 1909, 91% had petted; and of those born between 1910 and 1919, 98% had petted. The increase in percentages would seem to be an indication of the "sex revolution" which took place in the 1920s; women born after the turn of the century gradually, but steadfastly, became less sexually inhibited.[179, 180]

Simple kissing is engaged in at one time or another by nearly all women at all educational levels; more sophisticated methods of petting, however, are directly related to educational achievement, decade of birth, and incidence and frequency of coitus. The more advanced the level of education, the more liberal the girl is in the types of petting she engages in. Those women born after 1909 are more liberal in their petting practices than those born before 1910; and, as would be expected, frequency of coitus is directly related to freedom in petting. Furthermore, as one would also expect, at all educational levels, the more sophisticated and liberal the method of petting, the smaller the percentage of women who have participated becomes.

The type of petting that has been accepted more slowly and reluctantly than others, because of social taboos, is oral-genital contact.

This form of sexual stimulation, however, is apparently rather widely accepted as an erotic outlet — and a normal, healthy one — by the majority in the higher socioeducational groups. About 65% of the younger women at the upper educational levels who have had premarital coital experience more than twenty-five times have had their genitals stimulated orally prior to marriage; 62% of these same women have orally stimulated the genitals of their partners.[179, 180]

Between the ages of twenty-one and twenty-five, 31% of all women have established a pattern of regular participation in premarital petting to orgasm. The average occurrence in the age bracket of fifteen to fifty-five is four to six orgasmic responses through petting a year, although the frequency may be as high as seven to ten times a week. In the sixteen- to twenty-five-year-old age group, petting affords as much as 18% of women's total sexual outlet before marriage; it consistently provides a higher percentage of the total sexual outlet for women of all ages than it does for men in comparable age groups. More than a half of all women indulge in premarital petting for a period of six years or more. The number of partners with whom women engage in petting varies from one only (10%) to twenty-one or more (19%). In excess of 33% of all women have experienced premarital petting with more than ten men.[26, 179, 180]

In petting, as in most other practices in the sphere of sexual expression, women are influenced significantly by religious factors; the more pronounced the commitment to religious convictions, the more restricted the sexual behavior is. Interestingly, religion ultimately has little influence, one way or the other, on frequency of petting to orgasm, even among the most religiously devout. Once these devout women achieve orgasm through petting, they engage in such activity as often as less devout women.[26, 179] The rationale quite often is that petting allows a woman sexual gratification without depriving her of her virginity, a condition highly prized by many women.

HOMOSEXUAL RELATIONS

The term *homosexual relations* refers to the use of a partner of the same sex for sexual gratification. As a mode of sexual behavior in our society, it is greatly deplored, although sanctions against it are considerably more stringent for men than for women. In New York, for example, in a particular ten-year period of time, only one woman was convicted of "homosexual sodomy," while over 700 men were found guilty on the same charge.[179] Homosexual contact among infrahuman mammals is found among both males and females. Animal homosexuality is considerably more common than is popularly believed.[136]

Males. It is generally accepted by sexologists that about 4% of all white men are exclusively homosexual all their sexual lives, 8% are exclusively homosexual for at least three years between the ages of sixteen and fifty-five, and 37% have experienced at least some form of overt homosexuality to the point of orgasm.[180] While these data apply to white men, it has been estimated that the percentages are equally pertinent to the American Negro male population.[85]

Educational levels bear a different relationship to the incidence of homosexuality than they do to most other avenues of sexual expression.[180]

Homosexual Experience Among Men to Point of Orgasm

Educational Level	Single, to 35 years of age	Total male population
Grade School	50%	27%
High School	58%	39%
College	47%	34%

While the incidence of homosexuality among single men in the three educational groups is not significantly different, there is a great difference among the groups in the percentages of their total sexual outlet that homosexual practices constitute.[180]

Homosexuality Among Single Men Constituting Total Sexual Outlet

Educational Level	16-20 years old	21-25 years old	26-30 years old
Grade School	6.85%	8.06%	14.04%
High School	10.81%	16.31%	25.95%
College	2.43%	3.72%	8.82%

For all single men there is a gradual increase before the age of forty in the percentage of total sexual outlet that homosexuality affords, progressing from 5% to 22%. For married men, homosexuality represents less than 1% of the total outlet. For the previously married, there is also a gradual increase in total outlet, growing from 9% to 26%.

Some men who engage in homosexual practices are rather promiscuous: although 51% of them have only one or two sexual partners, 22% have over ten partners.

Generally speaking, the strength of the individual's religious convictions influences both the incidence and frequency of homosexual contacts; the more intense the commitment to religion, the less homosexual activity there is. The incidence is slightly higher among Catholic men than among the other two religious groups, the incidence among Jewish men falling behind that among Protestants.[180]

Females. The incidence of homosexuality appears to be somewhat less among women than it is among men; the occurrence of both exclusive and partial homosexuality among women is only two-thirds of that among men.[85]

The findings of some investigations indicate that as many as 50% of all women during their sexual life have harbored "intense feelings" for another woman or women. Most sexologists, however, agree with the more conservative conclusions of the Kinsey investigation: that 28% of women (compared with 50% of men) have experienced some sort of homosexual response.[93, 179, 180] Only about 1% to 3% of the female population between the ages of twenty and thirty-five are exclusively homosexual, although an additional 2% to 6% in this age bracket are "more or less exclusively homosexual" (meaning that, very rarely, there may be a heterosexual contact). Compared with 37% of all men, only 13% of all women have had homosexual contact to the point of orgasm. In homosexual relationships, then, twice as many men as women experience some sort of sexual response short of orgasm, while three times as many men as women respond to orgasm.[179]

In contrast to other types of sexual outlet, there is apparently no more female homosexuality (also called *lesbianism*) among those women born after 1900 than among those born earlier. The incidence of lesbianism at various educational levels differs, to be sure, but the figures do not correlate with those pertaining to male homosexuality. The percentages of women who, by the age of thirty, have experienced homosexual contact to the point of orgasm are these: those educated to the level of grade school, 6%; high school, 5%; and college, 10% (14% for women having attended graduate school). In the early years of active homosexuality, women in the two lower educational groups have a higher frequency of orgasm than college women do; but the differences subsequently disappear, and the frequency of orgasm then averages once in two or three weeks for women of all three educational levels.[179]

Female homosexuality is largely confined to single women and, to a lesser extent, to the previously married. The incidence, as well as frequency, of lesbian contact is negligible among married women. Although 19% of the total female population have had active homosexual contact by the age of forty, when the factor of marital status is introduced, this pattern of active homosexual incidence emerges in the same age group: 24% of the women who have never been married, 9% of the previously married, and only 3% of the married women.[179]

By the age of twenty, only 4% of the total female population have had orgasmic response through lesbian contacts; by thirty-five, the incidence of orgasmic response through homosexual outlets in the total female population has risen to 11%. The figure is 13% among women in their mid-forties. Of those women who have homosexual associations, from one-half to two-thirds experience orgasm at least occasionally.[179]

Homosexual activity does not last long for women. About one-third have fewer than ten experiences; for many, there has been only one or two. The homosexual experiences of half the women last for a total period of one year or less, while the activity of another quarter is spread over two to three years. Half the women (51%) involved in homosexual activity limit their experience to a single partner, another 20% have only two partners, and only 4% have ten or more partners (compared with 22% of the men who have ten or more partners).[179, 180]

Of those women who have the most extensive homosexual experience, only 20% express definite regret. Almost 90% of all women with homosexual experience themselves declare they would keep as a friend any woman with a history of lesbianism; they are less accepting (74%) of male friends with a history of homosexuality.[179]

In all three religious groups, the more devout adherents had less homosexual contact to the point of orgasm than the nondevout. Among women (as well as among men) only nominally affiliated with the Catholic Church, 25% have experienced homosexual contact to orgasm, while 5% of devout Catholic women have had this experience. Among Protestants and Jews, a similar correlation exists between casual or serious religious affiliation and homosexual experience.[179]

SEXUAL CONTACT WITH ANIMALS

The taboo against sexual relations with animals is well established in the Old Testament and in the Talmud. Sexual contact between humans and infrahumans (which is also called *bestiality*) has occurred since early civilization, but such behavior is highly abhorrent to most people who have not had a similar experience. The extent of such sexual activity among either men or women is extremely small, and the significance in studying it lies in its social impact rather than in its importance as a sexual outlet.[179]

Males. As would be expected, male contact with animals, whenever it exists, is found primarily among boys reared on farms. Between 40% and 50% of all farm boys have some sexual contact with animals, but only 17% experience orgasm as a result of animal contact. About twice as many men (32%) as women (16%) are erotically aroused by seeing animals in copulation. About 15% of rural males of only grade-school achievement have some sexual experience with animals to the point of orgasm, but there is an increase to 20% of the rural high-school group, and to about 27% of the rural males who are college-educated.

Sexual contacts with animals vary in frequency from once or twice a lifetime to as high as eight times a week for some adolescent rural boys; the average for those involved is about two times a week. The period of time over which these contacts occur is ordinarily limited to two or three years; most sexual contact with animals occurs in preadolescence before the boy is capable of orgasm. Sexual contact with animals represents considerably less than 1% of the total sexual outlet for men in both urban and rural communities.[179, 180]

City boys have limited sexual experience with animals. Their contacts are customarily with household pets, and with animals on a farm where they might visit during vacations.[180]

Females. An extremely low percentage of the total female population have ever had any sort of sexual contact with animals. About 1.5% of women have had sexual contact with animals during preadolescence (usually as a result of accidental physical contact with a household pet), and only 3.6% of the female sample have had sexual contact with animals after their adolescent years. Of those sexually precocious women who were able to have orgasms prior to adolescence, 1.7% experienced their first orgasm in animal contact.

Only about 16% of Kinsey's total female sample had ever been erotically aroused by witnessing coitus between animals. Out of the entire 5940 women in Kinsey's sample, twenty-nine had caused dogs or cats to stimulate their vulval area orally, and two had had coitus with dogs. In only twenty-five of these histories had women recorded being brought to orgasm by sexual contact with animals, and the method was primarily oral stimulation of their genitals. Of those women who engaged in bestiality, half had only a single experience, and a fourth had six or more contacts.[179]

HETEROSEXUAL INTERCOURSE

The average man or woman is more interested in coitus with a member of the opposite sex than in any other type of sexual outlet, although other methods of outlet are significant in the sexual lives of both men and women. Ordinarily, heterosexual intercourse is thought of in relationship to marriage, but premarital, extramarital, and postmarital heterosexual coitions are also to be considered in analyzing this type of sexual outlet.

Premarital Heterosexual Intercourse. The term *premarital hetero-sexual intercourse* is used to indicate that at least one of the heterosexual partners is single and has not been previously married. In our culture this act usually involves two single persons, although the second person may, of course, be married.[100]

Males. In the American culture, men are generally accorded considerably more latitude in sexual expression than women are; premarital sexual intercourse is the most controversial of these sexual outlets, and is the one most often considered in discussions concerning the double standard of morality.

At some time or another before they are married, 98% of men who have attended only grade school, 84% of men who have attended high school only, and 67% of men with college education will have sexual intercourse. The decade in which they were born appears to have little or no correlation with the frequency of premarital coitus among men, in contrast to the rather sharp differences found in the correlations between birthdate and frequency among women.[179, 180]

Between the ages of sixteen and twenty, the grade-school group has seven times the frequency of sexual intercourse that the college group has. Furthermore, this disparity in coital frequency lessens only slightly between the groups of older single men of the same educational levels. Depending upon their ages, the college group obtains from 4% to 21% of its total premarital sexual outlet from coitus; the high-school group, from 26% to 54%; and the grade-school group, from 40% to 68%. Also, unmarried college men commonly engage in coitus for the first time at an age five or six years older than that of the unmarried men of lower educational levels when *they* first experience coition.

The correlation between premarital intercourse with prostitutes and educational level follows the same trend. Of single men at the age of twenty-five, 74% of the grade-school group, 54% of the high-school group, and 28% of the college group have had coitus with prostitutes. The total sexual outlet sought from prostitutes by single men rises, between the ages of sixteen and forty, from 6% to 23% for the grade-school group, from 3% to 11% for the high-school group, and from less than 1% to 3% for the college group. Furthermore, sexual intercourse with any woman, prostitute or otherwise, never accounts for more than 21% of the total sexual outlet of single college men, whereas coitus may constitute as much as 68% of the total sexual outlet for single men in the lower educational groups.[180]

Among unmarried men who have coitus regularly, frequency is at its maximum during early adolescence, averaging about two contacts a week; among males in their teens and twenties, the average is about 1.4 times a week, dropping to a lesser frequency among older groups of unmarried men. The lowest education group maintains a level of two to four coitions a week—which incidentally equals the average incidence of coition among married men in the same age bracket.

The point should be made that the incidence of premarital sexual intercourse among men ranges from a single contact to such sexual activity as twenty-five or more coitions a week (the latter pattern sometimes persisting for as long as five years or more). Many men, particularly those at the upper end of the social-educational scale, limit their premarital coition to one girl—often the girl they eventually marry; other men, particularly at the lower end of the social-educational scale, may copulate with as many as several hundred girls.[180]

A few single men have sexual intercourse with older women—single, married, or divorced. However, almost all the coital experiences of single men are with single women, usually of their own age or slightly younger.[180] Studies have shown that boys of a higher social stratum often sexually exploit girls of a lower social stratum, but that, in college populations, young men and women will customarily have their sexual experiences with persons of an equal social class.[100, 163]

Religion, at all social-educational levels, has a direct relationship among men to the incidence and frequency of premarital sexual intercourse. Of Catholics and Protestants, there is much less premarital coitus among the devoutly religious than among the less devout. Interestingly, inactive Jews have less premarital coitus than do the orthodox Jews (although the incidence of experience does not differ greatly except among early pubescents up to the age of fifteen years). Kinsey speculated that this discrepancy could be a result of the strong condemnation with which the Jewish faith views masturbation; the religiously active Jew possibly feels less guilt over premarital coitus than over masturbation.[180]

Females. Kinsey drew his conclusions about premarital coition among women from data concerned only with sexual activity after early pubescence (about 10 years of age). Any earlier coital experiences among girls would not, therefore, have appeared in his findings. In any event, most sexual behavior during these early years is merely experimentation and sex play—although, of course, there are exceptions.

Prior to marriage, almost 50% of all women have experienced coitus and 67% have experienced orgasm. However, only about 17% of the orgasms that women experience result from coition, which lags far behind masturbation as unmarried women's primary source of sexual outlet. Girls younger than sixteen have only 6% of their total orgasmic experience from premarital coitus; girls between sixteen and twenty, 15%; and those still unmarried in their early twenties, 26%. After the early twenties, coition becomes more important to single women as a source of orgasm than petting is, and it is by this time not far behind masturbation as such a source.

The high percentage of women who engage in premarital coitus surprises and disturbs many people. It should be pointed out, however, that about half the single women who are coitally active have sexual intercourse only with the men they eventually marry; furthermore, most of women's premarital coition takes place only the year or two just preceding marriage. About 50% of the women who marry by the age of twenty have premarital sexual intercourse; the same percentage holds for those who marry between twenty-one and twenty-five. Of those women who marry between the ages of twenty-six and thirty, however, between 40% and 66% have experienced coition. Except for the girls who marry quite young, premarital coitus during the early teens is relatively rare; only 3% of all girls have premarital coition by the age of fifteen. The important conclusion to be drawn from these data is that females who marry at an early age will experience any premarital coition earlier than women who marry at a later age. This fact is significant in the consideration of premarital coital activity at the various educational levels, which will be discussed later.[179]

As is true with other types of premarital sexual activity, the frequency of premarital coitus does not reach its peak until the women involved are in their late twenties, after which it remains remarkably regular. Of those single girls under the age of twenty who engage in coition, sexual intercourse occurs on an average of once every five or ten weeks, while the frequency is about once every three weeks among older single girls. The frequency of premarital coitus among women as a group and individually often varies considerably. About 20% of the group who experience premarital coition have coitus as often as seven times a week (7% having it fourteen times in the same period), but there are usually intervals of complete (or relatively complete) sexual inactivity between the sexually active times.[179]

Some girls who have premarital intercourse are capable of multiple orgasms from the very beginning of their coital experience. About 14% regularly experience multiple orgasms, and a vast majority have a similar capacity.[179, 215, 217, 370]

Of all women who engage in premarital coitus (whether or not they eventually marry), 53% have a single partner, 34% have two to five partners, and only 13% have six or more partners. Of married women who had premarital coitus, 87% had at least some of their coital experience with the men they eventually married, and 46% only with their future husbands. Only 13% of these women had premarital coitus with men other than their future husbands, but never with the latter.

The age at which marriage occurs has a significant impact on the incidence of premarital coition at the various education levels. At first glance, Kinsey's findings would lead one to believe that single college girls are much more coitally active than girls of the two lower educational groups: the data show that 60% of the girls who have gone to college, 47% of the girls who have finished high school only, and 30% of those girls who have not gone beyond grade school have premarital coitus. (These statistics, incidentally, stand in striking contrast to those concerning men, wherein 67% of men with college education and 98% of those with only grade-school education were found to have had sexual intercourse prior to marriage.) Despite the seemingly high incidence of premarital coition among college girls, certain facts should be borne in mind: because girls who are schooled only to grade-school or high-school level tend to marry at a considerably earlier age than college girls, they obviously have fewer prenuptial years in which to form attachments that might lead to sexual intercourse. As Kinsey pointed out, among women within a given age group *after* the age of twenty, no matter what the educational background, coital experience before marriage is about equal.

The lower educational groups begin their coital experience at an earlier age than girls with more education do; between the ages of sixteen and twenty, 38% of the grade-school group, 32% of the high-school group, and about 18% of the college group have premarital sexual intercourse. The relationship between the *frequency* with which girls have coitus and their educational level is not as consistent as is the relationship between the *incidence* of premarital coitus in the female population and educational level.[179]

It was pointed out earlier that a rather noticeable change occurred in women's sexual behavior about 1920, affecting almost every aspect of their sexual lives. Two and a half times as many of the women born between 1900 and 1910 had sexual intercourse before marriage as women born before 1900 (36% as compared with 14%). Since that time the increase has leveled off onto a fairly consistent plateau. It is of interest to note that despite the increase in premarital coital *incidence* among women born in the decades mentioned above, the percentage of women who attained orgasm coitally before marriage remains about

the same—50% at the age of twenty, 75% by the age of thirty-five—
no matter which generation is under consideration. The *frequency* of
premarital coital experience has also remained remarkably consistent
for women of all generations.[179]

With regard to the site chosen for their premarital coition, over
half (58%) the women so involved have coitus at least some of the
time in their parents' home. Furthermore, while a small percentage of
girls attending college and living away from home have coition in the
college town, by far the greater number have it in their home towns
during visits and vacations. Almost half (48%) have some part of
their coital experiences in their partner's home, 40% have some part
in a hotel or in similar accommodations, and 41% have a portion of
their total experiences in an automobile. Kinsey found a correlation between date of birth and site of premarital coition; automobiles, for instance, doubled in popularity as a site over the thirty-year period
covered by his sampling.[179]

Premarital coital experience for women is directly related to their
degree of involvement in religion, whether Catholicism, Judaism, or
Protestantism; women who are the least active religiously engage the
most in premarital sexual intercourse, the moderately devout next most,
and the devout the least of all. By the age of thirty-five, slightly over
60% of the Protestant and Jewish single women who are inactive in
their churches or synagogues have had premarital coitus, as compared
with 55% of the inactive Catholic women. Of the single devout Protestant women of the same age, about 30% have had premarital coitus,
while 25% of devout Catholic and moderate Jewish women (no figures
on orthodox) have had the experience.[179] Of couples who attend church
regularly, 28% have engaged in premarital coitus; the percentage increases to 48% when one of the couple is a regular churchgoer, the
other not, and to 61% when neither of the pair attends church regularly.[178]

Marital Heterosexual Intercourse. According to the legal and moral
codes of our Anglo-American culture, coitus between husband and
wife is the one totally approved type of sexual activity (excepting, of
course, erotic dreams).[180] It is the sexual outlet most frequently utilized
by married couples; yet, as a conservative estimate, sexual relationships
in about one-third of all marriages are somewhat inadequate.[26, 50, 131] One
reason for marital problems stemming from the sexual relationship may
be that too much is expected of sex. Both the glories and the pitfalls of
sexual intercourse have been part of the preachments heard by almost
every man and woman. The negative aspects of sex (such as feelings
of guilt, and fear of inadequacy or rejection) are expected to be dis-

pelled as the groom carries the bride across the threshold of the bed-room. About 90% of husbands and 74% of wives cross that threshold with attitudes of eager anticipation; the remaining husbands and wives enter their marital chambers with attitudes of disgust, aversion, or in-difference toward sexual relations.[50] Of all married couples who stated that sex was about as important in marriage as they had anticipated, two-thirds rated their marriage as "very happy," whereas one-third rated their marriage as "average" or "less than average" in happiness.[26] Even from these very few examples, it can be seen that marital coition is affected by manifold emotional and psychological attitudes. The im-pact on marriage of these attitudes and resulting behavior is observed constantly by marriage counselors.

Males. Only an exceedingly small number of married men do not participate, at least occasionally, in marital coitus; even among hus-bands in their late fifties, only 6% refrain from marital intercourse. These statements, of course, do not mean that marital sexual activity is confined to marital coitus; actually, marital intercourse provides only 85% of the total sexual outlet for married men, the remaining 15% being derived from masturbation, nocturnal emissions, petting, homo-sexual activity, extramarital coitus, and, in some rural areas, animal contact.[180]

Many may be surprised to learn that about half the sexual outlets of the entire male population are socially disapproved, and, to a large extent, are illegal and punishable by law. Only 60% of the American male population are married at any one time, and between adolescence and old age, each 100 men average 231 orgasms a week; correcting for the increased incidence of coition and total sexual outlet in mar-riage, one is led to conclude that only 106 orgasms a week per 100 men are from marital coitus (45.9% of their total sexual outlet). If 5% of the total outlet is accounted for in nocturnal emissions, then approximately 50% of men's total sexual outlet is obtained through illegal or disapproved sources.[180]

An interesting contrast in incidence of marital intercourse in re-lation to total outlet for men at the various educational levels is pre-sented in Kinsey's investigations. In the lower educational groups, about 80% of the total outlet in the early years of marriage is pro-vided by marital coitus, and the incidence for this group increases to 90% as the marriages continue. For the college-educated man, marital coitus provides 85% of the total outlet during the early part of mar-riage, but by the time he reaches the age of fifty-five, only 62% of his total sexual outlet is provided by marital coitus.[180] The assumption is that these college-educated men have reevaluated the moral restraints placed on them during their early life and have found them to be less constrictive and threatening than they formerly were. These men then come to the conclusion that they should have the sexual experiences they missed earlier in their lives. However, it should be emphasized that half the remaining 38% of their total sexual activity aside from marital coitus is not with another woman (or man), but is in the solitary act of masturbation and through nocturnal emissions.[180]

The frequency of marital coitus decreases with age, dropping from an average of 3.9 times per week during the teens to 2.9 at the age of thirty, 1.8 at the age of fifty, and 0.9 at the age of sixty. If a man reaches pubescence as early as the age of ten or eleven, and marries between the ages of sixteen and twenty, he averages five to seven orgasms a week; if he reaches pubescence at fifteen or later, and marries between sixteen and twenty, his average is slightly over three orgasms a week.[180]

The sex drive is somewhat greater in men than in women, especially during the early years of marriage, although, curiously, each sex tends to overestimate the drive of the other.[50] One serious problem arises from this misjudgment: if their sex needs differ sharply, a husband and wife may work out some sort of compromise in the frequency of their sexual activity that, unfortunately, does not meet the needs of either.[26]

Petting in marriage is usually considered to be only an introduction to sexual intercourse, although every method of arousal known to man has been made a part of the erotic repertory of marriage. Educational achievement exerts considerable influence on attitudes towards precoital stimulation. About half the total population, especially those with less education, are uninterested in prolonging the sexual act; they want to proceed with coition as quickly as possible and to achieve orgasm in the shortest period of time. The man with only a low level of education may limit his precoital activity to a simple kiss without causing any upset to his wife; similar perfunctory behavior on the part of the college-educated husband, however, would be interpreted by his wife as rejection or a lack of interest. The average college-educated husband will spend from five to fifteen minutes—sometimes an hour or more—in precoital petting. Once coitus is under way, he will attempt, more often than a man of lower education, to delay orgasm (although three-fourths of the total male population reach orgasm within two minutes). About 90% of college-educated men prefer to have intercourse in the nude, but only one-half as many of the grade-school group have ever had intercourse without being clothed. Because college-educated men are capable of a higher level of abstraction than are men with only grade-school and high-school educations, they are also more excited by external erotic stimulation. Consequently, they prefer to have intercourse in a lighted room where they can observe the nude body of the partner and the act of coition itself.[180]

Because marital coitus (again, excepting nocturnal emissions and orgasms) is the only sexual outlet totally sanctioned by all religious groups, one would expect the frequency of marital coition to be greater among the religiously devout than among the religiously inactive—or that, at the very least, there should be no differences in frequency between the two groups. The frequencies of marital intercourse, however, are lower among religiously active Protestants than among inactive Protestants. (Insufficient data on Catholic and Jewish groups prevent similar comparisons.) It is difficult to escape the conclusion that the severity of early religious training of devout Protestants carries over into marriage and continues to inhibit sexual expression, despite the couples' conscious acceptance of the "rightness" of marital coitus.[180]

Marital coitus among older men occurs considerably more frequently than is commonly realized.[14, 180, 254, 282, 285] About three-fourths (73%) of all men between the ages of sixty-five and sixty-nine experience satisfactory coitus, as do about 60% of the men between the ages of seventy and seventy-four, and 48% of the men between the ages of seventy-five and ninety-two. [14, 254, 285, 366] The fact is interesting that elderly physicians seem to have one of the highest rates of impotency, while elderly clergymen, as a group, have one of the lowest impotency ratings.[285] Seven out of ten healthy married couples who are sixty years of age or older are sexually active, and the consistent clinical observation is that of both men and women, the ones with the strongest sex drive during youth retain the greatest sex drive and virility in old age.[198, 254, 282] Furthermore, another means of retaining vigorous sexual capacity is a consistent pattern of sexual intercourse through the years of marriage.[215] Once interest is allowed to wane, it is difficult to rekindle.

Studies of older men show that frequency of marital intercourse ranges from one to four times a month, with about 25% engaging in coitus four times a month.[285] Even the 25% of older men whose sexual potency is unsatisfactory report that they engage in sexual intercourse three or four times a month.[366] Over 60% of men seventy-five or older report having occasional morning erections, and 17% report that the condition recurs frequently.[284] It has generally been found that, among older people, Negroes are more sexually active than whites, and persons from low socioeconomic levels are more sexually active than those from higher socioeconomic levels.[254, 285]

The sexual drive of older people generally follows their overall pattern of health and physical performance. Secretion of the male sex hormone androgen decreases from fifty-five units per twenty-four hours when a man is thirty years of age to about eight units during the same period at the age of sixty; the secretion remains fairly constant thereafter. From the age of forty, women begin to experience a sharp decrease in the secretion of estrogen, a decrease which continues gradually for the remainder of their lives.[198, 282] However, over 90% of the older men studied reported that they had no physical disability that interfered with sexual frequency.[366] The factors that most often deter sexual activity in older men are such psychological agents as feelings of shame and guilt for having sexual needs and drives at their age, and the erroneous notion that older men are naturally unable to perform sexually.

Females. Practically all married women participate in sexual intercourse, although there is a gradual decline in frequency between the first two years of marriage and old age. Men, too, it will be remembered, experience marital coitus less frequently in later years of life, but the decline among women is somewhat steeper than among males. Kinsey showed that at the age of fifty, 97% of men and 93% of women are still having coitus; at the age of sixty, the percentages are 94% for men and 84% for women.[179, 180] Curiously, marital coition is the only form of sexual outlet among women that undergoes such a decline with advancing age.[179]

For women who marry in their late teens, the average (median) frequency of marital coitus is nearly three (2.8) times a week in the early years of marriage, 2.2 a week at the age of thirty, 1.5 a week at the age of forty, once a week at the age of fifty, and once every twelve days (0.6) at the age of sixty. About 14% of all married women have marital intercourse seven or more times a week, although the percentage of wives involved in such frequency drops to 5% at the age of thirty, and to 3% by the age of forty. This decline in frequency is rather puzzling in light of Kinsey's findings that women reach their peak of sexual desire between the ages of thirty-one and forty. However, since the peak of men's sexual drive is reached between the late teens and the age of twenty-five, and thereafter shows a decline, it must be assumed that the aging of men rather than women's loss of sexual interest causes the decrease in marital coital frequency.[14, 179] During the first year of marriage, 75% of all women attain orgasm at least once during coitus; the percentage gradually increases to 90% after twenty years of marriage.[179]

It should be remembered that the decline in frequency of marital coitus after the first two years of marriage does not mean that there is necessarily a decline in interest in other forms of sexual activity. The incidence of female masturbation and nocturnal dreams involving orgasm increases after marriage, and then remains fairly steady at its maximum level until wives become sixty years of age or even older. Between the ages of twenty-one and twenty-five, 89% of a married woman's total sexual outlet is derived from marital coition. After the age of twenty-five there is a gradual but consistent decline, so that by the time a woman reaches the age of seventy, only 72% of her total sexual outlet is provided by marital coitus.[179]

There is little evidence that aging produces any decline in the sexual capacity of women until possibly quite late in life. Apparently women struggle (with some success) through the years of marriage to throw off the inhibitory shackles forged by the taboos of their early sex education, and once they reach their maximum sexual peak (between the ages of thirty-one and forty), they maintain this level. By this time, however, the husband's interest in sexual intercourse typically begins to slacken, with the unfortunate result of all-round frustration that frequently leads the wife to seek out other means of sexual gratification.[254] From the late teens to the age of forty-five and after, the incidence of masturbation increases for all groups of women — from about 35% to 65% of single women, from 30% to 60% of the postmarital group, and from 25% to 45% of the married women.[179]

There are few differences in frequency of marital coitus among women at different educational levels; however, for every age group there is an increase in coition to orgasm as the education level rises. For example, during the first year of marriage, 34% of the grade-school group, 28% of the high-school group, about 25% of the college-educated group, and only 22% of the graduate-school women fail to reach orgasm during marital coition. During the later years of marriage, the incidence of female orgasm in coition increases for all educational levels, although the incidence is consistently greater among the higher education groups. No changes in frequency of female coital experience in marriage according to decade of birth have been observed, but there are significant differences between the decade-of-birth groups in the incidence of response to orgasm in marital coitus—the women born during the 1919-1929 decade showing about a 25% increase in the incidence of orgasmic response over those women born before 1900.[179]

It has been previously noted that the incidence of masturbation, premarital petting, and premarital coitus is significantly related to a woman's religious background—the more devout she is, the less likely she is to engage in such sexual activities. However, it has also been noted that once a woman has had these experiences, the frequency of her sexual activity continues, bearing little or no relationship to her religious background. This same pattern applies to marital coitus. A pattern of frequent coition is somewhat slower in developing among the more devout women, but once the frequency is established, there is no further relationship to the degree of religious involvement (in contrast to the findings concerning Protestant males).

There is a correlation, however, between the percentage of total sexual outlet provided by marital coitus and a woman's devotion to her religion, the more devout women experiencing from 4% to 12% more of their total outlet in marital coition than the women who are religiously inactive. Regarding religious affiliation, there are no differences in the incidence of sexual intercourse leading to orgasm, except that devout Catholic women are less likely to have orgasms during marital coitus than women of the other religious groups are.[179] This tendency probably stems from fear of pregnancy because of the Catholic Church's prohibition of certain birth-control measures that does not bind women of other religions.

Precoital techniques of petting in marriage are similar to premarital ones; however, since marital coition is readily available, the length of time devoted to petting is usually not as protracted within marriage as before. Precoital marital petting is limited to less than three minutes in 11% of marriages, four to ten minutes in a third of them, and eleven to twenty minutes in another third. About 22% of couples—primarily in the groups with higher education—extend petting beyond twenty minutes (occasionally for as long as an hour or more). Decade of birth also affects marital petting techniques. Eighty percent of those women born before 1900 have manually manipulated and 29% have had oral contact with their husbands' genitalia; while among those women born between 1920 and 1929, 95% have manually manipulated and 57% have had oral contact with the male genitalia. About one-third of the married women born before 1900 remained clothed during coitus, while only 8% of those born during the 1920s keep clothes on during coition.[179]

Kinsey[179] and Terman[370] have shown that almost 15% of all women regularly respond with multiple orgasms. Masters and Johnson[215] conclude from their investigations that the percentage is somewhat higher. Masters and Johnson say further that "woman is naturally multiple-orgasmic in capacity."[217]

Older women, like older men, are quite capable of sexual intercourse and other forms of sexual activity. About seven-eighths of all women aged fifty and 70% of those aged sixty continue to have intercourse with their husbands. Even of those women who no longer have husbands, 37% of the fifty-year-old group, 29% of the fifty-five-year-old group, and 12% of the sixty-year-old group continue to experience coitus. About 30% of the older married women supplement marital coitus with masturbation.[331]

Many women past sixty avoid having an orgasm because of the painful uterine cramping they often experience afterwards. This pain can be relieved by their taking the proper combination of estrogen and progesterone to correct the imbalance in the sex-steroid level caused by the aging process.[215, 217] However, despite some obvious and predictable physical changes resulting from aging, there are apparently no physiological agents that should prevent a woman in her postmenopausal years from continuing satisfactory sexual expression with the frequency of her younger years.[215]

Extramarital Sexual Activity. The phrase *extramarital sexual behavior* customarily means *adultery* in most people's thinking. However, many sexual outlets other than coition are technically implied in the total scope of extramarital behavior. In this discussion, unless otherwise indicated, extramarital sex relations will refer to extramarital coition only; that is, nonmarital sexual intercourse between a man and woman, at least one of whom is married at the time to someone else. Such behavior is condemned in practically all Western cultures because of the threat it poses to the family unit. Adultery, furthermore, is unequivocally condemned in Judaic-Christian moral theology.[157] Nevertheless, at no time in the history of any culture has men's extramarital coition been consistently controlled or severely punished, whereas women have universally been subjected to a much more stringent code of sexual ethics. Furthermore, wives at every social level are more permissive of their husbands' extramarital affairs than husbands are of such behavior on the part of their wives.[180] These differences in attitude are primarily a result of the fact that since the dawn of history, women have been regarded, more or less, as property of their husbands; if the woman were to engage in extramarital coitus, it would threaten the economic stability of the entire society, would reflect on the masculinity and social prestige of her husband, and, in the case of pregnancy, could raise the question of paternal responsibility.[157]

For men, the frequency of extramarital coitus, as with other types of sexual activity, decreases with age. For women, in keeping with certain other forms of sexual activity, both the frequency of extramarital coitus and the percent of total outlet that it represents increase with age.[157] Because of society's attitude toward extramarital affairs, the participants will usually go to rather extreme lengths to hide or deny their activity. As a result, only the most careful, detailed, and sophisticated investigations can uncover even an approximation of the actual incidence and frequency of extramarital coition—a state of affairs that is attested to by the experience of psychotherapists who find patients reluctant to admit to such behavior, despite an extended time in therapy and the confidential nature of the therapeutic relationship.

Although extramarital affairs incur moral, legal, and social condemnation, and often engender unique difficulties for one or both partners, the participants nonetheless frequently view their attachment as an opportunity for love, excitement, adventure, romance, renewed vigor, enhanced ego, and return to youth—all the dreams that marriage was supposed to fulfill, but did not, or no longer does. The partners, however, are frequently disappointed in their expectations. Although changing ethical values are producing a change of attitude toward both premarital and extramarital sexual activity, the censorious judgments of religious and social groups are still rigid and powerful enough to make adultery a relationship that is sometimes destructive to marriage—although it is questionable why couples would allow adultery, in most instances, to be so ruinous a force in their marriages.[157]

Males. Almost three-fourths of all married men admit at least to an occasional desire to have an extramarital affair, and a conservative estimate is that about 50% of married men actually do experience extramarital coitus at some point during their marriage.[180, 370]

Men of the lowest educational group have more extramarital coitus during the early years of marriage (as well as more premarital coition) than men at other educational levels do. College men have less premarital coitus and less extramarital coitus during the early years of marriage than other educational groups do. As marriages continue, however, the involvement in extramarital intercourse decreases for the lower educated group from 45% during the late teens to 27% by age forty, and 19% by age fifty. In contrast, among the male teenage married group, only 15% to 20% have extramarital intercourse, but the incidence increases to 27% by the time this group reaches the age of fifty.

Frequency of contact of men of lower education drops from once (1.2) a week between the ages of sixteen to twenty, to once in two weeks (0.6) by the age of fifty-five; extramaritally involved college men average one contact in two or three weeks between the ages of sixteen to twenty, and the average increases to almost once a week by the age of fifty.[180] Between the ages of sixteen and twenty, the men of lower education have over ten times (10.6) as much extramarital coitus as college men of the same age do; laborers and semiskilled workmen aged sixteen to twenty have almost seventeen (16.7) times more extramarital intercourse than do young men of the same age who later become members of the professions.[180]

Men frequently become promiscuous in their nonmarital sexual behavior once they begin it, no matter whether it involves premarital or extramarital coition or homosexual contacts. Ultimately, married men derive between 5% and 10% of all their orgasms from extramarital coition, intercourse with prostitutes comprising from 8% to 15% of all their extramarital coitus. The most common cause for men's seeking coition with someone other than their wives is, no doubt, their desire for sexual variety, although dissatisfaction with their marital coition leads many men to extramarital intercourse.[180]

Extramarital coitus causes more complications for the middle classes than it does for either the high or low social classes. Wives of low social status rather expect their husbands to form outside attachments, and they seem not to object to the affair so long as it is not conducted flagrantly under their noses. At the upper social levels, the persons involved in an extramarital affair exert sufficient and intelligent care so that no one becomes aware that it exists.[180]

Females. Among white American married women, about one-fourth (26%) will have extramarital sexual intercourse by the age of forty. During the fourteen years from the age of twenty-six to the age of forty, the incidence of extramarital coition rises from 7% to 26%.[170]

For most age groups, the incidence of response to orgasm in extramarital affairs is about the same as its occurrence in marital coition—from 78% to 100%, depending upon the group studied. For those having extramarital intercourse, the lowest frequency—once in ten weeks—is among married teen-age girls. From that point the frequency rises to one contact every two to three weeks by the age of forty. The notion is almost universal that men customarily prefer sexual intercourse with somewhat younger partners. Sexological investigations, however, have shown that men frequently prefer coition with middle-aged or older women. The reason is that since a woman's sex drive reaches its peak between the ages of thirty-five and forty, she therefore is ordinarily more responsive. Furthermore, she is more experienced sexually, and has a better knowledge of sexual techniques; she has also thrown off many of the taboos and inhibitions that plague most women during their earlier years, making her a freer and more responsive partner.[170]

Education, decade of birth, and religious factors have a direct bearing on extramarital coitus among women. Nearly a third (31%) of the college-level women have extramarital intercourse by the age of forty, as compared with about 24% of those in the same age group who have only grade-school or high-school education. Of those women born before 1900, 22% have had extramarital coition by the age of forty, while of those born after 1900, 30% have had the experience. At every age level, the lowest incidence of extramarital intercourse is among the religiously devout. For example, by the age of thirty, 7% of the active Protestant women have had extramarital intercourse, as compared with 28% of the inactive Protestant women.[170]

About 41% of the women who have extramarital affairs limit their activity to a single partner; another 40% have two to five partners in their total extramarital experience; 16%, between five and twenty partners; and 3%, more than twenty. Up to the date their histories were taken, about 33% of those women involved had had extramarital coitus ten times or less. Forty-two percent limit their extramarital affairs to one year or less; about a fourth have their affairs over a two- to three-year period; and about a third continue their extramarital sexual experiences over a period of four years or longer.[170]

The frequency of extramarital petting has risen in recent years, and all forms of petting are utilized. In fact, light petting under certain circumstances—for instance, at a cocktail party or dance—has become rather widely accepted in many groups. Almost 15% of married women reach orgasm when they engage in extramarital petting, including 2% who do not allow extramarital coitus but will pet.[170]

Of those women who experience extramarital coitus, 68% also have had premarital intercourse (in contrast to 50% of the whole female population who experience premarital coition). Of those women who have not experienced extramarital coitus, 83% state that they have no expectations of doing so, while only 44% of those who have had extramarital intercourse state that they do not expect to renew their activity.[170]

CHAPTER 13

Sexual Diseases
and Disorders

THE WORD "venereal" is derived from *venus,* the Latin name for love or sexual desire. It is a simple matter to see the relationship between the meaning of the word and the usual source of the disease, which is sexual contact. The causative organisms of venereal diseases are ordinarily found only in human beings, and they cannot live long outside the body. The diseases, therefore, are almost always acquired by direct sexual contact.

These diseases attack men, women, and children alike throughout the world, and are considered among the most serious afflictions of mankind. The discovery of penicillin and other antibiotic drugs has made it clear, however, that it is possible to control venereal disease. It now seems that complete eradication of the diseases is a realizable goal, if public apathy does not again hamstring the efforts of responsible agencies, as it did in the United States in 1956 just at the point when syphilis was almost eliminated as a major threat to health. At that time, faulty economic reasoning caused government officials to withdraw funds that would possibly have enabled public health agencies to eradicate the remnants of the disease. Those relatively few remaining infected persons quickly spread the disease again through the country, and after a short time, all progress—a near-victory over syphilis—was lost.

From 1957 through 1961, immediately after public funds to finance the control program were largely withdrawn, there was a marked increase in early infectious syphilis and gonorrhea, especially among teen-agers.[195] There were several reasons for this increase: physicians are reluctant to report new cases of venereal disease in private patients, but they are especially reticent when the patients are adolescents, among whom the increase was greatest. Therefore, the persons who infected the adolescents and the ones, in turn, whom the adolescents infected were not contacted and treated.

Adequate public funds needed to assist medical authorities in searching out and treating infectious contacts were not available; and the legal aspects of controlling venereal disease always present an almost insurmountable problem, especially since it is impossible to legislate effectively against acts which lead to the spread of VD. There is a natural reluctance on the part of both adults and teen-agers to divulge the source of their contacts (or even to seek treatment, in many cases). Certainly, most of these factors were somehow brought under control prior to 1957 when the incidence of syphilis was markedly reduced, despite the fact that most teen-agers do not feel free to turn to their parents with a problem of this nature, and the fact that they do not have ready access to physicians in whom they have confidence. (Even when they do, teen-agers are more reticent than adults to divulge their full sexual history and behavior.)

There is some encouraging news, however, from the Communicable Disease Center of the U.S. Public Health Service, which concluded from its study of a one-year period ending June 30, 1965, that the number of reported cases of infectious syphilis seems to be leveling off. There was also a continued decline of early latent syphilis for three consecutive years up to 1967. The avowed goal of the United States Public Health Service is the complete eradication of syphilis in the United States by 1972.[330] It is doubtful that such an ambitious goal will be reached.

Prompted into action by the increasing number of adolescents with venereal disease, public health agencies have made various studies to determine what sort of teen-ager becomes infected, from which stratum of society he comes, and to what extent ethnic, religious, and similar factors are involved. What unique pressures, if any, impel a 20th-century American adolescent toward premarital sexual experimentation, which too often ends with a venereal infection?

The studies reveal that there is no "typical" teen-ager who is more likely than another to contract venereal disease. The infected youngsters were of all personality types and represented the whole spectrum of American society. Of the cases treated at VD clinics, the majority, as might be expected, came from low-income minority-group families; the other infected youngsters were no doubt treated by their private physicians. Otherwise, the statistics showed that most of those infected had commenced high school, but only about 15% had graduated. A few were attending college. About 25% attended religious services, while 50% of their parents did so.[100]

There was no essential difference found in the degree of promiscuity among ethnic groups, although there was a higher rate of venereal disease among non-whites than among whites.[100] Promiscuity and homosexuality are considerably more prevalent among boys than girls, with a correspondingly higher rate among boys of venereal disease. The studies revealed an extremely high rate of venereal disease among male homosexuals, while its incidence was insignificant among female homosexuals. One of the segments of the population showing the greatest increase in venereal disorders in recent years has been the homosexual group.[367, 376]

The most significant fact uncovered in the public health agencies' studies was that teen-agers with venereal disease come from families lacking in wholesome interpersonal relations—families within which bonds of mutual understanding and confidence do not exist.[11] Only 21% of the group studied had obtained their knowledge of sexual matters from their parents, while 64% had obtained it from their peers. Those youngsters who had received sex education from adults who were meaningful to them showed less tendency toward promiscuity. All the teen-agers in the study lacked adequate information in the sphere of sex and venereal disease; all were extremely ignorant of the elementary facts of biology and hygiene; and all lacked serious involvement in school and work. They were frank in revealing their sexual behavior and ignorance about venereal disease, and expressed feelings of religious conflict and guilt over their sexual activity.[100]

Strong physical drive and lack of self-discipline are not of themselves breeders of promiscuous behavior; people are promiscuous because relationships encompassing mutual understanding and confidence have been absent from their lives.[11] Venereal-disease patients almost always see themselves as worthless, unlovable victims of some force over which they have no control. When seriously depressed by these feelings, they seek relief in irresponsible sexual relations. The traditional American attitude that relates security with love, and love with sex, accounts for their misguided attempts to correct their emotional problems with sexual acting-out behavior. If these people can be assisted toward a more satisfactory self-image, their general adjustment to life will quite naturally improve as well.[11]

In the urbanized and mobile society of 20th-century America, old cultural patterns have given way to mass conformity. Scientific, religious, and social concepts have changed with often bewildering rapidity. Adolescents are frequently left with no clearly defined ethical values—no rules of behavior. In a mobile society, their relationships are often of a transient nature, from which amoral attitudes and casual sexual encounters can easily grow. Venereal disease is, unfortunately, often the end result.

Sex education should begin with family-life education, with proper emphasis placed on individual duty and responsibility. Helping young people to understand themselves and their place in society is a worthwhile objective. It is guidance that should begin in the family and continue in school, in church, and throughout the life of the individual. Private physicians and public health agencies cannot eradicate venereal disease without the cooperation of the individual, the family, the school, and the church.

It is up to society to face the fact of venereal disease when it appears. Ancient as its occurrence is, in most cases it is easier to cure than the common cold. When there is even the slightest question that one's partner or oneself has VD, prophylactics should be used during sexual intercourse. The simplest and best prophylactic for men, if they suspect their sexual partner is infected, is the use of a condom ("rubber") during coition, followed by a thorough soap-and-water cleansing of the genitalia afterwards. Women with an infected sexual partner should use an antiseptic vaginal douche, also followed by a soap-and-water cleansing of the genitalia.

VENEREAL DISEASES

There now follows a discussion of most types of venereal diseases, both the well-known and the little-known. The discussion is presented in the belief that adequate sex instruction must include such information, and that the knowledge can help to curb promiscuity as well as the spread of the diseases themselves.

Syphilis

The physician Fracastoro in 1530 published a poem, which achieved wide popularity, about a shepherd named Syphilis who had been stricken with a disease that, until then, had been known as "the great pox." Since the time of Fracastoro's poem, the disease has been known as syphilis.

It is still debated to some extent whether Columbus and his crew brought syphilis to America from Europe, or whether they contracted the disease from West Indian women and then carried it to Europe. And, indeed, study of the bones of American Indians has revealed evidence that syphilis existed in America at least 500 years before Columbus's voyages.[318] But whichever the direction, syphilis spread in epidemic proportions across the known world within a few years after Columbus and his men returned to Europe from their historic journeys. Columbus himself probably died (in 1506) from general paresis, one of the neurological disorders resulting from syphilitic infections.[82] It was about 400 years later, in 1905, that the causative organism of syphilis was discovered; a short time later, the relationship between syphilis and paresis was recognized.

The origin of syphilis was found to be a corkscrew-shaped spirochete known as *Treponema pallidum,* a cylindrical body with eight to fourteen rigid spirals that is best seen with the aid of a dark-field microscope. Subsequently, in 1913, the scientists Noguchi and Moore found this same spirochete in the cerebral cortex of patients dying of general paresis.

Once the villain spirochete of syphilis was identified, extensive studies were made of the disease, and effective methods of diagnosis were developed (for example, the Wassermann test). Until 1943, when penicillin was discovered to be a quick and easy cure for syphilis, the best known treatment had been a combination of bismuth and arsenic administered alternately and slowly over a long period of time—up to two years, or longer—coupled with fever induced by typhoid germs or by extensive applications of heat. The drug in most common use today in the treatment of syphilis is penicillin, which can cure practically any case if it is caught in time; in many instances, only a single powerful injection is necessary. If the patient is penicillin-sensitive, Aureomycin or Terramycin can be used with equal success.[39]

Syphilis is considered to be in its early phase for a two-year period after infection, and early syphilis is subdivided into primary and secondary stages of infection (discussed below). It is important to recognize the disease during the early phase, because it is then that it can be most easily cured; the irreversible tissue damage has not yet occurred. This is also the period when the patient is most infectious, and is the greatest menace to public health.

The *primary stage* of syphilis is easily identified by a lesion or a *chancre* (sore) that usually appears in the anal-genital area following sexual contact with a diseased person. In about 10% of the cases, the chancre may appear in the mouth, or on the tonsils or lips, and the infection may be extragenital in origin.[106]

The chancre begins as a small red papule (circumscribed elevation of the skin) that becomes eroded and moist. The only other sign of infection at this stage is a painlessly swollen lymph gland at the site of the regional lymph drainage: for example, if the chancre is on the penis or labia minora, the glandular swelling will be in the groin. During the early primary stage, the microorganisms leave the bloodstream and invade other tissues of the body. This invasion usually causes lesions that are characteristic of the secondary stage of syphilis.

If the disease is adequately treated in its primary stage, a cure is easily effected and the danger of transmitting infection removed. Without treatment, the primary chancre heals in four to ten weeks; the surface warning signal is thus removed, but the danger of internal damage remains.

The *secondary stage* is characterized by a non-itching eruption (giving rise to the name "great pox" to distinguish the disease from small pox) or rash of the skin, usually on the trunk of the body. The rash is sometimes so indistinct as to escape notice.[197] Other symptoms appear at this time, and their significance as bearing a possible relationship to syphilis is usually recognizable only by a competent physician: glandular enlargement, throat infection, headaches, malaise, and a low-grade fever. Secondary lesions then heal, without treatment and without leaving scar formation, within a few weeks or months— possibly a year.

The *third stage* of untreated syphilis is called the *latent period,* and it commences at least two years after the initial infection. The latent period is further divided into early and late. The disease is called *early latent* when the patient has been infected less than four years, or is under twenty-five years of age.[197] Syphilis is considered to be in its *late latent* stage when infection has persisted longer than four years, or when the patient is over twenty-five years old. The latent period is dangerously deceptive; all symptoms associated with syphilis disappear, and the latency may last for months or years. It was at this stage during the great syphilis epidemic of the 15th century that the disease was thought to be cured. During latency, syphilitics do not infect contacts, but the results of a blood serology test are always positive, and such a test is the only reliable method of diagnosis. Without treatment, the disease can now progress to the destructive stage of late syphilis.

Late syphilis, the *fourth stage,* may manifest itself in any organ, in the central nervous system, the cardiovascular system, and, particularly, on the skin. These symptoms can appear as long as thirty years after the initial infection. Late lesions may appear in the mouth, throat, and on the tongue, usually accompanied by tissue thickenings or destructive ulcers. The late or tertiary lesions, as they are called, are responsible for the crippling, disabling, and disfiguring effects associated with syphilis. A chronic inflammatory process may develop in this late stage that involves bones, joints, eyes and other organs, and, especially, the cardiovascular system.

Modern methods of diagnosis and treatment have eliminated syphilis as "the great scourge"; but it still cannot be classified as a benign disease because of the deadly effects of an untreated case.

However, it has been shown that about 50% of those patients who contract syphilis and receive no treatment will not experience any disability or inconvenience; and another 25% will have some residual evidence of the disease, but will suffer no disability or shortening of life.[39] The reason that such a high proportion of untreated syphilitics suffer little or no ill effects from the disease is not known, but some speculate that a resistance to the disease is built up because penicillin and other antibiotics have been administered to these people in treatment of earlier illnesses.

The incidence of *congenital syphilis* has greatly diminished in recent years because of routine prenatal care and treatment of mothers, although it has not been totally eradicated. A syphilitic mother usually transmits the disease to any unborn offspring during the first two years of her infection. If the mother is treated before the fourth month of pregnancy, the child is usually born nonsyphilitic; in these instances, only one infant in eleven is born with the disease.[265]

Congenital syphilis is usually manifested early in life by certain pathological symptoms, although the symptoms may not appear until after the victim is ten or fifteen years old, and sometimes not even until he is as old as thirty years. The course of congenital syphilis is similar to that of the secondary and tertiary stages of the contracted form of the disease. Pupillary signs are frequently the only indication of congenital syphilis. More often, evidence of the disease is manifested in various degrees of mental defects ranging from mild deficiency to imbecility and idiocy. There are sometimes developmental defects, such as hydrocephalus or brain atrophies; sclerosis and convulsions are also an occasional development from congenital syphilis.

Untreated syphilis may produce disorders that are particularly disabling and devastating, the most two common being neurosyphilis and general paresis. In the past, about 5% of all untreated cases of syphilis developed into general paresis. Recently the figure has dropped to about 3%, although the exact cause of this decrease is not known.[82]

Neurosyphilis occurs in about 25% of untreated cases of syphilis.[265] It can affect every part of the cerebrospinal system in one or any combination of the three forms of the disease: meningovascular syphilis, paresis, and tabes dorsalis. Paresis and tabes dorsalis, especially, are frequently accompanied by vascular (blood vessels) or meningeal (a covering of the brain) complications.

Symptoms of neurosyphilis are many, but the affliction can also exist without any clinical indices to identify it. On the other hand, clinical signs may be mild or severe and acute or chronic, depending on the circumstances of the onset of the disease, the rate of its progress, and the extent and severity of it. There may be headache, dizziness, nausea, various subjective pains, numbness, attacks of unconsciousness, or epileptic-like convulsions. The list of personality disorders that may accompany neurosyphilis is also lengthy: restlessness, dullness, irritability, apathy, anxiety, depression, defective memory, mild or severe delirium, dementia, and so forth.

General paresis is a chronic progressive syphilitic disease with which certain physical symptoms are associated, as well as the better known psychological indications of psychosis and progressive mental deterioration.[52] The disease usually makes its appearance from ten to twenty years (occasionally longer) after the primary lesion of syphilis. It is commonly observed between the ages of thirty and fifty, more frequently in men than in women.

General paresis is often fatal; it may affect any and all areas of the nervous system, and is frequently confused with functional psychotic illnesses. Pupillary changes and a positive serology test are often the only factors calling attention to the actual nature of the disease. The symptoms, typically of psychotic proportions, may range from sudden manic or depressive reactions to a more complex syndrome of indications, such as anxiety, insomnia, hypochondria, fatigue, irritability, loss of interest, and a loss of power to concentrate. Because its symptoms resemble those of various psychological illnesses, general paresis is sometimes referred to as "the great imitator."

Juvenile general paresis usually manifests itself at some time between the age of ten and the time of adolescence. The symptoms typically involve delusional trends, depression or excitement, defective memory, general loss of interest, and disorderly conduct. These reactions are frequently masked by pronounced mental deficiency or convulsions. Juvenile paresis progresses more slowly and in a less clear-cut manner than the adult forms of the disease do, although the physical symptoms are the same. It is a disease rarely found today because of prophylactic measures taken with a syphilitic mother-to-be.[17, 82]

Gonorrhea

Gonorrhea is the most ancient, yet the most common, of the venereal diseases. Early Chinese writings and the unmistakable reference to the disease in the Bible attest to its existence for many centuries.[30] The word "gonorrhea" (Greek: flow of seed) was first used by the physician Galen in 130 A.D. to describe the disease, although the causative organism was not identified until 1839, at which time it was given the name "gonococcus." Until the advent, in 1943, of the "miracle drugs" and their remarkable effect on the organisms of venereal diseases, gonorrhea was not easily cured, and complications often resulted in ailments requiring specialized treatment. Since that time, however, the disease is ordinarily considered to be relatively minor and it is easily treated.

Gonorrhea is almost always contracted during sexual intercourse with an infected person. The organism usually restricts its attack to the genitourinary area, although the rectum may be infected by extension from the genitals or from anal intercourse.[39] Gonococcus has been known to involve the skin and joints and, much more rarely, the brain and blood system.

Gonorrhea in a man usually manifests itself by acute urethritis (inflammation of the urethra). A thin watery discharge from the penis commences from two to seven days following the date of infectious sexual contact, and becomes thicker and greenish-yellow in color within another day or two. The patient typically feels an urgent and frequent need to urinate and when he does so, the act is accompanied by a burning sensation at the tip of his penis, which is now swollen and inflamed.

Painful complications, which are sometimes serious, commonly result from gonorrhea. One of the most agonizing of these is epididymitis. This condition is characterized by a swelling of the structures leading to the testes, the latter sometimes becoming as large as an orange and extremely painful. Other complications are arthritis, iritis, conjunctivitis, skin infections, and, more rarely, endocarditis and meningitis. Gonorrheal infection of the prostate can become chronic, causing a man to remain infectious for a considerable length of time. Urethral stricture is another common and serious complication; the obstruction thus produced predisposes the patient to an attack of pyelonephritis (inflammation of the kidney).[39, 102] These complications, which are typically accompanied by fever, malaise, and marked debility, repeatedly caused the death of gonorrheal victims prior to the introduction of antibiotic drugs in the treatment of the disease.

The first symptom of gonorrhea in a woman is a vaginal discharge that begins two to seven days from the time of infectious contact. The vulva becomes red, raw, and irritated. There is an urgent and frequent need to urinate, and urination is accompanied by pain and a scalding sensation. Women can develop two important and distinct complications from this disease: infection of the Bartholin's glands (bartholinitis), and infection of the Fallopian tubes (salpingitis). In bartholinitis, the gland on one or both sides of the vulva swells and becomes tender and painful. An abscess or a cyst sometimes forms in the infected gland, requiring medical or, occasionally, surgical attention.[17, 39, 368]

Acute salpingitis often produces severe lower abdominal pain on one or both sides of the body, accompanied by fever and malaise. A tubal abscess can form on either or both sides, depending on the extent of inflammation of the Fallopian tubes. These conditions frequently cause severe colicky abdominal pain, menstrual irregularity, chronic invalidism, and sterility. Surgical treatment is often required if the conditions are to be properly corrected.[308]

Children are sometimes accidentally infected with gonorrhea, although its occurrence is uncommon, since the source of the infection is almost always sexual intercourse. However, children have been infected through mutual masturbation, sexual exploration and experimentation, and sexual assault. At one time, nearly one-third of all blindness in children was the result of gonococcal ophthalmia, which the newborn acquires in the birth process from its infected mother. This affliction has now been almost completely eradicated by treating all newborn babies with preventive medication: instillation in the eyes of a solution of silver nitrate or penicillin (the latter being the more modern technique).[30]

The diagnosis of gonorrhea is commonly made by microscopic examination of a smear of urethral or vaginal (cervical) discharge. A modern method of diagnosis known as the "fluorescent antibody technique" has been found effective in detecting the organism in patients who show no clinical signs of infection. Treatment of gonorrhea with antibiotics is simple and effective, but any complications stemming from the original infection will, of course, require specialized treatment. There are recent reports of a strain of gonococci that is highly resistant to treatment with penicillin and other "miracle" drugs, making its cure less of a certainty than that of other strains.

Chancroid

Chancroid (caused by the strepto-bacillus of Ducrey) is a highly contagious disease typically spread through sexual intercourse. The infection is characterized by ulcerations, usually at the points of physical contact, and by local lymph-gland swelling. The first sign of chancroid appears about twelve to sixteen hours after infectious sexual intercourse has taken place. It usually takes the form of an inflamed papule or pustule which soon breaks down to become a ragged-edged ulcer that is filled with dead tissue. The ulcer varies in size, but may become extremely large and destructive of the skin affected.[17, 30] There may be one ulcer, but ordinarily the matter suppurating from the ulcer will infect the contiguous area on a man's prepuce, frenum, or penile shaft, while in a woman, the ulcer usually forms on the labia majora, vestibule, or clitoris. Occasionally, the lymph glands of the groin may swell, cause pain, and rupture. If not treated, chancroid ulcerations can drain for months. The adverse effects of this disease are considerably greater in women than in men.[265]

Chancroid may be contracted in conjunction with other venereal diseases, such as lymphogranuloma venereum, granuloma inguinale (both discussed below), gonorrhea, and syphilis. It is plain to see that accurate diagnosis and treatment require expert clinical and laboratory techniques. Sulfonamides are the drugs commonly chosen to combat chancroid infection, and they usually produce a cure in as short a time as three to eight days. Certain other antibiotics are equally effective in bringing about a swift and permanent cure of this disease.[39]

Granuloma Inguinale

Granuloma inguinale is a chronic disease that is unique primarily because of its extensive ulceration and scarring of skin and subcutaneous tissues. The genitals are a special mark for attack, but extragenital sites are also frequently invaded. The disease is infectious, but it is not necessarily contracted through sexual intercourse; "venereal" is not, therefore, a wholly appropriate label for the infection. The disease is more prevalent in temperate and tropical zones than in milder climates.[20]

At the onset of granuloma inguinale, a small red papule appears, ordinarily on the penis or labia, but occasionally on other parts of the body, such as the face, neck, anus, rectum, or groin. Lesions enlarge and spread, and the ulcerations grow together to form a larger area of infection. The tissue degenerates into a red, moist, malodorous, granulated, and frequently bleeding mass. Spontaneous healing does not ordinarily occur, and a slow extension of the ulceration is capable of destroying much of the tissue of the entire genital region, which then becomes replaced by thick scar tissue.

The absence of lymph-node involvement is a marked feature of the disease and is an excellent diagnostic aid. The organism itself is difficult to isolate, even in scrapings from active lesions, and identification usually must be made by microscopic examination of stained slides. The disease can be cured by careful treatment with antibiotic drugs of the mycin family.[17, 39, 368]

Lymphogranuloma Venereum

Lymphogranuloma venereum is caused by a virus that invades the tissue in the anal-genital and inguinal areas. It is a systemic disease, and the primary lesion manifests itself within a few days of sexual contact in the form of a small blister that soon ruptures to form a shallow ulcer with clear-cut edges surrounded by reddened skin. The blister is painless and heals rapidly without leaving a scar. The initial lesion may appear on the glans, prepuce, vulva, vaginal walls, cervix, within the urethra, or in the anal region. If the virus is contracted during cunnilingus (oral-vulval contact), it can cause the tongue to blister and swell, reactions that are often followed by swelling in the glands of the neck.[37]

Approximately two weeks after the primary lesion, the invasion of the virus progresses to a secondary stage, which is characterized by pain in the groin followed by visible enlargement of the lymph nodes. These may be the only indications until the third stage, when symptoms become quite obvious: elephantiasis of the penis, scrotum, or vulva.

Diagnosis of lymphogranuloma venereum is rather difficult to make, even in the laboratory. The Frei skin test, however, has a high diagnostic accuracy, and should be performed in every suspected case. Antibiotic drugs have not elicited the near-miraculous cures in the treatment of this disease that they have in many other venereal diseases, but prognosis is rendered more favorable through treatment.[38, 368]

NONVENEREAL DISEASES

This section deals with diseases, infections, and inflammation affecting various parts of the male and female reproductive systems. The causative organism or condition may well not have any relationship to sexual activity, but in each instance some part of the internal or external genitalia is affected and may possibly be aggravated by sexual contact.

Nonvenereal Syphilis

Nonvenereal syphilis is an endemic infection acquired in infancy and caused by an invasion of a parasitic organism closely related to the treponemal organism that causes venereal syphilis, hence its inclusion here. The disease, frequently referred to as "yaws" or "pinta," affects many people in widely separated parts of the world, and typically thrives in warm, moist climates and in conditions of filth. Penicillin has been used successfully for mass treatment in many countries in eradication campaigns conducted by the World Health Organization.[39]

Trichomoniasis

Trichomoniasis is the most common of the minor gynecological diseases; it afflicts approximately 25% of all women patients, yet it is an infection that is seldom written about or discussed. Many married women and their husbands, as well, suffer from this annoying infection, although men seldom experience the copious discharge, itching, and burning that are symptomatic of the ailment in women. Until very recently, the infection has been extremely resistant to treatment.[252, 346]

Trichomoniasis is caused by a minute one-celled animal, the *trichomonas vaginalis*. The parasite is a flagellated organism approximating the shape and size of a paramecium and moving in the same manner. It propels itself by a constant thrashing of small whips at one end of its body. Thousands of these organisms can be seen by examining a bit of infected vaginal secretion under a microscope.

Trichomonads do not burrow into the tissues, but live on the surface of the membranes. They do not invade the womb or the Fallopian tubes, but normally limit their attack to the membrane of the vagina, including the cervix. The first indication of infection is usually a white or yellowish vaginal discharge, accompanied by itching and burning. Many women find this discharge extremely irritating with a constant inflammation and soreness of the external area of the vulva. A separation of the inflamed labia may reveal a thick, smelly, bubbly discharge in the vestibule.

To other women, trichomoniasis is not so irritating, but it does tend to cause severe itching. Practically all women who have endured this infection report that their underclothing is quickly soiled by the discharge which, together with the irritation or itching, seems to worsen immediately before and after menstruation. Some women experience severe symptoms; others have mild ones. Why some women are more susceptible to trichomoniasis remains a perplexing gynecological question.

Whether the symptoms are mild or severe, a doctor should be consulted immediately if there is the slightest indication of infection. Ordinarily, the infected husband has no symptoms except for a slight thin, whitish discharge, and occasionally urination causes an itching and burning in the urethral tract. If one marital partner is found to be infected with trichomoniasis, the other should be examined also; nothing is accomplished by curing one partner, only to have him or her reinfected by the other. Careful examination reveals that husbands of infected wives also have the infection in 60% of the cases.[315] It is possible for a couple to pass these infectious parasites back and forth for many years, especially as the husband frequently does not realize he is infected. Trichomonads house themselves under the foreskin of a man's uncircumcised penis, but in severe cases may invade his prostate.

It is not known just where these microscopic animals come from, or precisely how one contracts the disease (other than from an infected sexual partner). Many gynecologists state that there is a similarity between the trichomonads of the vagina and those found in the bowels.

However, parasitologists maintain that the vaginal type is quite different from the ones found in the bowels. They further claim that trichomoniasis is a venereal infection in that it is transmitted only by sexual intercourse. Some other scientists believe that the infection is not necessarily a venereal one, because the disease can be contracted in a swimming pool or a bathtub, where the organism may rather easily make its entry into the vaginal tract.

Recently, a new drug called Flagyl has come on the market in this country, and is reported to be almost 100% effective in the treatment of trichomoniasis.[346] The drug, obtainable by prescription only, is administered orally and renders a cure within ten to fourteen days for both men and women. If for one reason or another the drug cannot be used, some other form of medication can be applied to the vaginal area, and antiseptic douches are recommended.

Trichomoniasis is usually complicated by monilia (discussed below) and perhaps by one or several other of various associated pathogenic bacteria. Treatment of trichomoniasis and any accompanying bacterial infection should be rigorously pursued, for while the disease is not considered serious, it can nonetheless be a tormenting and a sexually inhibiting one.

Moniliasis

Moniliasis (commonly called "monilia") is a fungus infection of the genital region that can cause acute discomfort, primarily in women. The monilia organism is sporidiferous, which means that it has the power to lie dormant for long periods of time if circumstances are not ripe for its growth. The dormant organism can be harbored under the foreskin of a man's penis or in a woman's vagina until circumstances for its activation become favorable. More frequently than not, monilia accompanies other infectious organisms, such as trichomonads.[252, 316]

Examination of a genital area afflicted with monilia reveals white cheesy spots on the vulva, in the vagina, and on the cervix; minute ulcerations of the labia minora may also be present, accompanied in some instances by a thick or watery vaginal discharge. All these symptoms can eventually lead to a raw, bleeding surface if treatment is not prompt and careful.

Most organisms causing infection and irritation in the vagina thrive on menstrual blood. Therefore, women who are harboring such a fungus as monilia commonly complain of the greatest discomfort and distress just before and just after menstruation.

Monilia is sometimes found in children, and it is quite likely to afflict women who have diabetes, or who have been overtreated with antibiotic vaginal suppositories, which can kill off the native protective bacilli in the vaginal tract. A cure can be accomplished, however, with persistent and adequate treatment under the direction of a gynecologist.

Peyronie's Disease

Peyronie's disease is one in which a fibrous tissue develops in the space above and between the two large spongy bodies (corpora cavernosa) of the penis. Calcium deposits in about 20% of the cases develop in the fibrous tissue, and occasionally there is a hardening of this tissue into cartilage and bone. As the disease progresses, the penis may be deviated to the left or right, or upwards, often making erections extremely painful and sexual intercourse impossible.[252, 385] The only func-

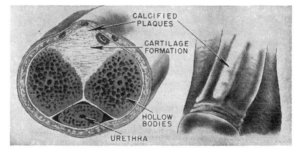

Fig. 13-1. Peyronie's disease. Abnormal formation of calcium shown along top of penis, between spongy bodies. Photograph courtesy *Sexology* magazine.

tion disturbed by this disease is erection. Treatment with drugs has been tried with unimpressive results; the advisability of surgical procedures is equally questionable, since they entail a particular hazard: the ability to achieve erection may be completely destroyed. X-ray treatment reportedly improved or cured the disorder entirely in 83% of patients treated.[105] The disease occurs primarily in middle or old age.

Venereal Warts

Venereal warts are actually benign tumors, and are probably a result of a filtrable virus infection. In a man, they usually appear around the base of the glans and develop quickly in the moist environment of a tight prepuce. A woman may develop venereal warts at the site of the labia and perineum, and the growths can spread to cover the entire area. They usually become manifest only after the menopause. Venereal warts may be transferred to other persons or to other parts of one's own body, and they should be examined microscopically in order that the seriousness of the condition can be determined.[38, 252]

Tuberculosis

Tuberculosis of various genital areas sometimes occurs in both men and women. *Tuberculosis prostatitis* is not a common disease, but it is found to invade the prostate gland in about 12% of all terminal cases of tuberculosis. Although the normal glandular tissue of the prostate is replaced by a crumbly fibrous growth and calcification as the disease progresses, tuberculosis prostatitis is almost always painless. Among women, tuberculosis constitutes about 2% of all diseases of the upper genital tract.[17, 252, 368]

Carcinoma

Carcinoma, of course, can strike any part, or related part, of the entire reproductive system. The symptoms are diverse, and upon recognizing any suspicious signals (such as those outlined by the American Cancer Society), one should immediately consult a physician.

There appears to be more than a casual relationship between cancer in specific areas of the body and certain physical, social, and health factors. For example, both penile and cervical cancers seem to bear a definite relationship to a man's having been circumcised or not. The theory is that smegma and other impurities that so easily collect under the prepuce of an uncircumcised penis predispose the man to penile cancer. Furthermore, the theory continues, these same impurities under a husband's prepuce predispose his wife to cervical cancer.[17, 190, 252, 352] The age at which a woman marries also seems to have some relationship to cervical cancer; women who marry very early are more likely to develop it than are those who marry later in life.[67]

The evidence further suggests that promiscuous sexual activity in women is positively correlated to the incidence of cervical cancer. Whether the explanation for this increased incidence lies with the frequency of sexual intercourse, the strength of the sex drive, personality factors, or the increased possibility for contact with men whose genitalia are unclean or diseased is not known.[257] Further support for the observation concerning cervical cancer and the promiscuous woman comes, perhaps strangely, from the fact that nuns have a considerably lower incidence of cervical cancer than is found in the general population; however, nuns have cancer of the uterus, ovaries, and breasts as frequently as women in the general population do.[324]

It bears repeating that all sensible precautions against cancer should be taken. The lives of thousands of women could be saved every year if they had regular—at least annual—gynecological examinations, including a Pap smear test. A simple and painless procedure, the Pap test involves taking a sample of cervical fluid by means of a cotton swab and examining the fluid for the presence of cancer cells. Cancer cells of deep tissue work their way to the surface and will appear in the smear taken from the surface of the cervix.

Elephantiasis

Elephantiasis of the scrotum involves a marked growth of its subcutaneous tissues and epidermis, producing an enlargement varying from slight to monstrous; in some extreme cases, the scrotum may touch the ground and weigh as much as 200 pounds. In women, the condition may manifest itself through excessive growth of the labia majora. This disease is only occasionally found in the United States; it is ordinarily indigenous to tropical regions.

Filarial elephantiasis is caused by a parasite which is carried by certain mosquitoes. Lymph glands are invaded by the parasite; the glands then usually swell and secondary infections develop, followed by scrotal enlargement. *Nonfilarial elephantiasis* results from disorders of the lymph glands, usually an aftermath of chronic streptococcal infection. Elephantiasis is treated through a proper support for the enlarged scrotum, and by the use of medication. Surgery is sometimes indicated.[38, 252]

Infectious Mononucleosis

Infectious mononucleosis is not, of course, a venereal disease or sexual disorder, and its inclusion in this section rests with its popular name, "the kissing disease." It is an acute infectious disease of the lymph glands, characterized by the sudden onset of fever, marked fatigue, chills, sweating, headache, sore throat, and loss of appetite.[38, 102, 314] There are occasionally severe and even fatal complications, and the instructions of the attending physician must be rigidly followed.

How the disease (which is caused by a filtrable virus) is transmitted has not been definitely determined, although many authorities suspect deep kissing with an infected person. One study found that seventy-one of seventy-three "mono" patients had engaged in deep kissing at the exact time the incubation period for mononucleosis would have commenced for them.[314] In the course of the disease, fever usually subsides after five days; other acute symptoms abate within three weeks, although some symptoms may persist for months.

Dermatoses

Dermatoses or skin diseases of the genital region are fairly common, and the causative organisms and substances are legion.

Chemicals, such as those contained in soap that is not rinsed off properly after a shower, can collect in the sensitive areas of the genitalia and produce irritation or burns.[84] The difficulty may be compounded by attempting a cure with medication too strong for the distressed area. Unfortunately, many people adopt the premise that if a little medicine is good, a lot will be even better.

Tinea crusis, or "jock itch," is another sort of dermatosis afflicting the genital region. It is a fungus whose initial symptoms are reddish, scaly patches that may then develop into large, highly inflamed zones with stressful itching and considerable pain. The affliction has a striking similarity to athlete's foot. Such conditions as sweating, tight clothing, and inadequate drying of the genitalia after a bath provide a favorable environment for the development and flourishing of this fungus infection.[252]

Scabies and *pediculosis* (crabs) are two forms of dermatoses caused by parasites that can invade the genital area.[122, 252] Scabies is a highly contagious skin disorder in which a female mite *(Sarcoptes scabiei)* burrows between the layers of skin and deposits her eggs. Little vesicles housing the mite and her eggs appear on the skin surface and soon develop into papules, pustules, and a rash that itches formidably, especially at night. Appropriate medication, prescribed by a physician, can usually rid the victim of scabies in a short period of time.

Pediculosis pubis is an itchy skin irritation caused by the minute bites of the crab louse *(Phthirius pubis).* Scratching produces further irritation and a brownish discoloration of the skin may develop. The crab louse usually buries its head in the follicles of the pubic hair and attaches its body to the hair itself. These parasites commonly pass from one person to another through sexual contact with an infected partner, although they may also be picked up from a toilet seat or from a bed.[122, 252]

Herpes genitalis is a condition of the external genitals, similar to the herpes simplex virus that assails the lips and nose. Little blisters develop that burst to form small ulcers, or that dry and harden into a crust.[38, 252]

Psoriasis is a disease of the skin characterized by scaly red patches. It may attack the genital region as well as other parts of the body.

Pruritis, an excruciating itching, typically accompanies psoriasis and other skin diseases. Medication usually provides relief for the itching, and the condition clears up in a short period of time.[252]

Folliculitis is an inflammation at the opening of the hair follicles that is precipitated by various sorts of infection, including staphylococci. The infection finds a suitable environment in which to flourish when the skin is not kept clean, clothing is too tight, and bodily resistance is generally low.[252]

Inflammation of Internal and External Genitalia

The suffix *-itis* added to the name of an organ indicates inflammation of that organ. Many disorders of the internal and external genitalia of both men and women fall into this grouping.

Vaginitis is a fairly common vaginal irritation; the inflammation is caused by such conditions as bacterial invasion, the introduction of foreign objects into the canal, and the use of strong chemicals. Children, especially, inject small objects (coins, marbles, pins, sticks) into the vagina, possibly in a clumsy attempt at masturbation. Douching with too high a concentration of chemicals, overmedication, tampons that are inserted and then forgotten, and incorrectly placed pessaries can all cause chemical burns and inflammation of the vaginal tract. Furthermore, it is well known that a general impairment of health can reduce bodily resistance to contagion, making one more susceptible to low-grade infections such as vaginitis. "Non-specific vaginitis" is an affliction that is considered gynecology's most perplexing unsolved problem. Sexual intercourse when such conditions exist may be the source of even further irritation to the vaginal tract.[252, 346]

Excessive douching or the use of overly strong solutions is the basic evil in many instances of vaginitis, because such douching destroys nature's protective organisms, Doderlein's bacilli, that normally inhabit the vagina. When this happens, the acid condition of the vagina is reduced and hostile bacteria find a suitable place for development; any of various vaginal maladies can be the consequence. All too often, women—especially the young and newly married ones—are overly concerned about feminine hygiene. They apparently feel that if a little douching is good, more must be better, and they therefore increase the strength and frequency of it; the results in the long run are often distressing. A recent study of prison women showed that daily douching with water, or with a mild vinegar or alkaline solution, did not produce the changes in the vaginal lining or any other ill effects claimed by some gynecologists.[325] The real danger, then, would seem to come from douching with harsh chemicals.

During and following menopause, the lining of the vagina undergoes a marked change. The decrease in hormonal production causes the membrane to become much thinner (perhaps one-fourth its former thickness) than it was during the period before menopause. While this change should in no way decrease a woman's sexual desire or ability, the tissue of her vagina does become more fragile, and she is more easily made uncomfortable, or even injured, by sexual activity. These difficulties are frequently corrected by use of an estrogenic (female hormone) cream or ointment as a vaginal lubricant, and through administration of female sex hormones orally or by injection. Such treatment should be prescribed and directed by a physician.[72, 282]

Probably the best method of warding off vaginitis is to maintain good general physical health, coupled with wholesome attitudes toward sex and feminine hygiene. Every woman should have a checkup by a gynecologist at least once a year—preferably semiannually.

Cystitis refers to inflammation of the bladder, and the disorder may occur in a variety of ways.[252, 368] Symptoms usually include a severe burning sensation in the urethra during urination, a frequent need to urinate, and sharp pain in the lower abdomen. Women who have inflammation of the bladder often report that the pain is especially severe when they have sexual intercourse, and that they must often discontinue coition because of the pain.[122]

The bladder may become infected when lowered bodily resistance facilitates the attack of existing internal bacteria on an already irritated bladder, or when germs enter the bladder via the urethra. Irritation of a woman's bladder may occur as a result of frequent sexual intercourse, since the bladder tends to become somewhat displaced by the pressure of the penis against it and the urethra through the vaginal walls. This condition occurs not infrequently during honeymoons, giving it the rather graphic name of "honeymoon cystitis." [276]

Obviously, bladder inflammation can be better controlled when the body is otherwise healthy. Furthermore, good personal hygiene will do much to combat the problem once it occurs. Treatment should include thorough daily cleansing with surgical soap of the external genitalia as well as of the urethral opening. In addition, a woman will fare better if she will empty her bladder before sexual intercourse, and if she will use a lubricating jelly when nature appears not to supply a sufficient amount of vaginal secretion; both these measures will decrease pressure on the abdominal organs through the vagina during coitus.

It should be pointed out that cystitis can have emotional as well as organic causes. Frequently it is related to conflict over sexual matters, and psychotherapy can be very helpful in bringing about a cure. As with all diseases and disorders discussed in this section, a physician should be consulted at the first signs of cystitis. Early investigation and treatment may enable the patient to avoid serious complications.

Epididymitis is a fairly common sexual disorder among men. It involves inflammation of the epididymis, that important structure closely attached to each testicle that receives and temporarily houses sperm as they are produced and then released from the testicles.[252] The epididymis is in a rather vulnerable position to become infected from the testis below, perhaps as a result of a blow to the testicle; and from above, by way of the vas deferens, as infection can spread from an affected prostate gland or seminal vesicle. Gonorrhea would appear to be a predisposing factor in epididymitis, for in one of five cases of the former, the victim becomes infected with epididymitis as well.

There are degrees of this infection, both in duration and in severity of symptoms. In mild cases there may be only slight swelling and tenderness, which respond readily to treatment; in severe cases, the entire testicular structure may be greatly swollen and painful. The disease can lead to growths and strictures that can result in sterility, and that only surgical procedures may be able to correct.

Some cases of chronic epididymitis persist for years. Nonsurgical treatment involves extensive use of certain drugs, a balanced and wholesome diet, rest, and a warm climate.

Prostatitis is an inflammation of the prostate gland and is a common problem among men. Since the discovery and use of antibiotics, acute prostatitis is a rare occurrence. Formerly, it was a frequent companion of gonorrhea, but now it is seen only occasionally, and then as a result of a staphylococci infection following catheterization.[122, 252]

Chronic prostatitis often follows prolonged infection of other parts of the body. It may also be the outcome of protracted but unrelieved sexual tension: certain secretions are activated that find no release, with the consequence of congestion and inflammation of the prostate.[356]

Symptoms in either acute or chronic prostatitis may include a thin mucous discharge, especially in the morning, and pain in the lower back, testicles, perineum, posterior scrotum, and perhaps even in the tip of the penis. Many prostatitis patients reveal a collateral emotional stress growing out of sexual conflicts, together with hypochondriacal complaints that are far out of proportion to the severity of the disease. Prostatitis may, however, cause loss of potency, painful or inadequate erections, premature and sometimes bloody ejaculations, and sterility.

Prostatic massage, antibiotic treatment, and prolonged warm baths are the weapons used by a urologist in clearing up prostatic infection and in bringing about drainage of the congested gland. It is, however, rather difficult to eradicate this infection completely because of the complexity of the ductwork of the sexual system.

As described earlier, the prostate gland surrounds the neck of the bladder in such a way that any inflammation, enlargement, or infection of the prostate can make urination difficult. The prostate tends to enlarge as a man grows older, and he is particularly so troubled after the age of fifty. Early symptoms of prostatitis usually include an increase in frequency of urination, day and night, and difficulty in starting the stream. The most serious problem associated with an enlarged prostate is that it interferes with the bladder's becoming completely emptied. This partial blockage can lead to infection involving many organs of the body other than the prostate and bladder.

It is not known definitely what causes the prostate to enlarge with age—about 20% of all men are affected after middle age—although the most widely accepted theory is that an excess of male hormones (androgen) is responsible. Hormone therapy is sometimes used in an attempt to control or correct the problem,[144] but in some instances all or a portion of the gland must be removed. Recently, Cryothermic surgery, a method of freezing rather than cutting (also employed successfully in the treatment of Parkinson's disease), has been used in prostatic operations, although the success of the technique in prostate surgery has not yet been proven by adequate follow-up studies.

Peritonitis is the infection of the peritoneal cavity that frequently results from the draining of any purulent matter from the Fallopian tubes into that cavity. The infection may be generalized, or it may be localized in the specific area where the drainage collects. The type and area of infection, the resistance of the patient, and the timing and type of treatment: all affect the mildness or severity, as well as the potential danger, of peritonitis. Even after the condition heals, adhesions result that cause the uterus, rectum, and so forth to change their fixed position. Backaches, pain during elimination, and distressful copulation are typical secondary symptoms. Diathermy, medication, and, occasionally, surgery are methods of treatment.[252, 368]

Balanitis causes the surfaces of the penile glans and prepuce to become swollen, tender, and itchy. The area also may reveal ulcers, venereal warts, and fissures—and in severe cases, even gangrene. Chemicals, drugs, infection, fungi, and special irritants in the urine caused by metabolic disorders act together or singly to produce this problem. Early medical attention is essential.[252]

Verumontanitis, inflammation of the verumontanum (an area located on the floor of the posterior urethra), is often caused by diseases of the prostate or seminal vesicles. Various disorders of this area, such as congestion, inflammation, granulation, and hypertrophy, may require hormone or other medical treatment, or even surgery. Premature ejaculation, frequency of urination, and obstructed ejaculatory ducts that produce low back pains may be symptomatic of disorders of the verumontanum.[252, 359]

SEXUAL DISORDERS

Sexual disorders are customarily considered to be physical anomalies of the genitalia caused by hereditary, constitutional, or postnatal factors.

Priapism is a continual and pathological erection of the penis. There is usually an erection of the corpora cavernosa without an accompanying erection of the glans of the penis or the corpora spongiosum (the small lower spongy body). The onset of priapism is sudden and painful, and is unaccompanied by sexual desire.[385]

The origins of this disorder range from leukemia to inflammation of the genital-urinary system to tumors and inflammation of the central nervous system. If erection persists for two days or more, thrombosis of the large spongy bodies occurs, followed by the possibility of a gristle-like replacement of the spongy bodies, thus rendering future penile erection impossible.[252]

Hypospadia occurs once in every 500 births, and is the second most common malformation, after club foot, found in male babies at the time of delivery. It is a congenital condition (although apparently no hereditary factor is involved) wherein the genital fold does not close completely during prenatal development, and the urethral opening is on the underside of the penis rather than on the tip end where it normally should be. In glandular hypospadia, the urethral meatus is slightly below and to the back of the customary opening; in penile hypospadia, the opening is somewhere along the lower part of the penile shaft. Plastic surgery should be performed as soon as possible on any child with this anomaly to ensure that the urethra and corpora cavernosa will develop properly and in straight alignment. Men in whom this condition remains uncorrected are usually quite able to engage in coitus; however, if the meatus is sufficiently recessed on the penile shaft, these men will obviously have difficulty in impregnating their wives.[252, 359] This disorder also occurs in women, but it is rarely bothersome.

Epispadia is much more rare than hypospadia and is usually associated with a congenital malformation of the bladder. In this disorder, the urethral opening is on the dorsum (top) of the penis. The epispadiac penis typically curves upward, is deformed, and requires early plastic surgery.[252, 350]

Phimosis is an anomaly in which the prepuce is abnormally long and cannot be pulled back or retracted over the glans of the penis.[196] Fibrous growths sometimes attach the glans to the prepuce, making it impossible to pull the foreskin back, and making even the attempt to do so quite painful.[252] Smegma may collect, leading to ulceration or inflammation of the penis. Surgery, usually in the form of circumcision, can correct this difficulty.

Strictures of the reproductive tracts. In the male urethral system, strictures can evolve in the prostatic, penile, and bulbous urethra. The symptomatology frequently involves difficulty in passing urine, accompanied by a burning sensation and mild urethral discharge. Psychological factors can enter the picture as well, frequently causing the added complication of impotency. The origin of these strictures is an infection of the urethral tract precipitated by scarring, blows, or injuries, or by tears and punctures made in the inept application of catheters and similar instruments. The disorder varies in severity.

In women, strictures of the reproductive tract are found not only in the urethra, but also in the internal cervical os and in the Fallopian tubes. If the cervical os is blocked, conception becomes impossible, and there will be a damming up of menstrual flow and other tissue debris. Dilation of the os or urethra gives some relief, although this procedure will not remove the scar tissue. A stretching process must be introduced, but it must also be gradual and extended over a long period if satisfactory results are to be obtained. Physicians believe that over-zealous treatment merely aggravates these conditions.[252, 368]

Polyps (papilloma) are pedunculated (stem-like) growths that arise from the mucosa and extend into the lumen or opening of any body cavity. They are true tumors, the inception of which is a morbid enlargement of the mucous membrane. Polyps may be found in any bodily area where there is mucous tissue. In the male genitalia, the tumors are benign and are usually found within the penile meatus. Urinary disturbances, such as painful, difficult, and urgent urination, and difficulties in sexual functioning are the usual symptoms of this disorder. Minor surgery is ordinarily sufficient to correct the problems.[252, 348, 368]

Cysts are sacs, containing a liquid or semisolid substance, that develop abnormally in some part of the body. They may appear in the bladder or urinary tract, in the prostate, Cowper's glands, or scrotum, and in the vagina, uterus, vulva, or Bartholin's glands, causing inordinate retention of urine and various sexual malfunctionings. The size of cysts varies considerably, and methods of treatment depend upon a number of circumstances, such as the location, size, and rate of growth of the cysts.[17, 252, 318, 368]

Edema (abnormal amount of fluid in intercellular tissue) of the scrotum results from inflammation or other disturbances in the vascular or lymphatic system. Such occurrences as physical trauma, allergic states, and insect bites may produce an edematous reaction that, because of the loose and elastic nature of scrotal tissue, causes the scrotum to swell to near basketball-size proportions.[252]

Hydrocele, a fairly common male birth malformation (ninth in frequency), is a collection of fluid within the two layers of tissue making up the tunica vaginalis (membranes covering the testes). As the testes descend from their abdominal position (usually at the seventh month of prenatal life) they carry with them two layers of the peritoneum; any abnormality in these layers of tissue can provide a natural environment for a variety of hydrocele conditions. Hydroceles can also follow physical trauma, operations, infection of the epididymis and other areas, gonorrhea, and tuberculosis. Suspending the scrotum and surgically removing the fluid and distressed portion of the tunica vaginalis are suggested methods of treatment. In some cases the fluid is drawn off with a hollow needle, although in this instance the possibility of infection is always present.[69, 252, 332, 350]

Spermatocele is a soft swelling on either side of the scrotum that develops because of an intrascrotal cyst. The cyst obstructs the tubular structure between the testicles and epididymis, causing a blockage of sperm and a collection of fluid. The fluid has a milky coloration because of the millions of sperm and lipids that are trapped there. Surgery is the usual method of treatment.[69, 252]

Varicocele is a swelling of the veins which lead to the testicles. Varicocele develop in 99% of the cases on the left side of the testicles; only 1% develop bilaterally. Perhaps one man in ten has some degree of spermatic vein dilation. There can be rather severe pain accompanied by a sensation of pulling and tugging at the testicles, although these symptoms disappear when the patient lies down and allows the blood to flow out of the veins. A suspensory can relieve the discomfort of the excessive weight, and cold baths may temporarily alleviate swelling and pain; but a surgical procedure is usually required to correct the condition.[69, 252]

Hematocele is an accumulation of blood in the tunica vaginalis usually resulting from an injury. Spontaneous hematocele may be a result of syphilis, arteriosclerosis, diabetes, or an inflammatory condition within the scrotum. Surgery is the treatment of choice.[69, 252] .

Cystocele is a hernial protrusion of the bladder through the vaginal wall. It is especially common, though in varying degrees of severity, among women who have had children. The muscle supports of the vagina become torn or considerably weakened, allowing the bladder to push through. A sensation in the lower abdomen of dragging or tugging, frequency of urination, incontinence, and infection are common symptoms. Sometimes pessaries may help correct the less severe of these conditions, but more often, surgical repair is required. Rupture of the perineal area, or damage to it, may produce *rectoceles*, wherein the vagina becomes closed by a bulging rectum.[252, 368]

Torsion of the testicle is an abnormal rotation of the testicle that causes a blockage of the blood supply to that organ. The rotation is caused by any of several physiological conditions. The amount of damage varies, depending upon the degree of torsion and how long the condition persists. If severe torsion is allowed to continue for as long as a few hours, necrosis of testicular tissue or even complete gangrene in the area can result. Survival of the testicle depends upon prompt diagnosis and appropriate corrective procedures, such as untwisting the spermatic cord. Manual efforts to correct the condition without opening the scrotum are unsuccessful; the condition should be rectified by open surgery.[252]

Undescended testes (cryptorchidism) are found in about one in fifty boys at the age of puberty, but this ratio dwindles to approximately one in 500 among adult men. The delay in the descent can be caused by an inadequate gonadotropic hormone secretion; a congenital defect in the gonadal germ cells, or the absence of them altogether; or physiological failure, such as a malformed inguinal ring, in the structure through which the testes pass from the abdomen to the scrotum.[122, 252]

Testes that remain undescended after puberty will progressively degenerate, and eunuchoidal (having only partial external genital structure) symptoms will develop, especially if both testicles are involved. Hormonal treatment will often effect a successful descent of the testicles. In instances where physical defects block what would otherwise be a normal descent, or where some cosmetic repair is desirable, surgery is indicated. In still other instances, the descent of the testes is faulty in that they enter foreign areas and lodge there. These *ectopic testes* require surgery to effect proper placement in the scrotum.[141]

Testicular failure may involve either the interstitial cells that produce male hormones, or the spermatic tubes where sperm develop, or both. In almost all instances, failure of the interstitial cells involves failure of the spermatic tubes, although the reverse is not necessarily true. *Hypogonadism* (insufficient secretion of the gonads) produces eunuchoidal characteristics, sometimes involving overmuch growth of the long bones. The boy, although shorter in stature than others his age, will have proportionately very long arms and legs. Approximately three-quarters of eunuchoidal boys are underweight because of poorly developed muscles and bones; but even so, these boys commonly develop excessive fat over the abdomen, around the mammary glands, above the pubis, and on the buttocks.[252] External genitals are extraordinarily small and poorly developed, and the prostate and seminal vesicles may also be markedly underdeveloped. Secondary sexual characteristics are typically feminine in appearance.

Testicular failure may be intrinsic, or it may manifest itself at any of the different stages of a boy's development and growth. Treatment usually consists of endocrine therapy, and meets with rather good success.

Ordinarily, the interstitial cells begin to produce the hormone, androgen, when a boy is about twelve years old. This hormonal production, however, can begin as early as eight years, or be delayed until the boy is, say, twenty-two.[252] When the production is impeded, the youngster frequently becomes obese and reveals retarded genital development. Diet sometimes hastens laggard pubescence. Hormonal treatment, however, is commonly used to accelerate the process, not only to avoid any physical problems (which will very likely correct themselves in time when the development eventually commences), but also to prevent psychological and emotional difficulties that are liable to develop from a feeling of "being different" and from the little cruelties inflicted by the boy's peer group.

Testicular failure can also manifest itself in sterility without the presence of any overt signs of changes in the external genitalia.

Sexual precocity may have its origins in a premature development of hypothalmic centers, in which event the disorder is said to be the *cerebral* type; certain dysfunctions of the adrenal cortex or the interstitial cells of the testes cause the *endocrine* type of the disorder. Primary and secondary sexual characteristics are prematurely well developed in young boys so affected. They may have the appearance of a small adult (endocrine type); or their physique may be inordinately muscular and their bone structure mature, yet they maintain other boyish characteristics and a normal development of the central nervous system (cerebral type).[252] Similar manifestations in girls are discussed below.

Neoplasms of the ovaries are new growths on or within the ovaries, sometimes so greatly affecting the hormonal output of these organs that marked changes in secondary sexual characteristics take place. Some *feminizing neoplasms* develop in prepuberal girls, typically resulting in rapid and premature enlargement of the breasts, premature development of the genitalia, and early growth of pubic hair. In the sexually mature woman, there may be irregular uterine bleeding, endometrial growth, or breast enlargement. Because they are the cause of hormonal dysfunction, *masculinizing neoplasms* produce changes in physical appearance, including hirsutism (abnormal hairiness), enlargement of the clitoris, overdevelopment of muscles, and a masculine lowering of the voice. The condition also can induce such defeminizing changes as sterility, amenorrhea, and decrease in breast size. Most incidences of masculinizing neoplasms occur in women between the ages of twenty-five and forty-five, although girls as young as fifteen and women as old as sixty-five have been affected by the anomaly. Other endocrine changes may result from abnormal growths in hormone-producing glands, such as the adrenal or the pituitary.[252, 348]

Chromosomal anomalies. Since early in this century, it has been thought that man's cellular structure contains forty-eight chromosomes (Latin: *chromo,* color; *soma,* body; so called because they become visible if put in special dyes). Recently, however, careful research revealed that there are normally only forty-six, represented by forty-four *autosomes* (non-sex chromosomes) and an additional pair of sex chromosomes labeled XX in the female and XY in the male. The phenomenon was first noted in 1938 (and has been studied in detail since then) that certain congenital sexual disorders are related to an abnormal *karyotype,* a term used to indicate an arrangement of chromosomes.[45, 377] Furthermore, it was discovered in 1949 that there is typically present in the cell nuclei of female mammals an extra piece of *chromatin* (stainable portion of cell nucleus shaped in the form of a drumstick) that makes women chromatin-positive; this extra bit of chromatin is absent in the cells of males—hence males are chromatin-negative. The substance is present in a week-old female embryo and will continue to be present throughout the individual's pre- and postnatal life. The presence or absence of sex chromatin also plays a crucial role in some congenital human sexual disorders.[18, 347]

Best known of these pathological disorders are *Turner's syndrome* and *Klinefelter's syndrome*, and the conditions are believed to arise from meiotic (reduction of two sets of chromosomes to a single set) or mitotic (method of cell division) nondisjunction. If the disorder is meiotic in character, some ova are produced during oogenesis which have twenty-two chromosomes, others containing twenty-four, rather than the normal twenty-three. If an atypical ovum containing twenty-two chromosomes is fertilized, an XO sex karyotype, or Turner's syndrome, is the result, rather than the normal XX or XY karyotype. If a twenty-four-chromosome ovum is fertilized, an XXY karyotype, or Klinefelter's syndrome, is the result. Similar abnormal karyotypes may be produced when normal ova are fertilized by spermatozoa that have twenty-two or twenty-four chromosomes.

In mitotic nondisjunction, there are originally the normal forty-six chromosomes; but the cell then divides into two unequally endowed daughter cells, one containing forty-four chromosomes, the other forty-six. If the cell with the abnormal number of chromosomes prevails, an abnormal karyotype results.

In Turner's syndrome (XO), one of the X chromosomes is missing, the total number of chromosomes being in this case forty-five: forty-four autosomes and only one X chromosome instead of the normal two. The abnormality will produce a woman who has the primary external sex structure of a female, although poorly developed and infantile in size; however, the ovaries are missing. Besides the deficiencies in the primary and secondary sexual characteristics, other typical indications of this disorder are a short stature, winglike folds of skin extending from the base of the skull to an area over the clavicle, and a broad, stocky chest; deafness and mental deficiency are also fairly common.[252, 347]

In Klinefelter's syndrome (XXY), an ovum contributes an extra X chromosome, making a total of forty-seven chromosomes upon fertilization. This additional female (X) sex chromosome and the presence of sex chromatin produce a man with a distinctly feminine physical appearance. The testicles are small and incapable of producing mature sperm.

As new scientific instruments are developed and techniques for investigation are refined, new discoveries in the field of chromosome structure are made. For example, individuals with XXXY, XXXXY, and XXXXXY karyotypes have recently been discovered.[45]

Atrophic conditions of the vulva may mean loss of fatty tissue in the mons pubis and labia majora; reduction in size of the clitoris and labia minora; loss of elasticity of the skin; inflammation, abrasions, and fissures of the vulva; and a development of a leather-like condition of the vulval tissue. **Atrophic conditions of the vagina** may mean a reduction or loss of its wrinkled surface; shrinking of the mucous membrane; narrowing of the canal, especially at the apex; formation of adhesions; and an ill-smelling, irritating discharge. Causality may be related to aging, removal of ovaries, X-ray, or fungal invasion.[252, 346]

Varicose veins of the vulva usually arise during pregnancy when intrapelvic pressure retards venous flow. An aching, "dragging" sensation may be felt in the pelvic region; the symptoms may be more severe while the woman is standing, then tend to disappear when she is in a supine position. Surgery can correct this and other circulatory disorders of the vulval region.[252]

Congenital anomalies of the vagina, uterus, and Fallopian tubes are more common than many realize. For example, the vagina may be entirely missing (gynatresia). (In this case, an artificial vagina that is functional for sexual intercourse can be surgically constructed.) Double vaginas also occur; one is usually considerably larger than the other, or the vagina may be divided into two parts by a septum, as the nose is. Similar anomalies are also occasionally found in the uterus (rudimentary, double, divided) and in the tubes (rudimentary, extra ampullae, blocked opening). And the uterus or tubes may be missing altogether. If the organs exist, even in a malformed state they may or may not be functional, depending upon how extensively they are affected. Such congenital anomalies are usually a contingency of imperfect development of the Mullerian system, involving failure of the Mullerian ducts to fuse completely or properly during prenatal development.[17, 215, 252, 368]

An **imperforate hymen** is a condition wherein the vagina is sealed off by a solid mass of hymenal tissue. Until the onset of menstruation, the condition may be unnoticed; but unless the hymen is punctured at the menarche, the menstrual fluid is perforce retained in the vagina and the uterus must enlarge in order to contain the flow. Incision of the hymen corrects the condition easily and quickly. A *fibrous hymen* is not a common occurrence, however often the condition is discussed in medical writings. The hymenal tissue in this instance is inordinately thick and tough. It must be surgically incised before there can be a normal opening to the vagina, and before penile penetration is possible.[252, 348, 368]

Vaginal fistulae are pipe-like openings that may develop between the bladder and vagina, urethra and vagina, or rectum and vagina. The etiology may be congenital, as in hypospadia (in which the urethra empties into the vaginal tract); or traumatic, such as in obstetrical or surgical injury. Malignant tumors can also produce these unwelcome fistulae. Urinary incontinence and severe infection are only two of the possible consequences of such anomalies. Surgical treatment is difficult and complicated; however, recent advances in operative methods used in the investigation and correction of pelvic disorders make prognosis more favorable than it was in the recent past.[17, 252, 348, 368]

Abnormal uterine bleeding is the most frequent gynecological complaint encountered by physicians, and the term "functional uterine bleeding" refers to hemorrhages not precipitated by detectable anomalies. If ovulation should not occur, too little or no progesterone is secreted; yet the secretion of estrogen continues. The result in some instances — although not all — is that the proliferation or growth phase of the menstrual cycle persists, and with it comes a thickening of the mucosa. There is no growth stimulation of the ovarian follicles because ovarian estrogen inhibits the release of FSH (the follicle stimulating hormone) from the pituitary gland. The endometrium lining, therefore, thrives under the continued flow of estrogen, and the nonstimulated and unruptured follicles gradually convert into cystic structures. This process reduces the level of estrogen, which causes some FSH production and hence the development of some *new* follicles; the growth process of the endometrium lining is repeated, eventually producing both gross and microscopic changes in the endometrium itself. The irregular hormonal interplay produces unnatural growth in the uterine tissue; and abnormal bleeding, both in frequency and amount, from the uterus may result. In about 66% of the cases of functional uterine bleeding, endometrial hyperplasia (that is, an excessive formation of the uterine lining) is present.

Endometrial hyperplasia may be induced simply by the presence of polyps, or by the more serious conditions of uterine carcinoma, pregnancy disorders, or psychogenic states. Birth control pills inhibit ovulation, but they do not cause a disturbance in hormone balance; they therefore act to prevent malfunctions of this nature. Women should not have to be encouraged to consult with their gynecologist regularly, most especially when any unusual or abnormal complex of symptoms pertaining to the reproductive system manifests itself.[17, 252, 348, 368]

Cervical erosion is in most cases due to congenital defects or childbirth injuries. The usual symptoms are red granular tissue in the area in and surrounding the external cervical opening or os. Any break in the cervical tissue, such as unhealed lacerations caused by childbirth, or any unusual exposure of the cervical mucous glands to the bacteria inhabiting the vaginal tract, makes the cervix susceptible to infection, which is usually chronic and low-grade. Infection of this area may lead to erosion and ulceration of the cervical tissue, and a partial excision of the cervix may be required to correct the condition.[102, 252, 348, 368]

Displacement of the uterus is said to exist when the womb becomes fixed in a position that it does not ordinarily assume. The normal position for the uterus when a woman is standing erect is approximately at right angles to the axis of the vagina, putting the uterus in an almost horizontal plane above the bladder. For various reasons, the ligaments which support and position the uterus may become too taut or too loose, and the uterus then shifts to an unusual position, showing varying degrees of deviation. This shifting frequently causes painful menstruation, backaches, and pelvic congestion, and makes sexual intercourse uncomfortable. If there is no pain connected with uterine displacement, there is no necessity to correct the condition; the displacement does not seem to interfere with the possibility of a woman's becoming pregnant, and properly positioning the uterus apparently does not increase the chances for pregnancy.[252, 368]

Prolapse of the uterus is the relaxation of the supportive uterine ligaments, allowing the uterus to descend into the vaginal canal. The degree of prolapse can be slight, wherein the supporting tissue relaxes minimally to permit only a small portion of the uterus to drop into the vagina; or second degree, wherein the cervix actually protrudes from the vagina; or complete, in which the entire uterus itself protrudes from the vaginal barrel. Prolapse of the uterus usually pulls down the bladder as well, and often there is an accompanying cystocele. Functional bleeding, backaches, a "bearing-down" feeling, and difficulties in elimination are frequent complaints associated with this uterine irregularity. Surgery is usually required to correct the condition, especially if the prolapse is second degree or complete.[17, 252, 348, 368]

Uterine myomata or **fibroid tumors** are found in 4% to 11% of women, and vary greatly in size and position. The description "fibroid" is something of a misnomer, in that these tumors form from muscle cells, not from fibrous tissue. Their incidence is greatest among women in their fifties, although women considerably younger may develop uterine tumors of prodigious size. It is thought that hormonal imbalance of some sort produces fibroid tumors, since it has been established that existing ones either shrink or remain static in their dimensions after menopause. In about 50% of the cases, excessive bleeding is a symptom, and eventual calcification in a fibroid tumor is not unusual. A gynecologist can easily determine in each case the most suitable method of treatment indicated.[17, 252, 348, 368]

Endometriosis involves the ectopic or aberrant growth of the endometrium (lining of the uterus). Symptoms of the disorder may include sterility (32% to 53% of the time), dysmenorrhea, backaches, and painful sexual intercourse. While the condition can exist as long as the ovaries produce hormones, it is most often found in women who are in their thirties. The tissue can commence growth in any of various parts of the body; the cervix, abdominal walls, intestines, Bartholin's glands, vulva, and even the umbilicus may be encroached upon by ectopic endometrium. But the tissue always retains the histologic and biologic characteristics of uterine mucosa. Treatment depends upon the severity of the symptoms, and includes cervical dilation, surgery, or simply encouraging the patient to become pregnant. Surgery usually involves the removal of the organs or areas invaded together with the surrounding tissue.[17, 252, 348, 368]

Menstrual cramps, if their origin is physical, are usually caused by a tilted or infantile uterus, inadequate dilation or blockage of the cervical os, endometrial disorders, and similar anomalies. Psychological factors are a more likely cause of menstrual cramps than physiological conditions are.[60, 76, 233, 234]

Hermaphroditism is a condition in which an individual has the gonads of both sexes; that is, both ovarian and testicular tissue is present.[252] Cases of true hermaphroditism are extremely rare, with perhaps fewer than one hundred valid incidences appearing in the medical literature of the entire world.[15, 239] It would be possible, technically, for a hermaphrodite to impregnate as a male and also to conceive as a woman.[252] Indeed, Brazilian doctors recently reported a case of a true hermaphrodite who had a developing fetus in the womb, and who also possessed testicles capable of producing sperm. Furthermore, the person claimed to be both the father and the mother of the child![239] There is some doubt that this was an instance of self-impregnation, however, because the female hormones of the ovary would ordinarily sterilize the testis, making the person incapable of fertilizing ova.

Pseudohermaphroditism is a much more common disorder than true hermaphroditism is; some form of it appears in about one of every 1000 infants born.[146] The male pseudohermaphrodite has gonads that are testes, at least from a histological standpoint, although he may exhibit varying degrees of external female characteristics. The gonads of a female pseudohermaphrodite are ovaries, but her external genitalia (and often other of her bodily characteristics) are those of a male.

During the normal development of the Wolffian and Mullerian ducts, the gonads develop into either testes or ovaries. When certain aberrations in the process of sexual differentiation occur, there results a reversal in cellular morphosis; either or both the gonads and genitalia, in addition to other bodily characteristics, assume the features of the opposite sex.[252] These people usually have both male and female sex organs in rudimentary form, and their true sex is difficult to determine. Because the sex of the pseudohermaphrodite can be so easily misjudged, it is not uncommon for such a child to be brought up as a

member of the wrong sex. Childhood influences quite naturally predispose the individual to assume the interests, attitudes, and sexual
behavior of one sex, however much his somatic characteristics may
be those of the opposite sex—another indication of the superiority of
psychological over physiological factors in sexual matters.[238]

When external somatic characteristics cause any ambiguity regarding the sex of a newborn child, it is essential that the parents
immediately seek the advice of specialists. Little success in accurate
sex-role rehabilitation can be expected after a pseudohermaphrodite
child has reached school age.[238] Sometimes surgery is indicated, not
only to alter the sexual characteristics of the child, but to alleviate
the emotional problems that typically accompany such anomalies.

Dyspareunia is painful coitus. It can happen to both men and
women, although women are affected far more frequently than men
are. Men sometimes have acute pain at the time of erection (which is
not actually dyspareunia). Dyspareunia occurs in men during intromission when they suffer severe, jabbing pain at the time of orgasm; it
is commonly caused by congestion of the prostate, seminal vesicles,
or ejaculatory ducts, or by an inflamed verumontanum. Otherwise,
dyspareunia in men is extremely rare.

Dyspareunia in women frequently has its inception in tension,
fear, or anxiety over initial sexual intercourse, and the pain can involve
vagina, cervix, uterus, or bladder. The vaginal muscles become taut
and coitus can be painful, especially if the husband is clumsy or
insensitive. Furthermore, depending upon the type and thickness of
the hymen, pain may be experienced when the tissue is ruptured by
penile penetration.[122, 177, 252] Some women suffer considerable pain when
the cervix is touched and moved by the penis during sexual intercourse;
coitus, in fact, becomes impossible at times. Surgically severing particular nerves leading to the uterus has given complete relief from this
sort of pain, and at the same time does not diminish the sexual enjoyment of 80% of the women so treated.[390]

Medical opinion is that if dyspareunia persists over a period of
time, small undetected lesions in the vagina are to be suspected, since
they cause the disorder 85% of the time.[188] Furthermore, any infection
of the vagina, uterus, bladder, or surrounding areas can obviously
mean painful intercourse for a woman. Dyspareunia in postmenopausal
women frequently occurs because the mucous membrane of the vagina
has become fragile and thin, sometimes shrinking in thickness to a
fraction of its fertile adult size, and does not secrete sufficient lubrication for easy penile intromission. Vaginal creams containing female
hormones are frequently prescribed in such cases to act as a lubricant

and to stimulate the mucous membrane.[72, 282] A displaced or prolapsed uterus is another persistent cause of a woman's having painful coitus; so also are polyps, cysts, and tumors of the reproductive system. Medical and surgical approaches are obviously of great value in attacking many of the causes of dyspareunia. Nevertheless, the value of psychotherapy should not be overlooked in those instances in which the foundations of the disorder lie in emotional blocks and fears.

Vaginismus is an extremely powerful and often severely painful contraction of the muscles that surround the vaginal tract. The anticipated pain of first penile penetration, or fear or guilt surrounding sexual intercourse, can cause these muscular spasms, which may persist for long periods of time. Even an attempt at intromission of the penis or the introduction of a finger into the vagina will often produce

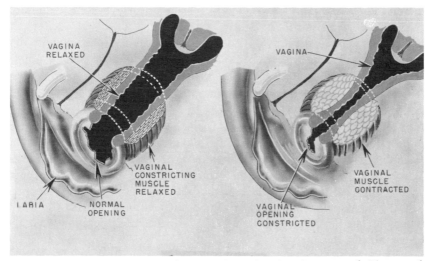

Fig. 13-2.　Diagram of vaginal muscles, relaxed and contracted. Photograph courtesy *Sexology* magazine.

agonizing pain. Husbands as well as wives must understand the dynamics behind vaginismus and avoid any behavior which will produce discomfort for either partner. A selfish, inconsiderate, and brutal husband can do irreparable damage to the marriage by forging ahead like a battering ram in his attempts at sexual intercourse when his wife is suffering these muscular spasms.

Vaginismus, strangely, seldom occurs in women of the lower socioeconomic-educational strata; it is an affliction almost exclusively of women in the upper levels of these groups.[177] Sometimes local anesthetics applied to the vulva, vagina, and hymenal area before intromission is attempted are successful in reducing the pain. A physician can also supply a young wife with a series of graduated dilators that will stretch the vaginal muscles to the extent of comfortable accommodation of her husband's penis.[348] Because vaginismus frequently has its roots in the psychological quagmire of fear, guilt, and shame, physical efforts at overcoming it may be unsuccessful and psychotherapy is therefore indicated.

Congested ovaries and testicles. Women may develop this condition when they participate in prolonged, sexually stimulating petting in which there is no culminating release through orgasm. As it is a common occurrence during an engagement period, the term "engagement ovaries" is frequently used. Protracted but unrelieved sexual tensions cause blood to concentrate in the ovaries and other areas of the internal genitalia, producing a swelling and congestion of the tissues, which is the source of the pain. A woman's vulva may also become painfully congested for the same reason. In men, protracted sexual excitement without orgasmic relief gives rise to a concentration of blood in the testicles, which creates conditions of swelling, pain, and aching, popularly called "stone-ache." [215, 235]

Congenital and acquired anomalies of the breast are found in both men and women. The most frequent of these disorders among men is *gynecomastia,* in which there is a feminization and abnormal increase in breast size. This disorder may have its inception in adolescence when an endocrine change ordinarily takes place. It may also occur in adulthood as a result of developed endocrine disorders, or because estrogenic substances have been medically prescribed to combat certain ailments, such as prostatic carcinoma. Endocrine medication to shrink excessive tissue, or simple surgery to remove it, are the most popular methods of treatment.

Women may possess one or more extra breasts *(polymastia),* supernumerary nipples *(polythelia),* or an abnormally enlarged breast or breasts; and, even more rarely, the nipple or areola may be missing altogether. These conditions are all congenital anomalies. Extra breasts and nipples usually follow the milk line, which starts under the arm, then extends through the breasts and down both sides of the abdomen in a line to the lips of the vulva, terminating in the inner thighs. Plastic surgery can correct these abnormalities once the enlargement has formed.[102, 252] Any unusual growth, pain, or change in the feel, function, or appearance of the breast should be investigated immediately by a physician.

CHAPTER 14

Sexual Aberrations

ONE OF THE major problems in the field of sexology—and indeed, in the whole realm of mental health—today centers around the question of what is normal sexual behavior and what is abnormal. The following discussion is not intended to add fuel to the fire of this controversy, but rather to present certain considerations so that the reader might come to view different forms of sexual expression in an objective light, and perhaps thereby attain a better understanding of certain of his associates.

Too many people are ready to stigmatize any sexual activity which deviates from their own method of sexual behavior as being aberrant or perverted.[119] What is usual in one culture may be unusual in another, and thus may become branded as abnormality, although unusual sexual behavior is not tantamount to perversion simply because it is out of the ordinary for that culture. The more scientists discover about sexual behavior, in fact, the less they are inclined to label unusual sexual expression as abnormal. It is generally accepted, for instance, by authorities in the field that about 70% of the American males will engage in some "perverse" sexual act or another during their lifetime; furthermore, about 60% will take part in such behavior on a fairly frequent basis, at least during some period of their lives.[178]

Society seems to be progressing toward a more liberal definition of what constitutes normal sexual activity. Generally speaking, if this behavior is not harmful to the participants, is carried out by consenting adults without any sort of coercion, and is out of sight and sound of unwilling observers, it should be considered acceptable, whether or not others would care to participate in similar acts. These criteria, then, would probably serve as a valid basis on which to judge what is and is not abnormal.[119]

Ordinarily, sexual aberrations or perversions may be classified according to (1) the method of functioning and quality of the sexual striving; (2) the choice of the sexual partner, either person or object; and (3) the degree of desire and strength of the sexual drive.[373]

273

ABNORMAL METHODS OF FUNCTIONING
AND QUALITY OF THE SEXUAL STRIVING

1. **Sadism** is a sexual abnormality wherein the disturbed person gains sexual gratification, or at least an increase in sexual pleasure, by inflicting either physical or psychological pain upon his partner in the sexual relationship. The aggressive act has no purpose other than that the pain thus caused is the source of sensual gratification.

The term "sadism" derives from the name of the French author the Marquis de Sade (1740-1814). This man wrote extensively of his erotic exploits, which included several marriages, arrests for cruel acts in houses of prostitution, the luring of a shopkeeper's wife into a house where he proceeded to horsewhip her at gunpoint, an elopement with his wife's sister, administering poisonous "aphrodisiac" drugs to guests, and inflicting hundreds of scalpel wounds and severing the veins of a woman whom he confined to a house.

The causes of sadism are as varied as the means of expressing it. The disturbed person may have been taught, consciously or unconsciously, to have disgust for anything sexual. Since normal sexuality is unacceptable to him, his acts of cruelty are a punishment of his partner for engaging in something so shameful. Another source of sadism is a fear of castration (feelings of inferiority) wherein the sadistic acts are a reassurance that he is more powerful than his partner, and therefore he need have no fear. Some sadists' behavior is merely a method of acting out repressed hostility towards parents.[52, 373]

Whipping, biting, pinching, and slapping are typical of the acts of physical pain inflicted by the sadist; if sadism is expressed verbally, it is in the form of sarcastic remarks, belittling, threatening, teasing, or bullying. As with nearly all sexual aberrations, sadism is found more frequently among men than women, probably because of its aggressive nature. It should be remembered, however, that this aggressiveness may be unconscious and expressed indirectly or deviously, as well as through the conscious and direct actions mentioned above.

Lust murder is the extreme of sadistic sexual perversion, as the victim must be murdered and mutilated in order to provide the perpetrator with sexual gratification. In true lust murders, no coitus occurs; orgasm is the outcome of the act of murder and mutilation. At least at the time of the act, these persons' mental illness is at the psychotic level. The underlying cause of such violence often relates to a fear of possible rejection by a mature woman, and an accompanying hostility and aggression.

2. **Masochism** is the mirror image of sadism. The disturbed per-

son receives sexual pleasure or gratification from being hurt, physically or mentally, by his sexual partner. The disorder also derives its name from a historical figure, the Austrian novelist Leopold von Sacher-Masoch (1836-1895). A Doctor of Law at the age of nineteen, he set out on a long career of masochistic involvements. His first love, an older woman who insulted and victimized him at every turn, finally left him for a Russian adventurer. He then met a princess who compelled him to serve as her valet and secretary until she tired of him. After affairs with two baronesses, the second a lesbian, he married an extremely ugly woman who satisfied his craving for punishment, but who eventually deserted him.

Masochism, like sadism, develops from an attitude of shame and disgust toward normal heterosexual relationships. The masochist uses the pain and punishment inflicted on him to wash away the guilt he associates with his sexual desires. In other cases, the masochist dominates his partner with his ability to endure punishment, which to his way of thinking proclaims to the world his strength and superiority, and which also serves to make him the center of attention. Often, the sexual partner is identified with a parent-figure who dominated him as a child. For example, the masochist may remember experiencing sexual excitement in childhood while being beaten, a sensation centered in the erogenous zones of the skin about the buttocks and the muscles below the skin. Finally, the masochist is so fearful of rejection that he is willing to be subjected to almost any humiliation or punishment that will please his partner and win for him, as he sees it, affection and acceptance.[82]

According to certain psychoanalytic interpretations, the masochist considers suffering a prerequisite to pleasure, since in his past experiences pain and sexual pleasure are somehow connected. In addition, stressing one's own helplessness is an appeal to the threatening or protecting power that now rests in his partner. In men, masochism is often a symbol of self-castration which, in their rationale, robs others of the power to castrate them.

This aberration may also take the form of mental masochism wherein the individual seeks out mental rather than physical suffering. Anthropologists and psychologists view sadomasochistic behavior as an essential part of the mating relationship of many lower primates and other animals; and in primitive societies, forms of sexual violence, such as deep scratch and bite wounds, are commonplace. However, when men deliberately conjure up fantasies of ill-treatment which are sexually exciting, or when they actively seek physical and psychological pain, such as from chaining, beating, switching, kicking, and verbal abuse, as means of enhancing their sexual powers and pleasure, there is cause for concern and psychological treatment is definitely indicated.[82, 373]

3. **Exhibitionism** is an aberration wherein sexual gratification is derived from exhibiting the genitals to unwitting (and typically unwilling) sexual prey. Its pathology lies in the fact that satisfaction is gained in a vicarious manner rather than through a straightforward sexual experience. It is a relatively common sexual problem, and is involved in 35% of all arrests for sexual violations.[6] Far more men than women are exhibitionists, although just how many women do actually exhibit themselves is impossible to determine. The public has a more tolerant attitude toward the exposed bodies of women than it does toward those of men, and women found exposing themselves would probably not be reported by the beholder—except perhaps to friends who are called in to share the view.

The inception of this behavior is classically the exhibitionist's feelings of insignificance or inadequacy: he hopes to gain the attention he craves through exhibition. Some psychoanalysts claim that this deviancy stems from a fear of castration, the exposure of self being explained as an attempt to deny it. Others believe that exhibitionism is an extreme form of autoeroticism based on narcissistic (self-love) impulses.

Typically, the exhibitionist is a quiet, timid, submissive person who is beset with feelings of inadequacy and insecurity. He is usually described as being "nice" but immature. He was characteristically reared in a cultural atmosphere of overstrict and puritanical attitudes toward sex, and his formative years were dominated by a powerful, engulfing mother. Despite the fact that most of these men are married, the sexual relationship with their wives is quite likely a poor one. All these influences work to create in exhibitionists pervading doubts and fears concerning their masculinity.[82]

The exhibitionist obviously hopes his actions will have a profound shock effect on the viewer, and the woman who responds hysterically to his behavior merely feeds his illness. Confronted by an exhibitionist, a woman's most sensible approach is calmly to ignore the act, making the suggestion, at the same time, that he stands in need of psychological help and can benefit from it.

There is also pseudoexhibitionism, which is often confused with true exhibitionism. In this syndrome, a person is under stress because heterosexual relations are not available, and he exhibits himself only as a poor substitute for the sexual intercourse he prefers.

Very frequently, exhibitionism is linked with a compulsive pattern of behavior wherein the display occurs in the same place and usually at the same time of day. In these linkage cases, the prognosis is fairly good. The factors involved in their exhibitionistic tendencies are more easily made clear and intelligible to the majority of these patients than they are to most nonlinkage ones. Understanding the etiology of their difficulties, they appear genuinely to feel that a serious effort on their part will lead to a more healthy sexual adjustment.

4. **Scoptophilia** and **voyeurism** are disturbances in which the viewer of sexual acts and erotic things derives unusual sensual pleasure and gratification. There is a difference between the two: scoptophilia refers to pleasure gained from observing sexual acts and genitalia, while voyeurism involves only the scrutinizing of nudes.[175] The terms are frequently used interchangeably, however, with voyeurism's having the more popular usage. In the case of the voyeur (commonly called a "Peeping Tom"), the viewing is usually done secretly. In his efforts to observe the sexual activity of others, he often hopefully peers through windows, or may go to such lengths as to bore peepholes through walls and doors of toilets, dressing rooms, and guest rooms.

Only a small number of women are known to be voyeurs or scoptophiliacs. According to FBI reports, nine men to one woman are arrested on charges of "peeping." Kinsey found that women generally are offended by the observation of sexual acts ("peeping" activities, pornographic films, lewd pictures), and denounce them on moral, social, and aesthetic grounds.[176]

Like other sexual aberrations, these two deviant phenomena are believed to develop as defense mechanisms against what the individual feels is a threat to his self-evaluation. By engaging merely in surreptitious examination of sexual details, he guards against any personal failure in coitus, while at the same time enjoying a feeling of superiority over those whom he secretly observes. According to psychoanalytic interpretation, fixations relating to certain events witnessed as a child, *e.g.,* seeing parents in the act of sexual intercourse, underlie voyeurism.

As in the case of exhibitionism, many of the milder incidents of voyeurism may in fact be classified as pseudovoyeurism, since they serve only as a substitute for preferred but unattainable sexual intercourse. Furthermore, the desire to view the naked body of one's sexual partner is certainly normal; so also is the pleasure a couple experience in viewing themselves by way of mirrors in the act of coitus itself. Viewing becomes abnormal only when it is preferred to petting or sexual intercourse.

5. **Troilism** (also **triolism**) is the sharing of a sexual partner with another person while that person looks on. The circumstances often involve two couples having sexual relations at the same time in the

visual presence of each other. The troilist is typically a sexual inadequate who cannot perform the sex act unless he is partaking in the "sharing" experience.[42] Troilism encompasses elements of voyeurism and exhibitionism. It can also constitute expression of latent or disguised homosexuality, since the troilist may identify with his marital partner during these erotic activities. This aberrant behavior is far more prevalent among men than among women in that men are the usual instigators and derive the greatest pleasure from it.

6. **Transvestism** refers to sexual excitement or gratification derived from dressing in the clothes of the opposite sex.[48] There is some doubt, because of the curious nature and ramifications of this behavior, whether it should be included in this or the second classification of aberrations. However, the disturbance seems more a matter of functioning than of abnormal object of sexual striving, hence its inclusion here. Although it is usually thought that transvestites are drawn primarily from the homosexual segment of the population, such behavior is sometimes found in heterosexual, asexual, and bisexual people as well.

The practice usually begins in early childhood, and is often evoked by parental rejection of the sex of the child. An unattractive woman will sometimes retaliate by dressing in a man's clothing. Whatever the cause, many transvestites engage only in normal and acceptable sexual activities, their strange dressing habits on "special occasions" being their only deviation. Most of these people are able to make a satisfactory adjustment to sex and marriage, especially when they receive understanding and cooperation from their marriage partner.

Herodotus, the early Greek historian, wrote of a primitive people living on the shore of the Black Sea in which the men not only wore female clothes but engaged in traditionally female activity. He attributed their behavior to repeated horseback riding accidents that led to atrophy of the reproductive organs, and subsequent impotence and effeminacy. Similar organic theories concerning transvestism persist today, along with theories placing the onus on hormonal imbalance, but these are discredited by practically all specialists in the field of sexology.[48]

Treatment in an attempt to correct this deviant behavior varies from psychotherapy to the administration of hormones. In some extreme cases, the individual actually seeks surgery to change his genital structure to that of the opposite sex. These people, however, usually have deep-seated and serious psychiatric problems, and more correctly should be called **transsexualists** rather than transvestites. Transsexualists constitute a severe form of a sex-role inversion in that they refuse to accept their genetic sex and seek surgery to make the necessary cosmetic and functional changes to transform them into the opposite sex.

Such surgical procedures have been practiced for a number of years in certain European countries, but only recently have they been performed in this country, the first hospital openly performing such surgery being Johns Hopkins in Baltimore.

7. **Sexual oralism** refers to pleasure obtained from the application of lips, tongue, and mouth to the sexual organs of one's partner. It is considered abnormal, however, only when it is used to the exclusion of all other methods of sexual outlet. True deviation from traditional techniques in sexual activity is becoming more and more difficult to pinpoint; what is considered a deviation by one group may be perfectly normal behavior in another. For example, methods of extravaginal intercourse are frowned upon by some people, yet readily accepted by others. To repeat the definitions given in an earlier chapter, fellatio is oral stimulation of the penis, and cunnilingus is oral stimulation of the vulva. There is reasonably wide acceptance of these methods of sexual foreplay and outlet, especially in the higher educational groups. Many people will not readily admit to these practices, however, out of fear that they might be denounced as abnormal.[111, 122, 204, 379]

8. **Sexual analism** refers to the use of the anus for copulation. **Sodomy** is another term for this act, although its legal interpretation may encompass a much wider range of sexual aberrations. Sexual analism is seldom practiced in heterosexual contacts, except for occasional experimentation; but about 20% of male homosexuals use this technique as a method of sexual intercourse.[180]

Homosexuals and, to a lesser extent, heterosexuals make use of other body parts in sexual relations—for example, using the space between the thighs, which is an act called *interfemoral sexual intercourse*. Scientific opinion is that there is nothing physically or psychologically wrong or abnormal with nonvaginal methods of coitus.

An excessive adherence to one technique only of sexual activity often indicates compulsive behavior utilized as a means of avoiding emotional stress that would accrue from a wider scope of sexual expression.[122] Furthermore, the limitation of sexual activity to the repetition of one or two techniques can lead to a sort of "bedroom boredom," which too often generates marital discord.

ABNORMAL CHOICE OF SEXUAL PARTNER, EITHER PERSON OR OBJECT

1. **Homosexuality** is a sexual attraction to a member of the same sex, or manifest sexual relations with that person. Kinsey and his co-workers established that there are degrees of sexuality, and devised a seven-point scale to categorize the heterosexual-homosexual balance.[180]

At one extreme is exclusive heterosexuality in which no homosexuality is involved. This is followed by predominant heterosexuality with only incidental homosexuality. Then follows predominant heterosexuality,

Fig. 14-1.   Continuum of heterosexuality-homosexuality. Photograph courtesy *Sexology* magazine.

but with more than incidental homosexuality. At midpoint, there is sexual functioning at equal heterosexual and homosexual levels. Still further along the continuum is predominant homosexuality, but with more than incidental heterosexuality; then predominant homosexuality with only incidental heterosexuality; and, finally, exclusive homosexuality with no heterosexual leanings at all.

To recapitulate the findings of the Kinsey research, 37% of the male and 13% of the female population engage at one point in their lives in some form of homosexual activity to the point of orgasm; 8% of men have been exclusively homosexual for a period of at least three years; and 4% of the men have been homosexual deviates all their lives.[180, 272] A study of 2200 college women showed that over 50% had experienced intense feelings for other women.[93] The consensus among authorities, however, is that male homosexuals outnumber female homosexuals about two or three to one, although the cause for this imbalance is frequently debated.[179, 180]

Homosexual expression falls into three patterns: (1) active, wherein the individual plays the male role regardless of his own sex, (2) passive, in which the participant, whether man or woman, plays the female role, and (3) mixed, in which the individual assumes an active role one time and a passive role the next. The mixed role is the pattern most frequently followed by homosexuals.

Principal homosexual practices include masturbation, sodomy, fellatio, cunnilingus, and interfemoral coitus. These activities may or may not also involve sadism, masochism, fetishism, and other behavior indicative of even further emotional problems.

Contrary to common belief, there are no physical characteristics common to all homosexuals. Far too often, passive or frail men and aggressive or robust women are unfairly stigmatized as homosexuals. It is not unusual, on the other hand, to find men and women, quite masculine and feminine, respectively, in their appearance and behavior, who nonetheless lead homosexual lives. Only about 15% of the males who have extensive homosexual experience and about 5% of such women can be identified by their appearance as being homosexual.[259]

Theories concerning the dynamics of homosexuality are various, emphasis being placed on the roles of hereditary tendencies, environmental influences, or sex hormonal imbalance.[82, 260]

The "nativistic" theorists argue that the perversion is inborn. They point out that most homosexuals grow up in a culture that encourages heterosexuality; that they are usually ignorant of their homosexual tendencies until they reach pubescence and first encounter opportunities for homosexual attachments and expression. Therefore, these theorists reason, the homosexual propensities must have been inborn and not learned. At first glance, the data on assumed anatomical differences between confirmed homosexuals and heterosexuals of the same sex appear to be rather significant and to uphold the nativistic theory. Close examination, however, reveals that these alleged dissimilarities are actually far from supportable on the basis of current scientific evidence.[112]

There is more convincing evidence, however, that homosexuality is an outgrowth of environmental pressures and other conditioning factors.[82, 179, 180, 260, 373] The individual may seek homosexual outlets, for instance, as a result of an accidental but pleasurable homosexual incident in childhood, or because of having been segregated with others of the same sex for long periods of time (*e.g.,* in boarding school or correctional institution). Unsatisfactory social relationships with members of the opposite sex may also direct a person to seek the companionship of his own sex and thus to avoid the possibility of similar failures in the future.

The most likely explanation probably lies in the realm of parental influence. Faulty attitudes of parents (or teachers) toward sex, the obvious marital unhappiness of the parents, fears of incest because of confusing the mother with all women or the father with all men, antagonism toward the parent of the opposite sex, strong attraction toward the parent of the same sex, rejection of the child's sex by his parents: any of these factors, or a combination of them, may well create an atmosphere so threatening that the individual attempts eventually to escape through homosexuality.

Pathogenic patterns in the family life of homosexuals have been noted. Typically, the mother is unhappy in her marriage. She turns to her son and develops a close and intimate relationship with him, one that is tinged with romance and seductiveness but that stops short of physical contact. The relationship engenders guilt in the son because of his own incestuous desires toward his mother, causing him eventually to avoid all women since they appear to him to be symbols of her. Because of his wife's obvious preference, the father comes to resent the son and discourages his growth along masculine lines; furthermore, the father typically shows a favoritism toward his daughter, if he has one. The son, envious of the father-daughter relationship and fearful of his incestuous feelings toward his mother, rejects the masculine role and seeks to assume the role of a daughter.[37]

Psychoanalytical explanations are based on several environmental circumstances, usually involving in men a strong castration fear and an Oedipus complex. A strong infantile, yet sexual (Oedipal) attachment to the mother puts the child in competition with his powerful father who could, the child reasons, attack and destroy the pleasurable area of his body (fear of castration). To protect himself, the threatened boy child avoids all women (they being confused with the mother), and turns to men with the same fondness that his mother demonstrated toward him.

A similar triangular interaction among a girl child, her mother, and her father may engender a comparable syndrome in a daughter's sexual development.

The third theory advanced regarding the cause of homosexuality concerns an imbalance of sex hormones. The urine of a normal man and a normal woman reveals hormones of both sexes; however, one dominates the other. It is suggested that if the dominance is reversed, homosexuality will result. This theory, which has gained little support through scientific investigation, is not usually considered significant in a study of homosexuality.

As long as the causes of homosexuality remain undetermined, curative efforts cannot be expected to meet with much success. Homosexuals themselves cling tenaciously to their deviant practices. They attempt to adjust to two societies, seeking to belong to both, and quite naturally they fall short of this goal. Those who do seek psychological help without outside pressure are usually far more concerned over their anxiety and fear of discovery than they are about their homosexuality, *per se*. Many authorities believe that those homosexuals who are turned from their deviance by psychotherapy are not truly homosexual but are, rather, pseudohomosexuals—people who turn to members of their own sex for love, affection, and sexual expression because, although they have an emotional preference for members of the opposite sex, they are distinctly afraid of the latter. Other authorities are firm in their conviction that true homosexuality exists, but can often be corrected if the patient has a desire to change.[37, 126] Still other authorities believe that psychotherapeutic efforts should simply be directed toward helping the patient accept his homosexuality and to adapt to it.[82]

The attitude of the average American toward homosexuality differs from that of many other cultures.[259, 260, 263] A study of 193 different societies throughout the world showed that 28% of them accepted male homosexuality, at least to an extent, but only 11% accepted female homosexuality.[260] Among 225 American Indian tribes, 53% accepted male homosexuality, again at least to a limited degree, but only 17% of the tribes accepted female homosexuality.[263] In the typical American community, however, the reverse of these acceptance patterns is true. Male homosexuality is severely denounced, often to the point of violence, while female homosexuality receives only token disapproval, if any at all.

Male homosexuality is much more of a threat to men than female homosexuality is to women. It is widely recognized among psychotherapists that men who have an underlying fear of their own homosexual tendencies frequently are vociferously abusive in their attacks against homosexuality.[302] Those who do not feel threatened by any homosexual leanings within themselves are more understanding and relaxed in their dealings with people of homosexual proclivities. It is believed that transsexualists, those persons who change sex by surgical means, are so afraid of homosexuality that they had rather give up their maleness altogether than face their homosexual tendencies.[262]

Men frequently become sexually aroused by a display of female homosexuality even though they may find viewing any sexual activity between two men offensive. Women usually show little interest in witnessing any manifestations of either male or female homosexuality.[263]

It should be remembered that homosexuals—or people with almost any other sexual problem—can be as religious, moralistic, loyal to country or cause, inhibited, bigoted, and censorious of other types of sexual abnormality as anyone else can.[329] They manifest no greater number of other serious personality problems than one would expect to find in the normal population.[165, 166] Fortunately, Western societies are finally making some effort to evaluate homosexuality with compassion rather than with condemnation.

That a youngster between the ages of seven and sixteen should be seduced by a homosexual is unfortunate, but the effects are seldom permanent. These boys are no more liable to become homosexuals than boys who have not been seduced, and the evidence is that they later marry and lead quite normal lives.[309]

2. **Pedophilia** is a form of sexual deviation wherein adults derive erotic pleasure from relationships of one form or another with children. Pedophilic practices include exposure of the genitals to the child, and manipulation and possible penetration of the child. Of all sex offenders, about 30% are classed as pedophiles, and most of them are men.[129] This group is usually less aggressive and forceful than rapists, although public outrage is often stronger in this area of sexual offense. Many of these offenders are mentally dull, psychotic, alcoholic, and asocial in their attitude. About 20% use physical violence. Older offenders seek out very young children while younger offenders appear to concentrate their attention on adolescent girls. The average age of the offenders is about 40 years.[82, 273]

It is an interesting fact that these offenders have a Victorian attitude towards sex in that they believe in the double standard, assess women as being either "good" or "bad," insist that their brides be virgins, and so forth.[142, 280] It is both curious and disquieting to note that imprisoned sex offenders in general exhibit strong religious convictions. They see themselves as being very devout, practice religious rituals faithfully, respect the ministry, read the Bible regularly, and take part in long and self-centered prayers that they think can also cure their illnesses. These same men, however, are overly concerned about sexual matters, feel guilty and doomed, think that life has been unfair to them, and are painfully pulled in the opposite directions of sex and rigid piety.[18] About 90% of sex offenders admit to having received religious training in childhood,[8] yet only from 0% to 33% (depending upon the type of sex offense) report that their sex education came from their fathers or mothers.[142]

The opinion of most psychologists is that sexual experiences at the hands of a pedophile are less traumatic to the child than to his parents. If parents can deal with such unfortunate occurrences in a controlled manner, the child will usually suffer no residual trauma.

This aberration usually develops as an attempt on the part of the pedophile to cope with a fear of failure in normal interpersonal and heterosexual relationships, especially with a sexually experienced adult; or to satisfy a narcissistic love of himself as a child.[180] Efforts to rehabilitate pedophiles through psychotherapy have shown promising results, although some of them become recidivists. A prison sentence, however, does little by way of altering the subsequent behavior of sexual deviates, although society is, of course, protected from them during their term of imprisonment.[82]

Not all men charged as sex offenders against children are disturbed or sick men; some have simply been trapped. It is a sad truth that our culture places far too much emphasis on physical beauty, and stresses through constant advertisements the advantages of being sexually attractive. Many girls in the twelve- to fifteen-year-old age bracket, especially those who have been poorly guided by their parents in the matter of healthy self-evaluation, feel inadequate because of their youth. Many therefore turn to cosmetics and sophisticated clothing and conduct in an effort to give the appearance of being older than they really are. Men are simply unable to judge such a girl's true age, and frequently get caught in the legal trap of a statutory rape charge.[142]

In their recent book, *Sex Offenders,* the Kinsey group reported a not untypical case in which a man was snared in such a situation. The girl involved had appeared to him quite mature, even though somewhat heavily made up and provocatively dressed; she drank her liquor with ease, and held her own in the sexual banter. She proved to be an experienced and satisfactory sexual partner. Unfortunately, she was under legal age of consent and the man was taken to court. "I knew I was done for," he stated, "when I saw they had braided her hair in pigtails and had given her a rag doll to hold."[142]

3. **Bestiality** is sexual gratification obtained by engaging in sexual relations with animals. Kinsey and his investigators reported that 17% of men reared on farms have reached orgasm through sexual relations with animals, and many others probably have had some sort of sexual contact with animals.[180] It is thought that in some rural societies where there is an insufficient number of cooperative women, this behavior has no more significance than masturbation as a sexual release.[82]

If the pattern of behavior becomes fixed, however, bestiality might be considered a mechanism to avoid feared failure with the opposite sex, or a means of avoiding distress or threat because relations with any woman signifies to the man incest with Mother. In many cases, the individual shows his hostility or contempt toward women by identifying animals with them, or by choosing animals in preference to them.

4. **Zoophilia** is an unnatural love for animals, although the term is usually used interchangeably with bestiality. The term *zoophilia erotica* was coined by Krafft-Ebing, one of the pioneers in the study of psychopathology of sexual behavior. This type of anomaly is fairly common among rural people and small children. As a sexual deviation it can take several forms, such as deriving sexual pleasure from fondling animals, from observing the sexual activities of animals, or from a fetish built around animal skins or furs.[6, 82, 373]

5. **Necrophilia** is a rare sexual deviation emanating from profound emotional disturbance, almost always of psychotic proportions. It involves sexual gratification stemming from the sight of a corpse, or actually having sexual intercourse with it, sometimes followed, in either instance, by mutilation of the body.[373] The necrophile may kill to provide himself with a corpse, have sexual relations with it, mutilate it, and even descend to cannibalizing his victim. This rare but obviously severe form of sexual deviation may be explained as an attempt by the individual to dominate someone, even if it is a cadaver.[8, 82]

6. **Pornography** is written or pictorial material deliberately designed to cause sexual excitement.[142] Usually the material is obscene or immodest, but the responsibility for labeling it as such lies with the courts. Only when perusal of such material is preferred to heterosexual activity should it be considered abnormal, as it is well known to psychologists and psychiatrists that normal, sexually well-adjusted people often enjoy the erotic stimulation of certain written and pictorial matter.

A continual battle rages around the possible dangers of pornography. Admittedly, pornographic matter can stimulate sexually, but there is no significant empirical or clinical evidence to support the contention that pornography causes sexual deviation or violence.[142] The greatest objection to it might well arise from its appalling lack both of good taste and of literary value. There is little likelihood that pornography will provoke excessive or abnormal sexual behavior; when such evidence appears to exist, tendencies toward such behavior on the part of that particular person were probably already present. Young people, it is generally conceded, are particularly vulnerable to the arousal of strong sexual desires from prurient material. But it is also possible that pornographic material serves as a harmless psychological release that might actually be an aid to those who are burdened with certain sexual repressions. Here again, there is no significant amount of empirical or clinical proof to support either of these latter contentions.[364]

It is known that strong response to pornography is related to imaginativeness, to an ability to make abstractions and to project, to sensitivity (all of which increase as education increases), and to youthfulness. Sex offenders respond *less* to pornography than those who do not commit such offenses, probably because they are not well educated and are not young. The Kinsey group[142] sums up the effects of pornography fairly well with: "Pornography collections follow the pre-existing interest of the collector. Men make the collections, collections do not make the men."

7. **Obscenity** consists of utterances, gestures, sketches, and the like that are judged repugnant according to the mores of our society. Most obscene behavior, such as crude writing on the walls, telephone calls (usually anonymous), or public remarks, is of a sexually assaultive nature. The subject of sex is no doubt chosen because of its almost certain shock effect, or because the behavior is indicative of actual fantasy. Both pornography and obscene conduct are illegal in all states, but there are widely varying interpretations of the offenses and their penalties.

Persons receiving obscene phone calls are advised to hang up immediately and without comment, and then to report the call to the police and telephone company. Any acceptance of the call by way of verbal retaliation or any show of shock only serves to reinforce the behavior of the disturbed person. Men making such calls are usually quite harmless, and they feel so sexually inadequate that they have neither the courage nor capability of coping with women and sex in open contact.

In two 1957 U.S. Supreme Court rulings lies an indication of the difficulty in defining what is and is not obscene. The rulings held that while the First and Fourteenth Amendments give no one the right to purvey obscene material, the Constitution does grant that freedom to any matter "having even the slightest redeeming social importance . . . ," however unpopular the ideas therein contained. But what the Court did hold as obscene is any material "utterly without redeeming social importance . . . in which to the average person, applying contemporary community standards, the dominant theme of the material taken as a whole appeals to prurient interest." One can see the endless possibilities for divergent evaluation of the same piece of material, since it is the responsibility of each township, county, or state to pass on the purity of a particular work. What might not cause an eye to widen in Greenwich Village might well cause near apoplexy in some small mid-Western town. Furthermore, the Supreme Court decisions allow blatantly pornographic material to circulate freely until it is so labeled by the courts; the police cannot legally seize it until then.

Obscenity, as well as pornography, is usually in the eye (or mind) of the beholder. For any damage from obscenity or pornography to befall a person, the impact must be upon previously prepared and receptive soil, because obscenity and pornography cannot, of themselves, produce such damage.[302]

8. **Fetishism** is defined as a psychosexual aberration in which an individual's sexual impulses become fixated onto a substitute, a sexual symbol, for the basic love-object.[60] Usually the articles are fondled, gazed upon, or made part of masturbatory activities. They may be articles of underclothing, hair, shoes (especially high-heel shoes), or gloves. (For some unexplained reason, rubber has very strong appeal to the fetishist.) Or the object of the fetishist's fixation may be a bodily part of the opposite sex, such as hair, hands, thighs, feet, ears, or eyes. The fetishist is almost always male, and in acquiring his sex symbols, he often commits burglary or even assault.[175]

Fetishists are typically aggressive and antisocial, and are beset with fears of impotency. Fetishism is a form of sexual regression; the individual obtains sexual gratification from a particular object or bodily part because of its unique relationship to some childhood conditioning. The particular fetish-object somehow became associated with sexual excitement, or with the love and acceptance the fetishist once received from his mother.[60]

Two fetishistic patterns that deserve attention are **kleptomania** and **pyromania**.[82] Kleptomania is compulsive stealing, usually of an object that is of no value to the thief, except for its sexual symbolism or because of its association with sexual gratification. The kleptomaniac is typically an emotionally disturbed woman who is beset with feelings of being unloved and unwanted.[4] Occasionally the thief is a boy or young man who takes women's undergarments (particularly panties) in order to achieve erotic stimulation through the symbolic nature of the clothing, and through the excitement and suspense of the very act of stealing.[82] When apprehended, these individuals are reluctant to admit to the sexual implications of their behavior.

Pyromania is compulsive firesetting that often has sexual overtones. The relationship between fire and sex is apparent from such terms as "in heat" and "becoming hot" for someone. Sexual excitement and gratification usually occur as the person — always a man, and usually young—sets the fire, or as he beholds the early stages of the conflagration. Once orgasm occurs, the individual usually feels guilty and frequently steps forward to extinguish the fire.[82, 145] Many pyromaniacs can give no reason for their impulse to set fires, and others claim revenge as their motive. A large number of these fetishists are psychotic.[361]

9. **Frottage** is an act performed for the purpose of obtaining sexual pleasure from rubbing or pressing against the desired person, and the perpetrator is called a *frotteur*. Such conduct often passes unnoticed, as it may be performed in crowded public places, *e.g.,* a subway or elevator. The dynamics behind this behavior are probably similar to those of exhibitionism. At worst, the frotteur is an unappealing, sexually inadequate man who would probably be frightened of the opportunity for sexual intercourse with an adequate, adult woman.

10. **Saliromania** is a sexual disorder, found primarily in men, that is characterized by the desire to damage or soil the body or clothes of a woman or a representation of a woman. These men frequently have marked feelings of sexual inadequacy, or have come to associate strong aggressive impulses with sex, the latter frequently being a consequence of unreasonable feelings of guilt surrounding normal sexual desires. The hostility often is expressed symbolically by the throwing of acid, tar, ink, or the like on a strange woman or a statue; by cutting and tearing women's clothing; or by defacing or disfiguring a painting or statue. The beheading a few years ago of the famous mermaid statue in the harbor of Copenhagen was very likely the act of such a disordered man. Saliromaniacs usually become sexually excited to the point of erection and perhaps ejaculation during their acts of destruction.

11. **Gerontosexuality** is a disorder in which a young person has a distinct preference for an elderly person as the object of sexual interest. The economic considerations of a marriage between a person who is quite old and one who is very young may well be more important than the sexual aspects.[6] However, when there is an actual sexual preference for a person of advanced years, there may be an indication of a sexual desire for a parent-substitute.

12. **Incest** is sexual intercourse between two persons, married or not, who are too closely related by blood or affinity to be legally married. Laws relating to incest bear little uniformity from state to state, and are often highly confusing.[350] For example, when marriage is involved, certain states have legislated separate penalties for the marriage itself and for the sex act.

Incest does not come before the courts often; of those convicted of sex offenses, only 6% had been charged with incest. Nonetheless, the act of incest probably occurs far more frequently than the average citizen realizes. The offense is more likely to occur in families of low socioeconomic levels than in others.[91] The person who commits incest against children usually comes from a sordid home background, shows a preoccupation with sex, drinks heavily, and is often unemployed, giving him ample opportunity to be at home with the children. The incest offender against adults is typically "conservative, moralistic, restrained, religiously devout, traditional and uneducated."[142, 289] In about 60% of the incidences of adult father-daughter incest, the daughter was a voluntary participant, and in only 8% of the cases did she resist.

The most common form of incest is probably brother-sister, especially in poor families where children of both sexes must share a bedroom; the next most common is father-daughter incest.[82] Mother-son incest is a rare occurrence. Its incidence may be somewhat higher than is suspected because when this incest does take place, it is not likely to be reported by either party.

Incest is not universally a taboo; most cultures, however, both primitive and modern, are of the opinion that family and subculture survival depends upon expansion through marriage outside the immediate family. Only recently has the interest of the scientists been directed toward this ancient problem, although novelists, poets, and scholars have often probed the subject and have contributed much to an understanding of it.[210] Sexologists are presently attempting to determine the real and measurable effects of incest on the contemporary world, without regard to the biases of ancient societies which obviously attempted to expand their strength and influence through marriage outside the tribe or family.

Many psychotherapists believe that the effects of actual incest involving a child are not so disastrous as are the effects of a parent's seductive behavior toward that child which never culminates in any manifest sexual activity. One theory is that the problem of unconscious incestuous desire may well underlie all cases of neuroses and psychoses, and that actual incest will not have such a deleterious effect upon the child since parental approval of the behavior is implicit. There will therefore be little residual guilt on the part of the child, except later, perhaps, when he grows older and reads and listens to the opinions of others on the matter of incest.[210]

13. **Wife swapping** in the American culture is generally considered to be a sexual problem, or at least a sign of personality maladjustment. Such a negative evaluation of the act does not necessarily hold, however, in all countries or cultures; in certain Eskimo tribes, for example, it is considered a matter of courtesy and hospitality.[363] Unless wife swapping carries the full approval of all parties concerned, strife in the marriages concerned is inevitable. And even with the approbation of all the persons involved, this type of behavior is liable to foster marital dissatisfaction, further promiscuity, and jealousies, all of which en-

gender unhappiness and hence pose real threats to the marriages. The wish for extramarital sexual experiences is understandable and normal, but to actualize such desires has too often irreparable consequences. The usual impetus in wife swapping would appear to be boredom in the marriage, although a wide variety of other reasons, most of them rooted in maladjustment, is often cited.

14. **Mysophilia, coprophilia,** and **urophilia** are descriptive words for several forms of obsessive interest in excretory processes.[6] The words are easily definable from their etymology: *philia,* deriving from the Greek word meaning affinity for; *myso-,* meaning filth; *copro-,* meaning dung; and *uro-,* Greek for urine. The causes of these abnormalities are usually related to repressed sexual yearnings, and the association of anything sexual with "nastiness" and "dirtiness." Some psychoanalysts see them as defenses against castration anxiety by such a symbolic equation as "feces equals penis."

It has frequently been observed that children often associate urination and defecation with the sexual acts of their elders. The child may make the further association between the protruding (fat) abdomen in pregnancy (sexuality) and food and the gastrointestinal system, setting the stage for unconscious association of sex with the processes of elimination.

While extreme forms of coprophilia are found mostly in men, urophilia is more generally associated with women. Perhaps the predilection in women is due to the anatomical proximity of urethra, vulva, and clitoris, and a greater likelihood of genital stimulation during urination.

15. **Masturbation** produces sexual gratification through stimulation of the genitals by manipulation, usually manual or digital. Only under extremely rare circumstances can masturbation be considered a sexual abnormality (especially since well over 95% of men and about 70% of women practice it at one time or another).[179, 180] Only because it occurs occasionally as part of the behavior pattern of psychotic patients, or among those people who use it as the sole method of sexual outlet (even when other outlets are readily available), is its inclusion here warranted. Indeed, those who do not practice masturbation, or have not done so, are far more likely to be sexually abnormal than those who have masturbating experience. Suppression of the tendency to masturbate usually occurs when the individual's thinking regarding sexual matters is beclouded with guilt, fear, and perplexity.[119, 122]

Long prior to the birth of Hippocrates, the "Father of Medicine," down through the ages to 1900, the medical world was rather ignorant of cause and effect in sexual behavior. Objectivity and a scientific approach were notoriously lacking in those paltry investigations that were made. Occasionally some brave scientific soul would reach out for enlightenment, but such men were few. Struggles through these dark ages towards an understanding of human sexuality were dealt a near death-blow in the mid-18th century when S. A. D. Tissot of France wrote his *Onana, a Treatise on the Diseases Produced by Onanism.* Projecting his personal problems into his writings, to say nothing of his super-abundance of ignorance, Tissot wrote of the viciousness of self-abuse, attributing most of the known medical disorders—including consump-tion, epileptic seizures, gonorrhea, and insanity—to the loss of semen through masturbation. It was Tissot who introduced the fatuous and totally unscientific idea that the loss of one drop of seminal fluid causes more bodily damage and weakness than the loss of forty drops of blood.[95]

Tissot's writings and theories captured the attention of many coun-tries, influencing medical men and laymen alike. Other "authorities" added their views to those of Tissot until even today there still persist irrational social prohibitions against the perfectly normal, and probably beneficial, act of masturbation.[122] Fortunately, the vast majority of people are almost ready to accept masturbation for what it is—a not immoral and certainly harmless act of sexual stimulation and relief. The tide of ignorance concerning masturbation began turning in 1891 when Dr. E. T. Brady became one of the first authorities to challenge the concept of masturbation as a pernicious act, but even Brady considered self-stimulation somewhat dangerous.[95]

The hysteria over masturbation reached such a pitch in the late 1800s that "depraved" women who resorted to it were frequently forced by their families to submit to a clitoridectomy as a method of control. French medical men, furthermore, expressed their dismay at an occupa-tional hazard peculiar to seamstresses: the masturbatory up-and-down movements of their legs as they treadled their sewing machines were wont to cause orgasms. In at least one establishment, a matron was appointed to circulate among the seamstresses to detect runaway ma-chines as the women became caught up in this "horrible" by-product of their profession.[103, 104]

In the light of today's prevailing opinion that masturbation is not harmful, it seems unrealistic that certain people and institutions still declaim against it as a dangerous and evil practice. For example, the June, 1940, United States Naval Academy regulations state that evi-dence of masturbation is adequate grounds for refusing to admit a man as a candidate to that institution. Considering the prevalence of mas-turbation among men, one wonders how the Naval Academy has managed to fill its ranks.

Only where abnormality already exists, as in the instance of severely disturbed schizophrenic patients, could there be the possibility of masturbation's being carried to extremes. Nature carefully regulates individual sexual activity, and any form of it becomes unpleasant to the person experiencing it when it is overdone. Even in the case, say, of an acute schizophrenia, the problem of excess may just as easily encompass coitus or any other sexual act; if the excessive behavior happens to be masturbatory, it is not the cause of the schizophrenia, but merely a symptom of it.[115]

The technique of masturbation customarily used by men is gripping the penis by the hand and moving the hand back and forth at the desired pressure and tempo along the length of the penile shaft. The glans is stimulated in somewhat the same manner as it is by the in-and-out body movements of penile penetration of the vagina. The degree of pressure, speed of stroking, the use of lubrication or not, naturally vary from man to man. About two-thirds of women who masturbate prefer to stimulate the clitoris by manual or digital friction of the vulval region,[137] although the Masters and Johnson research indicates that arousal is best accomplished when the stimulation is to the side of the clitoris rather than on the clitoris directly.[215] About 20% of women prefer vaginal to other methods of stimulation, and insert foreign objects into the vagina as a method of masturbation; about 11% prefer stimulation of the urethral meatus; and 2% attain orgasm by pressing their thighs together in a rhythmical manner.[137]

As mentioned in the chapter on sexual techniques, some women achieve self-arousal and orgasm through directing a stream of water onto the genitals while bathing—either from the faucet of a tub, or from the peppery spray of a shower.[191] Perhaps the use of water in self-stimulation has some psychological advantage in that an unconscious need to "cleanse away the guilt" engendered by masturbation is satisfied along with the sexual need.

Further information on frequency, incidence, and techniques of masturbation is given in Chapters 9 and 12.

Problems that people tend to consider outgrowths of masturbation in fact exist before masturbation ever occurred; the emotional problems are not a result of self-stimulation. The only conflicts that masturbation engenders stem from poor sex education and guilt on the part of the parents, other teachers, and peers who pass on to those young people whom they instruct their disturbed attitudes toward a perfectly normal act. [115, 119]

Certainly it is advisable that if an individual has anxieties concerning masturbation, and self-stimulation causes him extreme guilt, he should avoid it until the underlying psychological problem is corrected. Similarly, if one has extreme and severe guilt about head-scratching, one should also avoid head-scratching until the underlying psychological difficulty in this instance is rectified.

ABNORMAL DEGREE OF DESIRE AND STRENGTH OF SEXUAL DRIVE

1. **Frigidity** is a condition in which a woman has a total or a partial lack of sex drive. (It might be mentioned that men also can be frigid, although its incidence is rare. The term "frigidity" is typically limited in the literature as meaning an affliction of women.) A totally frigid woman has no desire for sexual expression, and may denounce such activity as disgusting. A partially frigid woman has only a mild interest in being sexually stimulated.

Frigidity has its genesis in organic, relationship, and psychological factors.[113] Organic factors include such things as inborn defects and injuries, constitutional deficiencies in sexual apparatus, hormonal imbalance, disorders of the nervous system, inflammation and lesions in the internal and external genitalia and surrounding areas, excessive use of drugs or alcohol, the aging process, and severe physical pain at the time of first or subsequent sexual relations, or associated with menstruation or other sexual processes.

Relationship factors suggest that the husband may be a "marital moron" whose selfishness, overeagerness, or stupidity throttles romance, and fills the wife with revulsion toward sex.[82] Or resentment on the part of one of the marital partners (usually the wife) for any of a variety of reasons can leave frigidity in its wake, as can any of a number of other realistic or unrealistic forces that interfere with sex and love, and hence with the overall relationship between husband and wife.[113]

The most common and by far the most important sources of frigidity have their roots in psychological considerations,[82, 113, 119, 122] typically in such emotional problems as shame, guilt, and fear. Many women in our culture are indoctrinated from an early age, either directly or by implication, into a warped sexual attitude.[113] All sexual relations, whether in or out of marriage, come to be judged as rather evil and something to be avoided. Even if sexual activity cannot be avoided on the physical plane, a woman can minimize her participation by refusing to become involved in the sexual response interaction. Inhibitory forces militating against sexual warmth and responsiveness are legion. A girl may expect physical pain at coitus, and therefore dread it; she may fear rejection or condemnation by her husband if she lets herself go sexually, or be frightened of becoming pregnant; or she may have homosexual tendencies, too strong feelings toward her father, or repressed hostility toward men in general, all of which can inhibit her from responding warmly to her husband.[113, 122]

One other notable and rather sad cause of many women's inability to respond sexually is their overconcern with orgasmic response; these women approach sexual activity with a grim determination, which is usually self-defeating, to reach a climax.[113] What is quite obviously needed is a more relaxed attitude toward coitus, and the women concerned should cease criticizing and condemning themselves because they do not have immediate orgasm, or multiple orgasms. They feel shame because their climaxes are not as monumental as they fancy "modern" woman's must be. Once they begin to enjoy coition for the pleasure it *does* give them (and their husbands), their chances eventually to have orgasmic responses will increase significantly.

Most barriers to warm sexual interaction can be toppled if handled with patience by both husband and wife. Albert Ellis, probably the most productive writer today in the field of sex, recommends coping with frigidity through self-therapy in conjunction with any medical or psychological treatment that seems advisable.[113, 122] These are some of his suggestions for arousing an unresponsive woman:

a. Select a suitable time for sexual activity, *e.g.,* when the woman is rested and as free from immediate troubles as possible.

b. There should be a minimum of disharmony between the partners at the time chosen.

c. Kindness, consideration, and expressions of love usually prove more effective than rough treatment.

d. The husband should acquaint himself with the parts of his wife's body that are especially responsive to stimulation, and they should be caressed.

e. It is often effective to take brief periods of rest between efforts at arousal.

f. Genital, particularly clitoral, stimulation should precede intromission.

g. Mild stimulants are sometimes useful.

h. The wife's focusing on sexually stimulating fantasy is helpful while the husband can offer encouragement through using terms of endearment and emphasizing his distinct interest and pleasure in her. Sexually arousing conversation often is of benefit.

i. If arousal is attainable but the woman is to an extent sexually insensitive, then one or more of the following procedures are recommended: steady and rhythmic pressure, intermittent or forceful strokings, and verbal encouragements. A woman's stimulating herself is often a valuable aid to her husband in his attempts at arousing her.

j. The use of deep, forceful penile-vaginal penetration is often helpful, although it may call for special coital positions together with prior or simultaneous noncoital stimulation. Orgasm, whenever and however possible, is the goal; simultaneous climax is not important.

Stimulative methods, such as oral-genital contact and especially the use of hand vibrators, are frequently successful in producing orgasmic response in a woman. Whatever technique promises success should be used; it bears repeating that orgasm, whenever and however achieved, is the objective. Once orgasm is attained and the woman gains confidence in her ability, no longer allowing fear and shame to act as such interfering forces, subsequent orgasms are usually more easily and more frequently reached.

2. **Impotency** refers to a man's inability to perform the sexual act, regardless of his desire, and it generally involves his being unable to attain or maintain an erection.

Three types of impotency are recognized: organic, functional, and psychogenic.[176] The first of these, organic impotency, is relatively rare and is caused by some anatomical defect in the reproductive or the central nervous system. Functional impotency may be caused by a nervous disorder, excessive use of certain drugs or alcohol, deficient hormonal functioning, circulatory problems, or physical exhaustion, any of which can act to interfere with the functions of the various sex organs. Psychogenic impotency, by far the most frequently encountered type of impotency,[158] is a disturbance brought about by certain inimical impulses from the brain acting on the spinal centers in such a way as to inhibit proper sexual functioning.

Emotional upset of one sort or another usually sets in motion the inhibitory processes entailed in psychogenic impotency, and fear is its most common underlying cause: fear that the sexual activity will be discovered, fear of impregnating, fear of venereal diseases, or fear of past sexual experiences and their effect upon present health and capabilities.[176] Guilt and shame, usually relating to some childhood experience or stemming from faulty sex education, are other common contributors to this disorder. Psychogenic impotency may also have its foundations in unconscious incestuous wishes and the association of all women with the mother image; in rigid, unbending religious scruples that are violated by such sexual transgressions as adultery; or in latent or active homosexuality when it results in guilt and shame. Some men become sexually incapable because of conscious or unconscious disgust, anger, or hos-

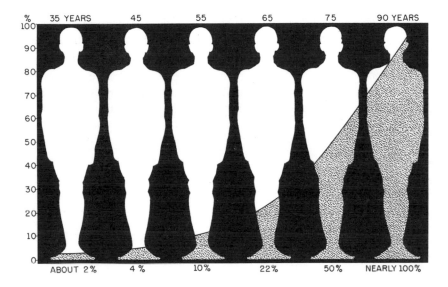

Fig. 14-2. Shaded areas indicate average percentage of males who usually suffer from impotency at various ages. The final figure represents an extension of the pattern in the first five. Photograph courtesy *Sexology* magazine.

tility toward their wives. Feelings of inferiority and inadequacy will often throttle a man's erectile ability, particularly if he has had one or two sexual failures. Concern over some such failures—which, it is important to emphasize, occur to almost all men occasionally—can also perpetuate the problem of impotency, unless a man has insight into what happened.[117]

Many men, especially as they get older, believe themselves to be impotent when actually they are not. Men are often made to believe that they have grown too old to function sexually; they convince themselves of this fallacy to a point that they do indeed become impotent. They had perhaps experienced the inability to attain or maintain an erection during a few successive sexual attempts, which to their way of thinking constituted proof positive of their impotence. Yet these men have morning erections that they associate with the need to urinate. It should be obvious that a full bladder is not necessarily the cause of the erection; if it were, all any man would have to do in order to assure an erection is to refrain from urinating. The one fact which emerges clearly is that a man with a morning erection *is* capable of having an erection, and any failure at other times has psychological rather than physical causality.[158] Furthermore, men who consider themselves unable to perform coition may have erections during their sleep; again, if they are capable of an erection during sleep, the physical capability for erections has not dissipated.[134] What does disappear during sleep and dreams is the fear, anxiety, and distractions that militate against a man during his waking hours to render him sexually incapable.

A man's virility is often a matter of great importance to him. Men have been known to go to incredible—sometimes terrifying—extremes to convince themselves and others that they are virile and sexually capable. These efforts have involved such divergent attempts at "proof" as rape, begetting a great number of children, physical aggressiveness, fast and reckless driving, and being tattooed.[360]

For purposes of easier comprehension of erotic drive and capacity, the varying degrees of men's sexual impetus can be conveniently arranged along an eleven-point continuum.[68] At one end of the scale there is a total absence of both desire and capacity for erection; followed by (2) the presence of erotic desires unaccompanied by a physical capability for erection; then (3) ability to attain semi-erection through special types of stimulation; (4) strong erections and ability to have sexual intercourse if tumescence can be maintained through special methods of stimulation; (5) spontaneous morning erections, but none at other times of the day no matter which stimulative technique is employed; (6) weak erections under almost any circumstance, but firm erections and vaginal penetration possible only after extensive caressing of the penis; (7) erections occurring from caresses of the body and other erotic stimuli; (8) spontaneous erections if the erotic stimulus is strong; (9) spontaneous, immediate erections even though the erotic stimulus is very mild; (10) strong, vigorous, spontaneous erections, accompanied by a strong sex drive; and at the far end of the scale, (11) very strong and vigorous erections and a powerful sex drive; this man can have many and prolonged acts of intercourse during one sexual contact, with or without ejaculation, and he may have two or more climaxes without loss of erection.

Impotency far more often than not has psychological rather than physical origins. The physical problems can be treated in manifold ways—pills, injections, hormones, rest, and surgery—often with rewarding results; but treatment of the condition when it has psychological roots requires a much more delicate and complex approach. The importance of the wife's role in aiding the husband in combatting his (actually, their) difficulties cannot be overemphasized; her efforts and attitude are of utmost value in helping him to overcome his emotional blocks. If a wife allows herself to display disappointment over her husband's failure, she will increase his tension, anxiety, and guilt which, in turn, only intensify his inhibitions. Not only should she be compassionate, but she should extend reassurance and any physical stimulation her husband may need to attain and maintain an erection sufficient to complete the act of coitus. Once these steps are taken, the emotional stress experienced by the husband is likely to disappear, together with his inability to perform the sex act. If understanding and cooperation between wife and husband do not correct the problem after a reasonable length of time, psychotherapy may well supply a solution.

Curiously, another sexual difficulty has somehow become associated with impotency—premature ejaculation. Technically, premature ejaculation occurs when a man's emission occurs before penetration or within a few seconds afterwards.[180, 246] However, because in our culture the ability to prolong sexual intercourse has become a primary criterion of masculinity, many men (and their wives as well) consider themselves sexually inadequate partners simply because for them coitus is a brief act, and they ruefully and erroneously label their hasty ejaculation premature.

About 75% of the males investigated by the Kinsey researchers reported ejaculations within two minutes of intromission, and in many cases the emission occurred within twenty seconds.[179, 246] Since a high percentage of sexually capable men have this experience repeatedly, it is difficult to comprehend why early ejaculation is so often thought of as a form of impotence.[179]

Physical factors, such as a hypersensitive glans or inflamed prostate, can cause ejaculations to occur earlier than the sexual partners may prefer, but emotional factors are usually responsible for this too swift response.[246] However, it should be understood that early ejaculation can happen to any man on occasion, especially if he is inexperienced and overexcited. Almost all men are liable to have a premature emission if they are sufficiently excited, have maintained an erection for a prolonged period of time before intromission, are sexually deprived, are tense, or are lacking in self-confidence.[372]

There are, to be sure, complications stemming from early ejaculation, the most common and most important one being that the wife is usually left sexually unsatisfied if the couple rely on intercourse to bring her to orgasm. It therefore becomes important in these instances that men learn to delay their ejaculation—and the technique can be learned—for a time sufficient for the wife to reach her climax.

These procedures have been found to be useful antidotes to premature or early ejaculation:

    a. It is universally recognized that worry and tension are the primary catalysts in early ejaculation, especially when they are outgrowths of unhappy initial sexual experiences. As explained earlier in the matter of overcoming impotency, the wife's role as an understanding and helpful partner is of inestimable value in reducing her husband's worry, fear, and anxiety. Muscular tension, which is a catalyst to ejaculation, is reduced in direct proportion to the reduction of emotional tension.

    b. Since muscular tension does indeed hasten ejaculation, a man can appreciably lengthen the time between arousal and emission if he assumes the lower position during coitus, allowing his wife to make the copulatory movements while he relaxes his body as much as possible. Muscular tension that terminates in early response for the man is one of the reasons (along with fear of detection) why sexual intercourse in the cramped confines of an automobile is unsatisfactory.

    c. The use of Nupercainal ointment or similar local anesthetics in an effort to control early ejaculation has frequently been recommended.[16, 170] The application of the ointment (1% strength in mild cases and 2.5% or 5% in severe cases) on the glans of the penis about twenty minutes before penetration will usually deaden or desensitize the nerve endings, making the man less liable to ejaculate prematurely. Since there are few nerve endings in the vagina, the ointment that rubs off from the glans penis into the vaginal canal fortunately does not interfere with the woman's pleasure. However, care should be taken at the time of penetration that the penis does not touch the vestibule, the minor lips, and, especially, the clitoris because the wife's response might otherwise be adversely affected. If this contact cannot be easily avoided, then a condom can be worn over the penis; the woman's vulval region is not only protected from the ointment, but the condom serves the further purpose of decreasing the friction, warmth, and moisture of the vagina to the penis, which ordinarily are sexually exciting to the man.

    d. Alcohol acts as a deterrent to physiological functioning of the sex organs and some people find a few drinks before coitus aids the man in prolonging his climax. Some people consider alcohol a sexual stimulant, but this assumption is untrue from a physiological standpoint Alcohol does, in fact, tend to reduce social inhibitions[136] and to relax emotional control. The relaxation, in some instances, permits greater freedom in sexual expression because the reduction in emotional tensions is more powerful than the accompanying physiological deterrent.

Study of the effects of alcohol on the sexual activity of dogs, whose behavior (contrary to human behavior) is not significantly complicated by psychological and emotional factors, provides some interesting insights on the workings of this depressant.[357] Dr. H. Horsley Gantt administered varying amounts of alcohol to dogs and found that even a very small amount of alcohol made it more difficult for the animals to achieve erection and to ejaculate; the larger the amount, the greater the difficulty, and very large doses destroyed altogether the capability for erection and ejaculation. Normal dogs were the least affected sexually by the alcohol; in some animals, temporary sterility was produced, with the sperm count's dropping in some cases as much as 92%. Each dog (like humans) in the experiment reacted differently to the alcohol. For instance, one very neurotic dog that was totally impotent attained strong erections after receiving a large amount of alcohol.

e. Men are easily stimulated by erotic material and thoughts; therefore, if the husband will direct his thoughts during coitus to such asexual matters as his car's balky ignition, multiplication tables, or the Green Bay Packers, he is frequently able to prolong the act of sexual intercourse (however unromantic this technique may seem to his wife—if the husband is foolish enough to tell her).

f. Having an orgasm and, after a short rest, attaining another erection often permit a man to experience a more prolonged act of coitus the second time. Some men masturbate shortly before they expect to have sexual intercourse, since their sex drive will thereby be decreased, and they can then prolong intercourse later.

g. Through cooperation between husband and wife, a man can be conditioned to a technique of delaying ejaculation. The wife should manually stimulate the penis until the husband feels the first sensations of impending orgasm; the stimulation should then cease to allow excitement to subside. Once the arousal has subsided sufficiently, the wife should again stimulate her husband to the same point of arousal, exerting care not to go too far. This pattern should be repeated several times. Repetition of this procedure on a number of subsequent occasions is frequently valuable as an aid in conditioning a man to delay ejaculation so that he can just about determine at will when ejaculation is to happen.

3.   **Nymphomania** refers to a sexually deviant woman whose abnormally voracious sexual hunger overshadows all her other activities. It is sometimes, although rarely, the outgrowth of certain physiological anomalies; more often, the disorder has a psychological basis.

Characteristically, true nymphomania involves an uncontrollable sexual desire that when aroused must be fulfilled, no matter what the consequences. The sexual craving is unquenchable regardless of the number of orgasms and the pleasure received from them. Nymphomania is compulsive sexual behavior in the true sense of the word, impelling the victim to irrational and self-defeating activities with all the stresses and problems that any compulsion causes. Typically, the nymphomaniac is consumed with feelings of self-contempt because of society's attitude toward excessive sexual behavior in any form.[130]

It must be stressed, however, that few words in our language are as misapplied as "nymphomania." It is bandied about by the man-on-the-street; it is a popular theme in Grade-B films, and a frequent topic of discussion in fraternity houses; and everyone from the minister to the mailman claims to know at least a half-dozen such women. Yet as a sexual disorder, nymphomania is quite rare. Many people have little general knowledge about human sex drive, let alone an understanding of individual differences in sexual needs. There can be, consequently, much bewilderment, and often consternation, when an individual is confronted with a type of sexual conduct that does not conform with his own narrow range of expectations.

Most men are sexually fulfilled after one orgasm, and care very little about continuing sexual activity afterwards. Most sexually mature women, however, are not usually satisfied with one climax only, most of them requiring two or more orgasms to reach sexual satiation, especially during episodes of clitoral manipulation. (Many women during masturbation may experience five to twenty, or more, orgasms during one episode.)[224, 225] Men who do not understand this normal sexual need of many women, are likely to believe they are involved with a sensual freak who refuses to recognize the end of a good thing when she arrives there. Since they do not understand female sexuality,

men often stigmatize a perfectly normal woman as being a nymphomaniac simply because she happens to have a healthy sexual appetite.

There is yet another type of man who through ignorance or,
perhaps, cruelty, accuses his wife of nymphomania simply because
her sexual desire exceeds his own. It is true that men on the whole
prefer sexual activity more frequently than their wives do, especially
during the earlier part of their marriages. But there are certainly
exceptions to this generalization, and some men simply do not realize
this fact or are not willing to admit it. Because their own desires are
quite satisfied with coitus two or three times a week, they are amazed
that a woman might wish intercourse six or seven times a week, which
is just as normal as their own level of sexual needs. If such a man
has feelings of inferiority and uncertainty about his own masculinity,
he is likely to be so threatened by a woman who desires more frequent intercourse that he must find some way to fight her. Hence
he calls her a nymphomaniac, and by branding her as "abnormal,"
he preserves his self-image of "normalcy" by implication.

The consensus of psychotherapists and marriage counselors is
that most cases of alleged nymphomania that they see are actually
not that at all. They are, rather, cases in which there are quite pronounced and disturbing individual differences between the sexual desire
and performance of husband and wife, both of whom are quite likely
to be within the realm of normalcy in their sexual needs. The gap in
sexual drives between husband and wife can only be filled by the less
sexually needful partner's finding some means other than coition to
satisfy the other partner; or by the partner with greater drive using
masturbation as a supplement to sexual intercourse. Compromise
frequently leads to frustration of one or both partners, as was discussed
earlier.

Psychological explanations for genuine nymphomania are that
the woman may be attempting to compensate for sexual deprivation
in adolescence and early adulthood, or that she is perhaps seeking
a means for release of excessive emotional tensions. Furthermore,
she may have fears of frigidity or latent homosexuality that through
her nymphomania she seeks to disprove, or she may be using the
opposite sex as an unconscious means of revenge against her father.[373]
Probably the most frequent cause is an irrational need to be loved and
accepted, involving a carry-over of early-childhood emphasis on the
value of the physical body as a tool to gain attention, recognition, and
acceptance. Through psychotherapy, the causative factors are uncovered
and the patient comes to have insight into her disorder. A therapeutic

program through which she can reevaluate herself is about the only successful method of treating nymphomania.

4. Satyriasis is an exaggerated desire for sexual gratification on the part of a man. Causative factors in this condition parallel those in nymphomania. An additional etiological factor may be an unconscious attempt to deny castration, or to reinforce a faltering self-view regarding masculinity and adequacy.

The public does not show as much concern over men who are "oversexed" as it does over similarly "afflicted" women. As might be expected, this divergency in attitudes has its roots in the traditional sexual role designated to females; women's deviation from their assigned erotically passive role is therefore likely to be more noticeable. The incidence of true satyriasis and nymphomania is about the same—both are very rare disorders—and each can be successfully treated with psychotherapy.

5. Promiscuity and **prostitution.** *Promiscuity* is generally defined as the participation in sexual intercourse with many people on a more or less casual basis. Promiscuity is to an extent condoned—or at least tolerated—for men, but it is strenuously condemned for women.

Studies involving personality and family backgrounds of promiscuous women indicate that they have generally made an uneven and perhaps incomplete progression to physical, emotional, intellectual, and social maturity. The investigations show that these women, before they left home, participated minimally in such group interaction as sports and other extracurricular activities. They could not enter into organized group experiences nor accept the responsibility for their own behavior. Parents, husbands, and friends were characteristically blamed for their failures and shortcomings. Their promiscuity was not caused by a strong sex drive, but, rather, sex came to be used in the attempt to cope with other emotional problems.[200]

To a large extent, men follow the same behavioral patterns in their promiscuity (which has been called "Don Juanism") as women do. In the case histories of almost all of the men studied, their promiscuous behavior proved to be the result of feelings of inadequacy, emotional conflicts, and other personality problems. There was no evidence that their sex drives, as such, were stronger than that of the average man.[183, 206]

A charge of promiscuity practically never appears on court dockets, even though laws against it abound. Fornication—coitus between unmarried persons—has, for instance, been legislated against in several states, but such acts are rarely penalized by the courts. Prostitution, on the other hand, is illegal almost everywhere in the United States[31] and is frequently prosecuted.

Prostitution, the participation in sexual activities for monetary rewards, has existed in one form or another throughout recorded history. It has been called, with much justification, the world's oldest profession, and through the ages it has been condemned, cursed, and attacked by people of nearly all societies and from all walks of life. Yet prostitution is with us today, and it is safe to predict that it will remain with us in the future.

As an example of the ineffectiveness of legal attempts to abolish it, a law was passed in Italy in 1958 aimed at stamping out prostitution and "freeing" the habitants of brothels. The effects of this legislation were quite the opposite of those expected: within a year, the incidence of syphilis had risen by 25%, and by 1961, the venereal disease rate in Italy was the highest in Europe. Furthermore, by 1965 the number of Italian prostitutes had increased from 18,000 to an estimated 200,000, the latter figure encompassing part-time practitioners.[311] Other attempts to eradicate prostitution have had similar consequences. The best that can be hoped for is to control the spread of venereal disease through contact with prostitutes, and to protect these women and their clientele from the exploitation of corrupt officials and blackmailers, which is a frequent correlative of prostitution.[31]

Kinsey and his associates[180] found that 69% of white males have had some experience with prostitutes. However, over the past several decades there apparently has been a steady decrease in the number of professional prostitutes in America, and in the frequency with which men consort with them.[31]

Men visit prostitutes for manifold reasons: desire for variety in their sex life; because they are too shy, embarrassed, or too physically handicapped to find heterosexual outlets elsewhere; because they need to gratify their deviate sex urges, such as sadomasochistic or fetishistic tendencies, and can pay to have them satisfied; because they wish to have sexual activity without the fear of troublesome obligations which are so often associated with less anonymous sexual intercourse; or because their wives are pregnant, or a child has been born and they feel they are in competition with it for the wife's affection. Men often forget, however, that since prostitution is illegal, they run the risk of blackmail, arrest, and scandal, to say nothing of the dangers of contracting venereal diseases or of being robbed.[7, 31, 215]

In ancient times, the prostitute was held in high esteem in certain Mediterranean societies; today, however, she is generally looked upon as the most derelict member of her sex. Many prostitutes enter the profession because of easy money, although many are disappointed in this respect, as they become victimized by pimps, corrupt city officials, or blackmailers. Some enter out of a sense of adventure, and others to find romance and a husband. (Far more often than many realize, the client develops a strong attachment to a prostitute and offers to marry her.) Still others become prostitutes because they are highly sexed and actually enjoy most of the sexual experiences prostitution affords them; some become so because of a neurotic need to punish and degrade themselves, or as an act of rebellion against parents and society. Many prostitutes are simply mentally deficient, emotionally disturbed, or lazy, and cannot therefore carry out regular employment.[31] A great many girls enter the profession on a temporary basis, and once their financial difficulties are in better control, they return to their work as salesgirl, teacher, secretary, or housewife.

The commonly held view that the prostitute is the prototype of a "bad girl" becomes interwoven into the pattern of many men's sexual conflicts. One such pattern has been called the "prostitute vs. princess syndrome"—the concept that "bad girls do, good girls don't." Boys are taught that their mothers and sisters are pure and good, and would never have involved themselves in the heinous act of premarital intercourse, and that the only sort of girl who would do so is bad—that is to say, a whore. The princess of this syndrome is the "girl next door" who is remindful of all mothers and sisters, and who is the type a man should marry. The prostitute of the syndrome is not, of course, actually a prostitute; she is merely from the "wrong side of the tracks," and hence is adjudged a sexual libertine, or she was a princess who fell from grace by allowing herself to become erotically active. The prostitute type, then, is seen as being sinful and lustful, and is not considered marriageable.

Paradoxically, the prostitute-princess ethic accepts sexual contact with a "bad," lustful, sensual girl as being not only permissible, but fun and enjoyable; whereas to express sexual endearments to a princess would be to defile her—in effect, a defilement of all mothers and sisters. It easily follows that men caught up in the prostitute-princess dichotomy find to their dismay that a marriage ceremony does not eradicate the notion that coitus with the princess is tantamount to coitus with Mother; the princess is not only besmirched, but symbolic incest now further distorts the picture. These men quite understandably find it impossible to function sexually with their princess-wives to any satisfactory degree, while they can perform most enjoyably with a prostitute, or with a girl whom they unconsciously identify as being a prostitute type because she enjoys her sexuality or because she comes from the "wrong side of the tracks." Fortunately, these men can usually be helped by psychotherapy.

6. **Rape** is sexual intercourse forced on an unconsenting person, nearly always a woman. Penalties for rape are quite severe, most states assessing a death penalty or life imprisonment as the maximum sentence. The rape victim is usually between eighteen and twenty-five, although of course the person attacked is occasionally a very young child or an old woman. Typically, the rapist is about twenty-six, is from a low-income, culturally deprived background, is mentally retarded or of dull-normal intelligence. The rapist is likely to have emotionally unstable parents and a weak, often alcoholic, father; the majority, however, come from broken homes. The rapist is usually emotionally immature, received little supervision in his youth from his parents, and is frequently physically unattractive.[142, 289]

Statutory rape concerns a girl under statutory age—usually eighteen years—and the legal definition of this felony revolves around the concept of "lawful consent." Despite the fact that many girls in these cases may well have lied about their ages and have purposely enticed the accused into coitus, they are nonetheless, because of their tender years, considered incapable of assessing and comprehending the nature of their actions. About one-third of the men convicted on charges of rape were accused on statutory grounds.[257] There is the occasional case wherein a woman is charged with raping a male; the charge is almost always statutory rape because the boy involved is underaged.

One fact should be noted: a woman who is emotionally disturbed may accuse a man with whom no intercourse has taken place (he may even be a total stranger) of rape. Furthermore, an adult consenting woman frequently charges the man with whom she has had intercourse with rape. The motive may be revenge; or she may be projecting her feelings of guilt, which her ego structure cannot handle, onto the man who in reality participated in coitus no more freely than she did.[23]

7. **Seduction** is any technique of persuasion or bribery used to obtain consent for unlawful sexual intercourse. In those instances in which difficulties arise, a promise of marriage is typically involved, and breach-of-promise lawsuits often follow. Seduction is not, of course, a sexual abnormality as such, but the manner in which seduction is carried out may be indicative of emotional or sexual problems— *e.g.,* "If you really love me, you'd prove it."

8. **Adultery** is an act of sexual intercourse between a married person and someone other than the legal spouse. Where legislation against adultery exists, prosecution is rare and penalties of the courts are usually relatively light. In American society, the traditional double-standard approach to sex has become modified over the past few decades so that both partners are now expected to restrict their sexual

activities to the marriage; earlier, husbands were accorded more sexual latitude.[26] The seriousness with which this violation of marital vows is held can be judged by the fact that in many states adultery is the only legal grounds for divorce.

Whether it is the husband or the wife who is the offending party seems to determine how serious a threat adultery is to the marriage —a remnant, perhaps, of the double standard. A single transgression by the wife may very well do irreparable damage to the marital relationship, while a similar transgression by the husband is often forgiven, unless there is involved a lengthy affair wherein love for the other woman has probably grown.[26] The explanation for these two divergent attitudes probably lies in the notion that a married man supposedly can have sexual relations with a woman other than his wife for physical pleasure only, conferring on the relationship no emotional commitment, whereas it is assumed that a woman must be in love with the other man before she wants a sexual relationship with him.[382]

Adultery is a more common occurrence than many realize. To repeat statistics set out earlier, Kinsey and his co-workers[170] found that by the age of forty, 26% of married women and 50% of married men have had adulterous relationships. Of the women, 41% restrict these affairs to one partner, 40% have had five or fewer partners, and 19% more than five partners. Most of those who have had an extramarital affair are not in retrospect distressed by the experience to the extent that they would not repeat the behavior in similar circumstances.

Approximately half the adulterous wives in the Kinsey sampling believed their husbands knew about their affairs, and in 42% of these instances the husbands took no retaliatory action nor posed any difficulty for the wives.[170] In addition, more often than many would think, these husbands had encouraged their wives to have extramarital affairs. Some wished to provide themselves with an excuse for their own adulterous behavior, but more commonly, the encouragement stemmed from a desire to allow the wives the "opportunity for additional sexual satisfaction." [170] Certainly this latter reasoning reflects a shift in attitude on the part of American husbands, and offers interesting grounds for speculation on the future of sexual mores in our culture. Even with these changes in attitude, however, adulterous relationships often put at least an additional strain on the marriage, and are more likely than not to cause greater unhappiness than the experiences are worth.

CHAPTER 15

Aphrodisiacs and Anaphrodisiacs

ALMOST SINCE the beginning of civilization, man has been interested in methods of controlling sexual appetite; most often he seems to be seeking ways to increase sexual desire (aphrodisiacs), but there are also times when he wishes to diminish the desire (anaphrodisiacs). He has sought to achieve these ends through a variety of foods, drugs, mechanical devices, and physical activities.

Aphrodisiacs. Certain foods have long been thought to have sexually stimulating properties. Ideas concerning the erotic value of various foods seem to spring from two sources. First, the rarity or newness of the food (such as the potato when it was first brought to England) has given hope to some that at last a great sexual stimulant has been discovered. Second, "the doctrine of signatures" is applied wherein it is assumed that sexual strength can be gained by eating foods that have external characteristics resembling a sex organ—for instance, bananas and oysters, with their superficial resemblance, respectively, to the penis and testicles.[203] Oysters have long been adjudged to contain sexually arousing properties, but a chemical analysis shows no ingredient which could have an arousal effect. It should be fairly obvious that there is no relationship between a food's shape and its sexual arousal properties, although if a man has strong enough faith in his convictions that added sexual prowess can be gained by eating a certain food, the psychological effect may be sufficient to provide some increase in sexual ability, at least temporarily.

The most famous of the alleged sexual stimulants is alcohol. It is presumed that alcoholic consumption propels sexual drive to new heights of capability and desire. The truth is that when it is taken in considerable quantity, alcohol is a depressant, narcotizes the brain, thus retarding its reflexes, and dilates the blood vessels, thus interfering with the capacity for erection. Physically, alcohol decreases sexual abilities. On the other hand, while it decreases certain physical powers, alcohol also tends to remove, temporarily, feelings of guilt and fear from the minds of some people, making them less inhibited than they normally would be.

The removal of inhibitions often more than counterbalances loss in physical ability, and there can therefore be an actual increase in sexual functioning despite depressed physical reactions. It can generally be accepted, however, that if a person's sexual drive and ability increase after the use of alcohol, he has some emotional blocks in the area of sex. It would appear that if he could rid himself of his emotional conflicts in this region, his sexual ability would be even greater than ever.

The most popularly known drug used to reinforce sexual drive is *cantharides* ("Spanish Fly"), derived from the *Cantharis vesicatoria,* a beautiful beetle found in southern Europe. The insects are dried and heated until they disintegrate into a fine powder, which is then taken internally, causing acute irritation of the genitourinary tract, specifically the mucous membrane of the urethra.[203] Accompanying this inflammation is a dilation of associated blood vessels, all of which produce a certain stimulation of the genitals. The drug can thus indeed produce penile erection, but usually without an increase in sexual desire. Furthermore, if cantharides is taken in excessive doses, it can cause violent illness or even death. The drug is not an effective sexual stimulant and is seldom used in modern medical practice.

Another substance to which aphrodisiac qualities are attributed is *yohimbine,* which is taken from the yohimbe tree, native to Africa, and which the natives have long used to increase their sexual powers. This plant is used to augment the excitability of the lower areas of the spine where erection and ejaculation centers are located. Any present-day use of yohimbine should be under the direction of a physician, and even then there is some doubt about its real effectiveness. Effective or not, yohimbine is generally conceded to be the most widely used drug for increasing sexual drive.

Erotic pictures, songs, and literature, as well as recordings of squeaking bedsprings accompanied by heavy breathing, moans, and gasps, are employed by some to increase sexual interest and drive. Some methods are more successful with one sex than the other, and their effectiveness varies from person to person of the same sex.

Aphrodisiacs are not likely to increase sex drive unless a psychological component of suggestion is present that might whet the sexual appetite and increase the drive momentarily; or unless the individual is physically debilitated, in which case such treatment as hormonal therapy might be of benefit.

All in all, good health, plenty of rest and sleep, an adequate amount of exercise, and freedom from emotional tension remain the most effective aphrodisiacs for man.[177, 282]

Anaphrodisiacs. Techniques used in an attempt to decrease sexual interest and drive have varied through the ages—from cold baths and going barefoot, as suggested by Plato and Aristotle[203] (one can well imagine what happens to amatory desire when a bare foot steps on a sharp stone); to wearing chastity belts and penis cages, as suggested by the Romans and British at one time; to the use of chemicals and tranquilizers.

The best known method for decreasing sexual appetite is the use of the chemical *potassium nitrate,* or saltpeter. Actually, this is an almost completely neutral chemical, except that it is a fairly effective diuretic, which perhaps accounts for its far-flung but undeserved reputation as a sex deterrent. It is a failure as an anaphrodisiac.

Recently, experimentation with the drug "Ismelin" *(guanethidine sulphate),* used for the treatment of high blood pressure, showed that erectile potency, ability to ejaculate, and intensity of climax were all reduced significantly by intake of the drug. Side effects of stomach cramps, diarrhea, and general loss of physical energy were reported by one-half the subjects.[240]

Physicians occasionally prescribe certain tranquilizers in an attempt to decrease sexual desire. Limited success has been reported. Some doctors shy away from their use, however, fearing that tranquilizers might have the same effect as alcohol: that the removal or reduction of emotional blocks might produce results opposite to the desired ones by releasing even stronger sexual yearnings or unusual sexual behavior.

In summary, it can be stated that most information regarding aphrodisiacs and anaphrodisiacs is based more on folklore than on scientific evidence. In those instances where there seems to be some change in desire and ability, the drugs are probably affecting some bodily function only remotely related to sexual function, and sexual ability is affected indirectly, if at all. Any changes, therefore, would be based on psychological, not physiological, factors. Any of the drugs is potentially dangerous if used without medical advice.

CHAPTER 16

Myths and Fallacies

WHEN ANY FACET of the human condition becomes as shrouded in misinformation and downright superstition as human sexuality has, it is almost inevitable that a welter of myths and fallacies should mushroom. And the tragedy is that misinformation not only becomes perpetuated by the distortions of truth communicated laterally by the peer group to its members, but also by those legitimately in a position to educate. Scientists have made notable advances in sex research, yet the educators—parents, teachers, clergymen—because of their own equivocal sex education, or their fear of freedom of expression on what they consider the hypersensitive subject of sex, ignore modern scientific contributions toward greater understanding in this vital area. Just as contradictory maternal attitudes toward sex are transmitted through successive generations of daughters, so sexual illogicality and bigotry become the bequest of one generation to the next.

Beliefs for which there is no conceivable foundation in truth are by no means limited to the uneducated and the unsophisticated. Highly educated professional people, as has been said, can harbor a rather harrowing collection of sexual misconceptions that, if not corrected, will almost certainly be handed down as indisputable truth to those whom they influence and instruct. This book has emphasized the vital importance of possessing accurate sex information, and the dispensing of that knowledge in an honest, direct manner to those under one's charge. This same approach can be used successfully when one encounters anyone caught up in some of the mythology obscuring the realities of sex. Some of the most common of these myths will now be discussed.

1. That each individual is allotted just so many sexual experiences, and that when they are used up, sexual activity is finished for that person.

This notion has troubled mankind for centuries, yet it is totally false. In fact, the degree of sexual activity that humans are capable of maintaining throughout the years seems to be correlated in quite an opposite manner: the earlier men or women mature physically, the longer their sexual reproductive ability continues; and the more sexually active a person is and the earlier the age at which he begins that activity, the longer it continues into old age.[179, 180, 278, 282] These observations do not mean necessarily that if a person starts his sex life early he will be guaranteed a longer and consistently vigorous sex life; it means that ordinarily the person with a stronger sex drive than average will commence sexual activity earlier in life and continue it longer.

A similar fallacious assumption is that men have only a certain amount of semen or a certain number of sperm cells in their bodies, and that once the supply has been discharged, no further reservoirs remain and no further manufacture is possible. Certainly this argument has been used—often with detrimental results—by adults in an attempt to discourage boys from masturbating. Most boys have heard that each ejaculation takes from his body some fantastic amount of protein, blood, strength, and the like, most of which, they are warned, will be difficult to replace—if replacement is possible at all. Experts in hormonal functioning have shown that the chemical constituents of semen are constantly being replenished by a normal intake of food, and that the production of sperm is also a continuing process. Ejaculated sperm are, therefore, easily and quickly replaced in the healthy body, much in the same way that saliva is constantly replenished.[59, 278]

It is a physical near-impossibility for a person to experience orgasm or ejaculation too often. When one has functioned to his or her physiological limit, the sexual act becomes repelling; and for the man, it becomes impossible to perform. After a normal rest or recovery period, however, both the desire and ability to engage in sexual activity return to normal.

2. That an unborn child can be "marked."

Because of the close connection between fetus and mother, it is understandable why many people assume that such experiences as sudden shocks or fright to the mother would cause her baby to be born with some physical or emotional "mark," most commonly a birthmark. There is no direct connection between the nervous systems or between the blood systems of mother and fetus, and the idea of prenatally "marking" the child in the manners mentioned is, therefore, completely false.

Most often when a child is born with an unusual birthmark— for example, a skin discoloration in the general shape of a bird—the parents' faulty memory processes will cause them to "remember" an incident while the mother was pregnant wherein she was attacked or in some way frightened by something of that shape.

Misinformed scientists have also been party to perpetuating the "marking" myth. For example, in 1836, eight physicians signed a report, which appeared in an American medical journal, that a man had a face like a snake and could coil and uncoil his arm in a snake-like fashion because a rattlesnake had frightened his mother during her sixth month of pregnancy.[241]

It is true, of course, that the mother supplies nourishment for the fetus; her diet and chemical intake can have a direct effect on certain physiological reactions of the child, both before and after birth. For example, if the mother grossly overeats certain foods, it is some-times possible to cause an allergic condition in the child that continues after birth. Also, it is well known that the physical condition of infants whose mothers smoked tobacco during their pregnancies will be af-fected by the smoking.[245] However, these reactions are not the same as those ordinarily considered when one discusses "marking" a baby; the latter theory is a physiological and psychological impossibility, so far as scientific investigation has been able to determine.

3. That sexual intercourse should be avoided during pregnancy.

Considerable investigation has been made into the pregnant wom-an's physiologic and psychologic patterns of response to sexual stim-ulation.[215] In general, there is little change from the nonpregnant state in sexual interest or capacity for satisfying coition during the first three months (first trimester) of pregnancy; and during the second trimester, there is usually an increase in erotic feelings, even beyond those of the nonpregnant state. During the third trimester, most women show a loss in sexual interest. There is no evidence to indicate that the pregnant woman with no unusual complications should not regularly engage in sexual intercourse or automanipulative activity to orgasm until late in the third trimester. Quite naturally, sensible precautions should be taken against excessive pressure on the abdomen, deep penile penetra-tion, and infection.[215]

It is now well known that there are rather strong contractions of the uterus during a woman's orgasmic response that are not unlike those experienced during labor. Couples should be warned, therefore, that the uterine contractions of orgasm may cause labor contractions to begin if the woman is within three weeks of term.[215, 217]

On the whole, sexual intercourse during pregnancy is valuable for both the wife and husband. The nature of a man's sex drive, and the

psychological stresses he experiences during the pregnancy and immediate postpartum period cause him to be more likely to seek out extramarital sexual activity in the last six weeks of his wife's pregnancy and
the first six weeks after delivery than at any other time.[215] Continuing
sexual activity as long as possible during pregnancy is, therefore, quite
likely a hedge against future marital discord and unhappiness if the
husband would otherwise feel driven during these weeks to seek sexual
release elsewhere.

Sexual intercourse may continue up to the time of labor if three
conditions are met: (1) if there is no pain during the act, (2) if the fetal
membrane is intact, and (3) if there is no spotting or bleeding.[215] It now
appears that unless these adverse conditions exist, coital abstinence
during pregnancy and after delivery (that is, after the time postpartum
vaginal bleeding has stopped and any vaginal incisions have healed)
is not called for. To the contrary, sexual intercourse during this period
probably should be encouraged, if the woman is psychologically dis-
posed toward it.[215, 217] However, whether or not sexual intercourse should
take place during the third trimester and the early postpartum period
is an *individual* matter that should be decided by the woman and her
physician, without the latter's arbitrarily following a set of rules that are
not equally applicable to all women. If for some reason coition is contra-
indicated, most couples would benefit from an understanding of the
value of automanipulation and of mutual sexual stimulation to relieve
both the husband's and the wife's sexual tensions during this time.

4. That oral-genital sex between a man and woman indicates homo-sexual tendencies.

Homosexuality involves sexual contact between members of the
same sex. The choice of a partner of the same rather than of the
opposite sex is the determinant in homosexuality, *not* the technique
used in sexual activity. Some of the most genuinely masculine of men
and feminine of women often enjoy oral-genital contact. But unless
that type of outlet is preferred with a member of the same sex, it is no
more an indication of homosexual tendencies than if sexual intercourse
were the technique of choice.[281]

Probably this idea is an outgrowth of the fact that homosexuals
often employ oral-genital techniques in their sex-play activities. It does
not follow, however, that the same technique cannot be employed by
heterosexual partners with pleasure and without the implication of the
slightest trace of homosexuality.

5. That repeated sexual experiences with one man will leave a mark on a child later fathered by another man.

The influence of a "previous sire" on a later conception is a theory known as *telegony*. Despite its rather widespread acceptance among breeders of animals, and regardless of the writings of such scientists as the great Charles Darwin, there is no scientific basis for the theory, whether one is discussing humans or animals. Inadequate knowledge of the laws of heredity and unscientific methods of observation and control in animal breeding have led some people to the conclusion that, on the human level, the offspring of a second husband might be affected by the fact that the wife was impregnated by her first husband or simply had sexual intercourse with him. There are cases wherein a woman, who had previously borne children of a Negro man and then had later married a white man, subsequently bore children with "Negro traits." However, these latter children were either fathered by a man with "Negro traits," or the woman had some Negro blood in her own heritage. It is a genetic impossibility that there could be a causal relationship between her previous Negro husband and the fact that children born after her marriage to a white man have Negroid features.

A common occurrence that appears to give credence to the telegony theory concerns female dogs. Bitches remain in heat for several days, during which time they may mate with several males. Since female dogs have the maddening capacity for escaping the watchful eye of their owners and mating with almost any male that happens along, it is quite possible to find a litter of puppies of which none resembles the intended sire. There is in this instance no "carry-over" from the bitch's previous matings; it is simply that the puppies of the same litter have been sired by different dogs.[161]

6. That heart patients need not worry that sexual activity will be detrimental to their health, as long as they remain physically inactive and quiet during coitus.

Heart patients who do not understand the marked changes that inevitably occur in heart rate and blood pressure during human sexual response may be endangering their lives or health by sexual arousal.[114, 278] During sexual excitement and fulfillment, the heart rate may increase from 70 beats per minute to 150 or more, and blood pressure may rapidly increase from 120 to 250 or more. Both husband and wife should understand that even if the heart patient plays a passive and physically inactive role during the sexual act, the heart beat and blood pressure will unquestionably rise to very high peaks as a result of the sexual response alone.

This is not to say that considerable benefit cannot accrue from sensible sexual behavior. What the heart patient *is* warned against is prolonged coition, fatiguing sexual positions, and extended sex play. Control of these factors can allow him the fulfillment and release of coitus with no undue threat to his health. Death can be (and has been) caused by violent coronary reaction to sexual acts, and the increase in blood pressure may lead to rupture of blood vessels, especially in older persons. Such severe reactions, however, are rare, and the admonition to observe total (or near total) sexual abstinence is not applicable to most patients suffering from heart disease; the advice, rather, is directed to those with serious coronary involvement.

It is quite possible for heart patients under proper circumstances to lead an active sex life; but in this as in other medical questions, a physician should be consulted and his prescriptions (and proscriptions) followed carefully. In addition to controlling physical factors of sex play and coition, one should be reminded that control of anxiety from any source is of utmost importance in the management of cardiac conditions. Tensions can frequently be alleviated by the patient's discussing whatever is disturbing him with his wife (or wife with husband, as the case may be) and with the physician; in severe or persistent cases of tension, a psychotherapist should probably be consulted.

7. That the virginity of the woman is an important factor in the success of a marriage.

Most of the scientifically sound investigations into the effect of a woman's premarital sexual experiences on marital adjustment show that there is only a slight correlation between happiness in marriage and premarital experience.[9, 50] However small the correlation, the indications are nevertheless slightly in favor of premarital chastity.

The importance to either men or women of their prospective marriage partner's chastity at the time of marriage is apparently diminishing gradually. Studies were made at the University of Wisconsin in 1939 and 1956 to determine the components that students considered important in a happy marriage. In the intervening years between the two surveys, chastity dropped in importance from tenth to fourteenth place. Kinsey's studies indicate that over 40% of men wanted to marry virgins, while only 23% of women expected their prospective husbands to be without coital experience.[170]

As indicated earlier, even though mothers who had premarital sexual intercourse admit they are not sorry for their actions and would do the same thing again, they do not want their daughters to experience sexual intercourse before marriage.[50, 88, 179] Mothers are more rigid in their attitude toward premarital coitus than their daughters are. When both groups were asked, "How important do you think it is that a girl be a virgin when she marries?" 88% of the mothers replied "very important," and 12% said "somewhat important"; none indicated that it was "not important." The percentage of the daughters replying in the same three categories was, respectively, 54%, 33%, and 13%.[20]

During the early part of marriage, those women who have had premarital coitus seem to enjoy sexual intercourse more than those who have not, but the differences eventually diminish as the marriages grow older.[9] Because sexual compatibility in marriage is dependent upon compatibility at the many levels of a couple's day-by-day living together, having premarital sexual intercourse, however satisfactory, will not assure them of a happy sex life after marriage.[159] This truth stands in opposition to the arguments many young men present to sexually reluctant girl friends, and to their threadbare cliche that "only a foolish person would purchase shoes without trying them on."

In summary, whether or not a woman has premarital coitus is not nearly so important to marital adjustment as are other factors, such as adequate sex education, emotional stability, dependability, and economic security.

8. That there is a difference between vaginal and clitoral orgasms.

Since the time of Sigmund Freud (and perhaps before), there has been considerable controversy over the difference between vaginal and clitoral orgasms—that is, orgasm produced by penile penetration of the vagina, as opposed to orgasm produced by some form of manipulation of the clitoris. Indeed, in the early days of the controversy it was considered—especially by the psychoanalysts—that only mature women had vaginal orgasms, while clitoral orgasms were sure signs of narcissism and sexual inadequacy. Freud taught that a girl can achieve orgasm by clitoral stimulation, but that as she matures into a "real" woman, she will transfer her sexual response from the clitoris to the vagina.[44]

For years, physiologists have recognized that the vaginal walls contain few erogenous nerve endings and that it is *only* stimulation (direct or indirect) of the clitoris that produces orgasmic responses in women. It has taken, however, the recent Masters and Johnson research to convince many medical men and scientists that "from an anatomic point of view, there is absolutely no difference in the response of the pelvic viscera to effective sexual stimulation, regardless of whether stimulation occurs as a result of clitoral area manipulation, natural or artificial coition, or, for that matter, from breast stimulation alone."[225]

Many women have been concerned over their sexual adequacy because they are unable to achieve orgasm through coition. The research findings of Masters and Johnson should once and for all dispel the myth that women have two kinds of orgasms—one clitoral and the other vaginal. From a purely physiological viewpoint, direct clitoral stimulation usually produces a somewhat stronger orgasmic response than does the indirect stimulation of the clitoris in vaginal penetration; but many women find the latter more satisfying because of various psychological factors.[217] Apparently these women feel that orgasm by vaginal penetration places them in a more traditional female role, and allows more "togetherness" with their husbands during the sex act, producing more satisfaction. Other women receive more gratification from clitoral stimulation alone; in fact, many women are unable to achieve an orgasm in any manner other than direct stimulation of the clitoral area.

9. That menopause or hysterectomy terminates a woman's sex life.

Kinsey and other researchers have shown that a woman's sexual desire ordinarily continues undiminished until she is sixty years of age or older.[179, 215, 282, 331] This is long after menopausal changes in hormonal functioning have occurred, and clearly indicates that ordinarily no physical reasons exist for a woman's sex life to end because of menopause or hysterectomy.

It is understandable that in the relatively unenlightened medical world of the 1800s, physicians would reason that since the ovaries dwindle in their production of female sex hormones at and after the climacteric, women's sex drive would accordingly decrease. It is now known that women's sex drive often does not diminish even when the ovaries are surgically removed. Hormones are only one of many factors affecting the capacity for sexual response; more crucial factors are the woman's emotional stability and attitude toward sex.[278]

Total hysterectomy is the removal of the uterus; panhysterectomy is removal of uterus, Fallopian tubes, and ovaries. In the first instance, there would not even be the reason of hormonal imbalance to account for loss of sex drive; if the woman's surgeon carefully explains the effects of the operation, neither should she have any diminution of sex drive because of psychological factors. If any change does occur, in fact, it might be in the direction of increased drive, since fear of pregnancy is now removed. If ovaries and tubes are also removed, some hormonal changes will occur, although medication can make up any deficiencies.

Considering all the factors, a woman can expect to maintain her sex drive at approximately the same level between the ages of about thirty to sixty years, despite menopause or hysterectomy.

10. That Negroes have greater sex drive than whites, and that the penis of the Negro male is larger than that of the white male.

There is no scientific evidence to support the contention that one race is more sexually active than another. The basis for the prevalent notion that Negroes are more sexually immoderate than whites to a great extent lies in certain general conclusions of research groups. Their findings reveal a greater amount of sexual activity among poorly educated Americans of low socioeconomic status than among those who are more fortunate. Since a greater number of Negro citizens—sadly, a majority—fall into the first group than whites do, many people erroneously conclude that racial rather than environmental or class factors account for the differences in sexual activity. The recent Duke University investigation[254] into sexual behavior during the human aging process demonstrated that Negro subjects between the ages of sixty and ninety-three were more active sexually than were whites, but the researchers also pointed out that the Negro subjects were of the lower classes.

We have also been taught—mistakenly—that people from culturally and economically deprived strata are more primitive and aggressive (and thus, presumably, more sexually potent) than are people from higher strata. This prejudicial belief exaggerates in many people's minds the sexual powers of the Negro.

Many people have the notion that the Negro's penis is larger than the white man's, and that the larger the penis, the greater the man's sexual powers. Many studies have proven that the size of the penis has absolutely nothing to do with the sexual ability of a man, except, of course, in those cases where hormonal deficiency has stunted both penile growth and sexual drive.[215, 300, 389] It is believed by some[49] that because body configurations of Negro and white males are somewhat different, the flaccid penis of the Negro is accordingly somewhat larger than that of the white man. However, even if this were true, there appears to be little or no relationship between the largeness or smallness of the penis when it is flaccid and when it is erect.[215] This misconception has helped in the evolution of a related fallacy, which is discussed next.

11. That a large penis is important to a woman's sexual gratification, and that the man with a large penis is more sexually potent than the man with a small penis.

As was discussed in Chapter 4, the size of the penis has practically no relationship to a man's ability to satisfy a woman sexually. The only exceptions would be these: the instances in which there is the psychological influence of a woman's *thinking* penile size makes a difference;[217] or when sexual pleasure is diminished because the penis is too large and causes the woman pain; or when the penis is so pathologically small that penetration and pelvic contact cannot be maintained.

The vaginal walls themselves have few nerve endings. But it is true that in penetration, the penis that is larger in circumference will be more likely to make contact with the labia minora and vestibular tissue, pulling them in and out during coital movements. This contact causes a tugging of the clitoris which stimulates it and produces erotic pleasure. A very long penis may also put pressure on the cervix, producing pain and detracting from some women's excitement. Yet other women will report that such pressure gives added pleasure, apparently because of psychological reasons, or because the pressure pushes the uterus in such a way that the erogenous nerve endings of the inner abdominal wall are stimulated. With the exceptions stated, however, the size of the penis is not related to the sexual gratification experienced by a woman.

To recapitulate what has been said earlier, there is little correlation between body and penile size—far less correlation, in fact, than there is between the dimensions of other organs and body size.[218] Penile size is dictated by heredity, and in no way affects, either adversely or favorably, sexual potency. The mystique surrounding the large penis no doubt has its beginnings in the prepuberal boy's awe at the postpuberal boy's larger penis—an awe augmented, quite likely, by the braggadocio of adolescent youths in their accounts (usually fantasied) of herculean sexual achievements. The younger boys thereby come to associate larger genitals with extraordinary sexual ability, and the attitude is carried into adulthood.

12. That today's young adults are "going wild" sexually.

Since the beginning of recorded history, older generations have been in a state of shock and horror at the immorality and other unacceptable behavior of younger generations. It is not surprising, then, that newspaper and magazine articles, organized groups, and individuals are crying out that the nation is on the brink of ruin because of the sexual misconduct of its young people. There are, to be sure, those incidents that incite public outrage and that are offered as evidence of general moral degeneration among the young. But there have always been such occurrences, and there are no more now—if as many—than in the past. As has been mentioned before in this book, the evidence is overwhelming that the young people of today are as well-adjusted mentally, as mature in their responsibilities, and as decent a group of citizens as America has ever known.

Sociological and psychological investigations indicate that very few changes are occurring in the sexual mores of boys and girls of today, although, as one expects of members of any new generation, they are working out new standards of thinking, believing, and behaving.[109, 179, 180, 280] Americans are not having sexual relations at an earlier age than before, promiscuity is not rampant among college students (only about 20% of college girls, for instance, are not virgins), and there has been no great leap forward in sexual permissiveness since about 1920.[83] There is, on the other hand, considerable evidence that today's young people—especially the college populations—are behaving responsibly. Indeed, they demonstrate moral strength in their concern for the welfare and rights of others.[185]

There will always be rebellious youth whose behavior will outrage certain segments of the citizenry, and such outrage has a tendency to radiate to include all youth. But every new generation has contained a core of rebellion, and the only surprise is that today there are not more rebellious acts—certainly there are no more than in past generations. As a matter of fact, group rebellion has often forced some of our most needed social reforms, although when such insurgence begins, it is interpreted by many simply as further evidence of the failure of adults to maintain proper control of their charges.

13. That frigid women, promiscuous women, and prostitutes are not so likely to conceive as women whose sexual activity is more normal.

Since frigidity in women is practically always based on psychological factors, and since conception has nothing whatever to do with whether or not a woman enjoys sexual activity, it is obvious that there is no foundation to the first part of this myth. If in an attempt to prevent conception a woman holds herself back from orgasm, or remains passive and indifferent during coition, she is running the risk of pregnancy. Neither orgasm nor active participation in coition is in the slightest degree necessary to conception.

If promiscuous women and prostitutes do not appear to become pregnant as readily as the average woman does, it is because they take better precautions against the possibility.[22] Sometimes promiscuous women begin their coital activity at a very early age, even before they produce mature ova. They are not, of course, able to conceive at that time of their lives, which perhaps leads to the false notion that a woman's "sexual excess" will cause her to be sterile. (Men *do* lower their ability to impregnate by frequent ejaculations because their sperm count is thereby reduced. The average man requires about thirty to forty hours to regain his normal sperm count after ejaculation.)[217]

Prostitutes who allow themselves to become pregnant are putting themselves out of business; one would quite naturally expect them to take extra precautions against such an eventuality, which they probably do. Furthermore, some prostitutes are sterile because of present or past venereal infection. But frequent sexual intercourse of itself will not lessen the likelihood of these women's becoming pregnant, nor strengthen the possibility of their becoming sterile.[22]

14. That it is dangerous to have sexual intercourse during menstruation.

This erroneous idea, along with other myths about menstruation, has been with mankind for centuries. As early as 60 A.D., the Roman historian Pliny declared that the mere presence of a menstruating woman will cause "new wine to become sour, seeds to become sterile, fruit to fall from trees, and garden plants to become parched." Furthermore, according to Pliny, menstrual fluid can blunt the edge of steel, kill a swarm of bees, instantly rust iron and brass (causing an offensive odor); and if, by chance, dogs were to taste the menstrual flow, they would become mad, and their bite venomous and incurable.[242] Small wonder, then, that couples shy away from sexual intercourse during menses. The taboo against "wasting sperm" by having intercourse during the "safe period" of menstruation undoubtedly has added to the cluster of misinformation surrounding coition during this time.

Menstrual blood is perfectly harmless in content to both man and woman; the source of the flow is uterine rather than vaginal, and no tissue damage occurs from penile penetration; and a woman's sex drive ordinarily does not diminish during the menstrual period: these facts point up the irrationality of any arguments against coition during menses, if the couple desire it at that time.

A related myth concerning menstruation is that women should not bathe during the time of flow. It is true that sharp changes in temperature during bathing may temporarily stop the bleeding, but a woman should take precautions against any abrupt temperature changes. Otherwise, there is no reason why bathing, as well as other normal everyday activity, should not be carried on.[242]

15. That humans can get "hung up" (i.e., experience penis captivus) during sexual intercourse.

This is another faulty notion that results from man's observing the behavior of animals and attributing the same possibility to himself. Dogs do get "hung up" because of the peculiar anatomical structure of the male dog's sexual organs. There is a bone in the animal's penis *(os penis)* that enables him to penetrate the bitch's vagina before full erection. With ensuing tumescence, the head of the penis fills the vaginal barrel and at the same time the walls of the bitch's vagina swell, all of which serves to "trap" the penis and prevent its withdrawal before ejaculation.[99]

Most people have heard stories of couples who became locked together while copulating, the services of a physician being required before the penis could be released. The story is characteristically told as the truth and as having happened to a friend (or to a friend of a friend), although no one has ever witnessed the phenomenon or experienced it. It is, of course, theoretically possible for a woman to experience sudden strong muscle spasms of the vagina *(vaginismus)* during sexual intercourse, and the vagina may momentarily tighten around her partner's penis. But even in these circumstances, the pain or fear the man would experience would cause loss of erection, permitting easy withdrawal of the penis. There are no scientifically verified cases of *penis captivus* among humans in modern medical literature.[99]

16. That nature compensates for the number of males killed during time of war.

For his own stability, man depends upon the laws of nature to keep his life in balance. Particularly after the shattering experiences of recent wars, he finds some comfort in the notion that nature compensates for the combatants killed during hostilities by increasing, in some mystical way, the ratio of male to female births. Indeed, at first sight, it seems that just such a miracle occurred after World War I and II when there was, in fact, an increase in male births. Scientists, however, have fairly sound explanations for this phenomenon.

It is an established fact that many more males than females are conceived, whatever the reason may be. From this point on, the female survival ratio is higher than that of the male: the conception ratio is about 160 males to 100 females, the zygote implantation ratio is about 120 males to 100 females, and the birth ratio is 105 males to 100 females. The noted biologist and anthropologist, Ashley Montagu, offers this explanation for what happens in wartime. People marry, he points out, at a younger age; the younger mothers, being strong and healthy, give fertilized ova a greater chance for survival and implantation, and hence tend to give birth to a higher percentage of males than older mothers do. Furthermore, since these young mothers are separated from their husbands, the enforced spacing between births is longer than usual, leaving the wives in a stronger physical condition to carry the next child to term, and thereby increasing the likelihood of a male birth. Following Montagu's reasoning, what actually happens is that more male zygotes are implanted in the uterus and fewer male embryos die, producing a greater male to female ratio of births.

17. That circumcision makes it difficult for a man to control ejaculation.

Until the recent Masters and Johnson research, this fallacy was frequently accepted as a biologic fact.[215] The assumption had been that the glans of the circumcised penis is more sensitive to the frictions of masturbation or coitus; the circumcised man cannot, therefore, delay ejaculation as long as the man whose foreskin is still intact. Neurological and clinical testing of tactile discrimination has failed, however, to reveal any differences in the sensitivity of a circumcised and an uncircumcised penis. In most instances of the latter, the foreskin retracts from over the glans during a state of penile erection, especially during coition, permitting the same exposure of the glans that the circumcised glans receives during the sex act. But even in those cases where the prepuce does not fully retract, the response to stimulation of the uncircumcised penis is the same as that of the circumcised penis.[215]

18. That urination by the woman after coitus, or having sexual intercourse while standing, will prevent pregnancy.

Since the bladder does not empty through the vagina, urine cannot possibly wash out sperm deposited in the vaginal canal during sexual intercourse. There is some remote possibility that the position assumed for urination, if the woman voids immediately after coitus, might aid in preventing the sperm from the entering the uterus. But the act of urination itself will not prevent impregnation.

Sexual intercourse, whether experienced in a lying, standing, sitting, or some more unusual position, can produce a pregnancy. Sperm are deposited at or near the cervix upon ejaculation, and almost immediately afterwards they begin to move toward and into the uterus. The standing position is not likely to cause the sperm to spill out of the vagina before they can enter the uterus and make their way towards the ovum, if one is present in the uterine tubes.

19. That humans and infrahuman animals can crossbreed.

Not only is it impossible for humans to crossbreed with infrahuman animals, but interbreeding among the various genera of lower animals is equally impossible, although members of different species of the same genus may produce crossbred offspring. For example, a man and an ape cannot interbreed, nor can an ape and a tiger; but two members of different species in the cat family, for example, may crossbreed.

Undoubtedly, our knowledge of the wondrous creatures of Greek and Roman mythology—the centaurs, sphinxes, mermaids, and satyrs—has given status through the years to the myth that humans and lower animals can interbreed.

20. That simultaneous climaxes are necessary if conception is to take place.

The best proof of the erroneousness of this belief is that a woman can be made pregnant through artificial insemination, at which time no orgasm—alone or simultaneous—occurs. The presence or absence of orgasmic response on the part of the woman has nothing to do with whether or not she becomes pregnant. If she produces a mature healthy egg that is penetrated by a normal sperm, conception has taken place.[22]

There are many other myths and fallacies revolving around human sexuality. There now follows a list of several more of them, and in each instance, the statements are false as set out. The chapters containing the correct information on each subject are listed parenthetically.

1. **That an intact hymen is proof of virginity, and the absence of a hymen proves nonvirginity** (Chapter 5).
2. **That masturbation is dangerous, and causes pimples or acne** (Chapters 3, 9, 14).
3. **That men and women lose their sex drive after the age of fifty** (Chapter 12).
4. **That alcohol is a sexual stimulant** (Chapter 15).
5. **That sterilization diminishes the sex drive** (Chapter 8).
6. **That castration completely destroys the sex drive** (Chapter 8).
7. **That removal of a man's prostate gland will keep him from attaining and maintaining an erection, from having children, and from enjoying sex** (Chapter 4).
8. **That it is the woman who determines the sex of the child** (Chapter 2).
9. **That there is an absolute "safe" period for sexual intercourse insofar as conception is concerned** (Chapter 8).

10. That sexual intercourse must be had twice at the same encounter in order to conceive twins, three times for triplets, and so on (Chapter 7).

11. That the diet of a woman during pregnancy will help determine the sex of the child (Chapter 2).

12. That the fetus sleeps during the day and awakens (and kicks) during the night (Chapter 7).

13. That a seven-month-old fetus has a better chance to survive than an eight-month-old fetus has (Chapter 7).

14. That the menarche occurs earlier for girls from countries with hot climates than for those from cool climates (Chapter 3).

15. That the Bartholin's glands supply the major lubrication for the vagina (Chapter 11).

16. That the uterus "sucks up" seminal fluid (Chapters 7, 11).

17. That women ejaculate as do men (Chapter 11).

18. That lower animals menstruate (Chapters 3, 6).

19. That the sperm from one testicle will produce males and from the other, females; or that the ova from one ovary will produce males, and from the other, females (Chapters 3, 4).

20. That abortions are necessarily dangerous (Chapter 8).

21. That pornography leads to sexual excess and sexual acting-out (Chapter 17).

22. That the age at which a man is most likely to molest children is after sixty-five (Chapter 17).

23. That sex criminals are impelled toward their actions by narcotics or pornography (Chapter 17).

24. That sex offenders are typically antireligious (Chapters 14, 17).

25. That chronic sex offenders are oversexed (Chapters 14, 17).

26. That sex offenders cannot be cured (Chapter 17).

27. That typical sex offenders, especially those who molest children, are aggressive, sadistic, homicidal, and physically dangerous (Chapter 17).

28. That homosexuals are "born that way" (Chapter 14).

29. That all people are either totally heterosexual or totally homosexual (Chapter 14).

30. That hormonal imbalance produces homosexuality (Chapters 3, 14).

31. That homosexuals are more creative than heterosexual individuals are (Chapter 14).

32. That homosexual offenders are a menace to society (Chapter 14).

33. That a child conceived in a rear-entry coital position will be homosexual (Chapter 4).

34. That men who enjoy having their nipples stimulated have suppressed homosexual desires (Chapter 9).

35. That most prostitutes are lesbians (homosexuals) (Chapter 14).

36. That the typical career woman is a suppressed lesbian (Chapter 14).

37. That any lesbian will prefer a man if a "real man" will just use the right technique (Chapter 14).

38. That if a woman desires sex more often than her husband, there is no way the couple can become sexually compatible (Chapter 9).

39. That women cannot have multiple orgasms (Chapter 11).

40. That women who have strong sex drives, come to easy climax, and have multiple orgasms are nymphomaniacs (Chapters 11, 14).

41. That nymphomaniacs and satyromaniacs—women and men with insatiable sex appetites—are fairly numerous in the population (Chapter 14).

42. That premature ejaculation is caused by an abnormally sensitive penis (Chapter 14).

43. That nocturnal emissions or "wet dreams" are indicators of sexual disorders (Chapter 4).

44. That women do not have nocturnal orgasms (Chapter 12).

45. That simultaneous orgasm is necessary for sexual compatibility in marriage (Chapter 9).

46. That sexual intercourse will weaken an athlete, and that he should abstain from sexual activity; and that females should avoid participating in sports during the menstrual period (Chapters 5, 6).

47. That the best health is enjoyed by those who abstain from sex (Chapter 8).

48. That aphrodisiacs are valuable in increasing erotic desire (Chapter 15).

49. That a woman's wearing high heels during pregnancy will cause the baby to be cross-eyed or to have some other physical problem (Chapters 3, 5, 7).

50. That the only normal method of sexual relations is penile-vaginal intercourse, and that unusual or excessive practices can cause mental breakdowns (Chapters 9, 12, 14).

CHAPTER 17

Sex and the Law

IF IT WERE not for the tragedy involved, one of the great farces of this nation would be its laws designed to control and regulate sexual behavior. Even a cursory examination of legislation attempting to regulate sexual expression reveals amazing vagueness and inconsistency, not only among the various states, but frequently within the same state.[350]

Much of this confusion can be accounted for historically; for the past fifty years, there have been few attempts to amend or repeal laws governing sexual matters. Generally, the laws of the nation are undergoing constant scrutiny and change, but this type of flexibility is not found in legislation governing sexual matters.[350] A short time ago, a man in North Carolina was convicted and sentenced to thirty years' imprisonment for homosexuality, "the abominable and detestable crime against nature, not to be mentioned among Christians." Upon appeal, the U.S. district judge who heard the case suggested it was time that the state legislature redraft this criminal statute, since the law was first enacted in 1533.[24]

The resistance to changing these laws is a result of the fears and anxieties of the nation's citizenry when it must deal with anything sexual; and of the lawmakers' reluctance to do anything that might cause their uneasy constituents to view their attitudes on sex, punishment, or morality as libertine. Progress in this realm of legislation is thus blocked; consequently, such relatively current problems as artificial insemination are virtually untouched by direct legal interpretation, while unrelated laws have unrealistically been extended to apply to them.[350]

In addition, the enforcement and administration of laws pertaining to sexual matters are inconsistent. It is well known that the ratio of enforcement to violation is very low.[118, 120, 350] For example, there are 3 million homosexual acts performed in America for every *one* conviction, and laws on abortion are especially archaic and unfair. Yet jurists have steadfastly refused (until recently, in some states) to consider even a slight relaxation and reworking of legal codes, despite pleas from physicians, psychologists, penologists, sexologists, sociologists, and many members of the clergy, as well as from private citizens.

At present, laws regulating abortion, for instance, favor the woman who can "afford to pay." In New York City in 1965, as an example, only 17% of maternal deaths among white women were caused by abortion, while 57% of the maternal deaths of Negroes and 70% of Puerto Rican women's were so caused. The more prosperous woman can go to a hospital and have a "perfectly legal" dilation and curettage performed by a physician (perhaps for a fee of $1000, but at least the operation is safe). A woman from the slums, on the other hand, often must turn to a practical nurse or to a poorly trained abortionist who might use a knitting needle or coat hanger in an attempt to produce the abortion. The more likely result is death for the mother.[24, 60, 301]

Some hope can be taken from the fact that at least a few states are making concerted efforts to revamp their abortion laws. In June, 1967, for instance, California enacted new legislation liberalizing the grounds for therapeutic abortion. These grounds now include pregnancies resulting from rape and incest, and pregnancy posing danger to the mother's physical or mental health.

The extent to which some of our present laws are at odds with reality is evidenced by the fact that in certain states a married couple can, at least theoretically, be arrested and convicted for any sexual behavior, conducted in the privacy of their bedroom, that goes beyond the insertion of the penis into the vagina.[24, 60, 350] Furthermore, according to the fuzzy laws of most states, 95% of adult American males and a large percentage of American women have experienced orgasms in an illegal manner.[24, 118, 180]

Only in June, 1967, did the United States Supreme Court declare unconstitutional those laws banning interracial marriages (such legislation still remaining on the statute books of at least sixteen states). There still exist, however, certain state laws that forbid sale and use of birth-control methods, although, fortunately, the constitutionality of these statutes is currently under the scrutiny of the Supreme Court. Even some religious leaders have grown more realistic than some lawmakers and are pushing for reform of certain laws relating to sex. Cardinal Cushing of Boston made this statement, in support of legalizing birth-control information and methods in Massachusetts: "It does not seem reasonable to me to forbid in civil law a practice that can be considered a matter of private morality."[322]

Laws concerning obscenity and pornography are also ambiguous. They are subject to a variety of interpretations, and frequently appear to be used in the course of legal prosecution to satisfy the unconscious needs and desires of the accuser rather than to protect society from the accused. The American culture regards sexual behavior with such intense emotionality (shame, guilt, and fear) that almost any literary or pictorial representation of sexual interaction is liable to be interpreted by *some*one as being obscene, hence unlawful.[164]

The United States Supreme Court has been called upon several times recently to settle questions of law regarding obscenity, and as was pointed out in Chapter 14, there remains much ambiguity over what is and is not obscene and pornographic.[181] Such ambiguity in the past, as a matter of fact, has led to the censorship, at one time or another, of such classics as *Alice in Wonderland, Huckleberry Finn, Adventures of Sherlock Holmes, Robinson Crusoe, On the Origin of Species,* and *The Scarlet Letter.*[308] One authority on censorship has declared that "had the Holy Bible been written today, the most we could hope for would be an expurgated edition—if it could be published and distributed at all."[350]

There also exist inconsistencies in enforcement under sex legislation, and these inconsistencies often directly relate to the liberal or strict religious beliefs and social attitudes of the judge and law-enforcement officers. Incongruities in enforcement also stem from confusion over what specific acts a law is intended to define as being sexual offenses. The whole enforcement picture is muddled even further—if one can concede the possibility—by the great variance in penalties prescribed for the same offense by various jurisdictions.[60]

Public opinion also reflects many inconsistencies in attitudes toward sex crimes. Periodic public clamor for stricter laws in this area has received the support of such personages as J. Edgar Hoover, who, when testifying before the House Appropriations Subcommittee in January, 1962, advocated the fingerprinting of all teachers because he considered them as being potentially dangerous sex offenders; he cited one instance of a child's having been molested by a teacher to support his position.[132] On the other hand, many scientific investigators contend that there has been no drastic increase in sex crimes in recent years, despite an increase in public outcry and the number of arrests. (These investigators say further that there should be a more realistic attitude toward sex offenders along the lines of understanding and treatment rather than of punishment.)[24, 118, 129, 132, 142, 350] The news media may on occasion be guilty of presenting a distorted picture of the extent of sexual criminality through exaggerations or faulty reporting.

In the United States, about 40,000 arrests a year are made for major sexual offenses. New Jersey, for example, made this breakdown of such offenders: exhibitionists, 18%; rapists, 45%; perverts, 14%;

those involved in commercial sex, 7%; and unclassified offenses, 16%.[118] (It might be noted that most rape cases in the United States involve statutory rape, which is voluntary coitus between partners, one of whom—almost always the girl—is under the legal age of consent.)

In England and Wales, 16,000 arrests were made for sexual offenses in 1954. The detentions were broken down into these categories: indecent assault on females accounted for almost 50% of the arrests; attempts to commit unnatural offenses and indecent assaults on males, 21%; indecency with males, 13%; defilement of girls between thirteen and sixteen years of age, 9%; unnatural offenses, 7%; rape, etc., 2%; incest, 2%; and defilement of girls under twelve, 1%.[266]

Turning from the crime to the criminal, one becomes aware that the sex offender is rarely involved in nonsexual crimes. Rather than making a progression through the gamut of paraphilia (unacceptable or illegal sexual acts) to more serious and diversified criminality, he seems to become relatively fixed in his offensive erotic expression.[82] Very few of the convicted sex offenders resemble the "sex fiend" of popular fiction, most being rather harmless minor deviates.[118, 129, 142, 289] Only a small percentage (about 20%) use force or duress on their victims, and homicide seldom occurs in conjunction with sexual offenses. On the other hand, one might consider that nine of ten cases of homicide occur within the family group or within a close circle of friends. The probability, then, of being murdered by a "sex fiend" is considerably less than that of being murdered by a relative or close friend.[118, 132] When homicide does occur in sex crimes, the offender is usually insane as well as sexually deviated.[82]

The sex offender who is arrested is usually found to be suffering from personality disturbances. In a study of 300 typical sex offenders at a New Jersey diagnostic center, only 14% were psychologically "normal," 29% were classified as mildly neurotic; 35% as severely neurotic; 8% as borderline psychotic; 5% as organically brain-damaged; 4% as mentally deficient; 3% as psychopathic; and 2% as psychotic.[129]

The majority of apprehended sex offenders come from low socioeconomic backgrounds, are poorly educated, and fall well below the average in intellectual capacity. Subnormal intelligence is more typical of offenders convicted of statutory rape, bestiality, incestuous relations, and sexually aggressive acts against little girls, than of offenders convicted of forcible rape, exhibitory acts, homosexuality, and the dissemination of "obscene" material.[118, 129, 142]

Few sex criminals take narcotics or are under the influence of drugs at the time of the sex offense. However, a large percentage (32%) of the convicted sex offenders are under the influence of alcohol when they commit their crimes, especially in cases of sexual assaults and incestuous relations with children.[118, 129, 142]

Some studies show that certain types of imprisoned sex offenders profess strong religious convictions, and that only a small percentage (10%) claim to have received no religious training in childhood. They read the Bible regularly, faithfully practice their religious rituals, and see themselves as devoted to their religion.[8] Other studies—notably the Kinsey group's *Sex Offenders*[142]—do not concur, finding that, generally speaking, the convicted sex offender is less religiously devout than the average citizen. The exception is the incest offender, whom the studies found to be especially moralistic, traditional, and religiously devout.

Quite contrary to popular notion, the typical convicted sex offender is undersexed rather than oversexed, and is likely to be afraid of sexual contact with the adult female and to be severely inhibited sexually, except when the crime is statutory rape or incestuous acts against minors. The less emotionally disturbed the sex offender, the less sexually inhibited he tends to be.[60, 129, 142]

Although the age of the convicted sex offender varies according to the specific type of sexual act committed, the majority of offenders are rather young—in their late teens or early twenties. Between 50% and 60% are unmarried.[118]

Most convicted sex offenders are the "losers" of society. They are usually so inept and severely disturbed emotionally in all their behavior that their sexual offenses are likely to be carried out in a stupid or indiscreet manner and to be found out. The actions of the intelligent sex offender are not nearly so likely to be discovered, nor, if found out, is he so likely to be convicted for his offenses.[118, 142]

Because of his emotional problems, there is danger of repeated offenses unless the sex offender receives psychotherapy to help him understand and control his problems.[118] Even so, the recidivism rate among convicted sex offenders is lower than that of other criminals. During a recent thirteen-year span, less than 10% of 4000 convicted sex offenders studied and treated at the Menlo Park Diagnostic Center of New Jersey became known recidivists. Attention, unfortunately, centers on the 10% who do revert to their old patterns of behavior rather than on the 90% who do not. The consequent public outcry and newspaper headlines persuade parole boards to the belief that all sex offenders are poor parole risks.[336]

Many psychologists and psychiatrists object to the term "sexual psychopath," which is in popular usage as a label for sex offenders. True sexual psychopaths (3% of all convicted sex offenders) may use force or serious threat, are unable to control their unacceptable erotic impulses, form no close emotional attachments, show a lack of anxiety and remorse concerning their sexual behavior, may disrupt social organization, and are not psychotic or feebleminded; indeed, they may give the appearance of being perfectly normal in all respects. The "sexual psychopath," then, is a far cry from the *typical* convicted sex offender, who is characteristically mentally disturbed, suffering from brain damage, below average in mentality, or who does not understand why he committed his offense.[82, 118, 129, 231]

Studies of known sex offenders generally delineate two broad categories of their offenses.[118, 129, 142, 289] One group of sexual violations encompasses more or less normal behavior that does not deviate very far from that of the normal populace, and is not considered to be motivated by unusual desires. Such transgressions do little or no psychological damage to the people involved, and have no adverse effect on social organization. For various reasons, however, the conduct is considered by society to be inappropriate and punishable (for example, the man who occasionally becomes a Peeping Tom). Society is not harmed by this type behavior, and the punishment should not be severe; nor should much money or time be spent on such cases. Effort is more appropriately directed toward helping these people to make a better adjustment to their life situation.

The second class of sex offenders is uncommon, and their truly unacceptable behavior is motivated by abnormal factors in their personalities. Their offenses may constitute a public nuisance, be socially disruptive, and cause individual psychological damage to those involved. It is toward these offenders that attention and money should be spent for detection, research, and treatment.[142, 289]

The purpose of laws insofar as sexual conduct is concerned should be to protect the individual from violence, to protect the young against the unworthy designs of adults who would take advantage of them, to protect the public from flagrant display of sexual acts that may disturb the peace, and to protect the institutions of family and marriage. The purpose of such laws should not be to determine and enforce standards of morality.[86] These were the principles set forth recently by the Illinois and Chicago Bar Associations in their formulation of a legal code governing sexual behavior that, they suggested, would adequately and realistically meet the needs of a modern society. These two groups of lawyers propounded and had accepted by the State Legislature what is probably the most sensible and enforceable set of sex laws ever found in America.[86]

Under the new Illinois code, the legal definition of rape no longer includes "statutory" or "nonviolent" rape. A sexual act is not rape unless the male uses force against the female; if she gives her consent but is not of legal age, the offense is handled under that section of the penal code dealing with "contributing to the sexual delinquency of a child." Furthermore, no offense is committed under the Illinois code for engaging in bestiality. Acts of sexual gratification involving the sex organs of one person and the mouth or anus of another are no longer punishable, unless such acts are brought about by force, threat, or violence, or unless one participant is underage, or if the act offends public decency. Such acts, whether heterosexual or homosexual by consenting adults and if conducted in private are not punishable.

Punishment for incest in Illinois now takes into consideration the closeness of the relationship between the parties, and the age of the participants. Aggravated incest incurs the most severe punishment, and the forbidden sexual relations include father-daughter (no matter what her age), father-stepdaughter, and father-foster daughter (in the latter two instances, only if the girls are under the age of 18). The strictness of this law is based on the strong position the father often holds in the family, and the influence he can exert over the daughters.

Public indecency or public exposure is related to the place in which the sex act is carried out. A public place is "any place where the conduct may reasonably be expected to be viewed by others." Thus, while a boy and a girl may be permitted to engage in light petting on a park bench, two men could not expect to get by with similar activity. However, a man would not be punished for suggesting to another man that they engage in such acts in private.

The Illinois law punishes men and women alike for prostitution, solicitation for a prostitute, operating a place for prostitution, and patronizing a prostitute. While the law defines prostitution as accepting money for sexual intercourse or deviate sexual conduct, it does not define accepting nonmonetary gifts (such as jewelry) for sexual favors as prostitution.

In May, 1967, the President's Crime Commission recommended removal from the domain of criminal law many sexual acts now considered to be crimes; the commission stated that these matters are often social ills and should be treated as such. States other than Illinois are, fortunately, beginning at least to recognize the need for similar revamping of legal codes to cope more realistically with the sexual activity of their citizenry. At the Fourth International Convention on Criminology, held in 1960 at The Hague, Holland, which was attended by over 600 governmental representatives and criminal law professors from almost every nation in the world, various resolutions to correct inequities in and misuse of sex laws were adopted. They included declarations calling for removal of fornication and adultery from the list of criminal offenses; relaxation in the interpretation and punishment of acts of incest; liberalizing laws concerning birth control, abortion, and artificial insemination; granting equal rights and freedom to homosexuals; and the toughening of laws concerning nonsupport of wives and children.[249]

Universal adoption of these legislative principles would be of immense value to both individuals and society. A burden of fear, guilt, and shame would thereby be lifted from the minds of citizens who, because of existing archaic laws, might otherwise be victims of entrapment, blackmail, unfair fines, and even imprisonment.[86]

Since the first Kinsey reports, the thinking of many experts in the legal, psychological, and sociological fields has been that laws pertaining to sex should be limited to those sex acts that (a) involve the use of force or threat of force, (b) involve minors, or (c) are performed in public. By concentrating on these regions, many problems are bypassed—especially those problems generated by laws that are unenforceable, useless, antiquated, inapplicable, or simply not within the province of law enforcement in any event. In addition to these basic criteria, other measures geared to prevent potential sex offenses and to provide better care and treatment of acknowledged offenders have been suggested by Albert Ellis,[118] who has been prominent in the study of the psychology of sex offenders:

1. All laws pertaining to sexual behavior should be rewritten in more definitive and meaningful terminology.

2. Before the accused is sentenced, a complete psychological examination should be performed to determine whether he is sexually or psychologically deviated, or is psychopathic.

3. Psychological treatment should be provided for offenders in their own community while they are on probation; or by a mental hospital or similar institution that affords specific psychotherapy for sex offenders, if incarceration is ordered. In the event of institutionalization, protective custody should be maintained as long as the patient is adjudged to be a menace to society.

4. Sex offenders should be offered help and understanding, rather than contempt and punishment.

5. If a preventive approach to sexual offenses is to be effective, there must be a wider dissemination of accurate sex information. Through such education, children will be provided with

more scientific and objectively stated facts regarding human sexuality.

When a society refuses to seek improvement of the conditions of its sick and downtrodden, and when overly severe punishment is meted out to transgressors, something assuredly is wrong. An objective evaluation of the members of a society who would so treat the unfortunate will quite likely reveal hostilities and conflicts within those members rather than any altruistic desire on their part to protect the community.

The prime example on the American scene of this type of hostility masked as public altruism is the person most responsible for our present-day rigid and often senseless laws pertaining to sex—Anthony Comstock (1844-1915), "the most aggressive opponent of personal liberties ever to soil the pages of American history."[35]

Comstock developed a hatred for liquor, and for a number of years directed much of his efforts toward the eradication of this "evil" from the world. His hostility toward liquor was mild, however, in comparison with his feelings about sex. He obtained employment as an investigator for the New York Society for the Suppression of Vice, and reveled in his duties as he raided theatres, harassed publishers and booksellers about what he decreed to be "impure" literature, and confiscated paintings revealing (for his tastes) too much of the female form.[35]

March 3, 1873, was a black day in the history of individual rights in this country: on that day (or night, rather), Comstock was able to force passage, through his successful lobbying, of the infamous Comstock Law. This statute set forth the most unreasonable restrictions against "obscenity" of any law ever passed in America at the same time leaving wide the interpretation of the word. Furthermore, it allowed savage punishment for anything that by the slightest twitch of imagination could be construed as "obscene." One wonders how such an unrealistic statute could have gained sufficient support for passage. Probably the New York legislators were tired and wanted to go home, for it was one o'clock in the morning when the law was finally passed, and one suspects they were at that time disinclined to study the bill in any great detail. Surely if the legislators had had any inkling of what they were really signing their names to, or of the hypermoralistic invasion into America's cultural and private life that they were unleashing, Comstock's proposal would have been quickly voted down.

With the passage of the bill into law, however, Comstock now held the legal right to open other people's mail, and he began to employ trickery to entrap people whom he believed to be involved in obscenity (which he had considerable latitude in defining), or whom he suspected of disseminating information about or practicing birth control. For example, he regularly wrote kindhearted physicians pretending to be a sick and frail mother of many children, begging the doctors for information on contraceptive methods. If the doctors responded, as Comstock of course hoped they would, they were apprehended and frequently fined and imprisoned. Worst of all, their careers were usually ruined.

Typically, Comstock devoted much of his lifetime attempting to ensnare Margaret Sanger, the founder of the planned-parenthood movement in America. He never succeeded in trapping Mrs. Sanger, but did contrive to have her husband, William Sanger, arrested and convicted. A Comstock agent begged Mr. Sanger for a copy of his wife's pamphlet, *Family Limitation,* and when he obtained it, he had Mr. Sanger arrested. Mr. Sanger refused to pay a fine, and served a thirty-day jail sentence for his "crime." (Perhaps his sentence was made lighter when he learned in the middle of it that Comstock had suddenly died.)[85] Even after his death, however, the spirit of Comstock lives on, and his influence continues to deprive people of their personal liberties through antiquated sex laws. The effects of his bigotry and supermoralism are felt still in almost every city, county, and state in the land.

In the final analysis, the social responsibility requisite to any improved legislation governing sexual affairs is a clearer understanding of the character of the sex offender. Implicit in this understanding is an insight into the significant roles that guilt and conflict play in sexual difficulties. Guilt regarding sexual matters begins early in childhood when the child engages in sexual exploration and is censured, or when any questions concerning sex are avoided or hushed up by his parents. As a result, the youngster's sexual acts and desires, such as they are, become to him an arena of guilt. His ability to respond normally and naturally to his sexual drive thus becomes impaired. Out of this sort of guilt spring almost endless possibilities for psychosexual disturbances. A denial of sexuality, and deviant or furtive methods of expressing sexuality, are among the potential aberrations that can result from defective sexual training.

Hopefully, we are finding our way out of the morass of sexual ignorance and guilt. Perhaps with the next decade will come a better all-round understanding of human sexuality, and with it, a comprehension of sexual problems. For it is *only* with such knowledge that society can work out effective methods of prevention (again, hopefully) or treatment of sexual conflicts and abnormalities.

Glossary

abortion. Premature expulsion from the uterus of the product of conception—a fertilized ovum, embryo, or nonviable fetus.

abstinence. A refraining from the use of or indulgence in certain foods, stimulants, or sexual intercourse.

adolescence. The period of life between puberty (appearance of secondary sex characteristics) and adulthood (cessation of major body growth).

adultery. Sexual intercourse between a married person and an individual other than his or her legal spouse.

afterbirth. The placenta and fetal membranes expelled from the uterus following the birth of a child.

amenorrhea. Absence of the menses (menstruation).

amnion. A thin membrane forming the closed sac or "bag of waters" that surrounds the unborn child within the uterus and contains amniotic fluid in which the fetus is immersed.

ampulla. A flasklike widening at the end of a tubular structure or canal.

anal eroticism. Pleasurable sensations in the region of the anus.

anaphrodisiac. A drug or medicine that allays sexual desire.

androgen. A steroid hormone producing masculine sex characteristics and having an influence on body and bone growth and on the sex drive.

anomaly. An irregularity or defect.

aphrodisiac. Anything, such as a drug or a perfume, that stimulates sexual desire.

areola. The ring of darkened tissue surrounding the nipple of the breast.

artificial insemination. Introduction of male semen into the vagina or womb of a woman by artificial means.

autoerotic. Pertaining to self-stimulation or erotic behavior directed toward one's self; frequently equated with masturbation.

Bartholin's glands. Two tiny glands in a female, located at either side of the entrance to the vagina.

bestiality. A sexual deviation in which a person engages in sexual relations with an animal. *Cf.* ZOOPHILIA.

birth control. Deliberate limitation of the number of children born—through such means as contraceptives, abstinence, the rhythm method, *coitus interruptus,* and the like.

bisexual. Literally, having sex organs of both sexes, as in hermaphrodites; having a sexual interest in both sexes.

blastocyst. The fertilized egg in the early stage of cell division when the cells form a hollow sphere.

breech presentation. A birth position in which the baby is presented and delivered buttocks first.

339

Caesarean birth (also **Caesarean section**). Delivery of a child through a surgical incision in the abdominal and uterine walls.

carpopedal spasm. A spastic contraction of the hands and feet.

castration. Removal of the gonads (sex glands)—the testicles in men, the ovaries in women.

castration complex. In psychoanalytic theory, unconscious fears centering around injury or loss of the genitals as punishment for forbidden sexual desires; a male's anxiety about his manhood.

celibacy. The state of being unmarried; abstention from sexual activity.

cervix. Neck; in the female, the narrow portion of the uterus or womb that forms its lower end and opens into the vagina.

chancre. The sore or ulcer that is the first symptom of syphilis.

change of life. See CLIMACTERIC, MENOPAUSE.

chorion. The outermost envelope of the growing zygote (fertilized ovum), which later contributes to the formation of the placenta.

chromosome. One of several small rod-shaped bodies found in the nucleus of all body cells, which contain the genes, or hereditary factors.

circumcision. Surgical removal of the foreskin or prepuce of the male penis.

climacteric. The syndrome of physical and psychologic changes that occur at the termination of menstrual function (*i.e.*, reproductive capability) in the woman and reduction in sex-steroid production in both sexes; menopause; change of life.

climax. See ORGASM.

clitoris (adj. **clitoral**). A small, highly sensitive nipple of flesh in the female, located just above the urethral opening in the upper triangle of the vulva.

coitus. Sexual intercourse between male and female, in which the male penis is inserted into the female vagina.

coitus interruptus (also **premature withdrawal**). The practice of withdrawing the penis from the vagina just before ejaculation.

coitus reservatus. Prolonged coitus in which ejaculation is intentionally suppressed.

colostrum. A thin, milky fluid secreted by the female breasts just before and just after childbirth.

conception. The beginning of a new life, when an ovum (egg) is penetrated by a sperm, resulting in the development of an embryo; impregnation.

condom. A contraceptive used by males consisting of a rubber or gut sheath that is drawn over the erect penis before coitus.

congenital. Existing at birth, but not necessarily inherited.

contraception. The use of devices or drugs to prevent conception in sexual intercourse.

coprophilia. A sexual deviation in which sexual gratification is associated with the act of defecation; a morbid interest in feces.

copulation. Sexual intercourse; coitus.

corona glandis. The rim surrounding the base of the glans penis in the male.

corpus luteum. A yellow mass in the ovary, formed from a ruptured Graafian follicle, that secretes the hormone progesterone.

Cowper's glands. Two glands in the male, one on each side of the urethra near the prostate, which secrete a mucoid material as part of the seminal fluid.

cremaster (adj. **cremasteric**). The muscles that elevate the male testes.

criminal abortion. Illegal termination of a human pregnancy by any type of medical, surgical, or other means of interference, as distinguished from *therapeutic abortion*, which is done to protect the health or life of the mother.

cryptorchidism. See UNDESCENDED TESTICLE.

cul-de-sac. The "blind alley" ending of the female vagina just beyond the opening into the womb (cervix).

cunnilingus. The act of using the tongue or mouth in erotic play with the external female genitalia (vulva).

curettage (also **curettement**). Scraping the lining of the uterus with a *curette,* a spoon-shaped medical instrument.

cystocele. Hernial protrusion of the female bladder through the vaginal wall.

cytogenic. Forming or producing cells.

defloration. The rupture of the hymen in a virgin's first experience of coitus or through vaginal examination.

detumescence. Subsidence of swelling; subsidence of erection in the genitals following orgasm.

diaphragm. A rubber contraceptive, used by women, that is hemispherical in shape and fits like a cap over the neck of the uterus (cervix).

Doderlein's bacilli. The bacteria (germs) normally present in the female vagina.

dorsal. Pertaining to the back (as the back of the hand, of the whole body, or of the upper surface of the penis), as opposed to the *ventral* (front) side.

douche. A stream of water or other liquid solution directed into the female vagina for sanitary, medical, or contraceptive reasons.

dysmenorrhea. Painful menstruation.

dyspareunia. Coitus that is difficult or painful, especially for a woman.

ectopic. In an abnormal place, *e.g.,* an *ectopic pregnancy,* in which the unborn child develops outside the uterus, either in an ovary, the abdominal cavity, or in a Fallopian tube.

ejaculatio praecox. Premature ejaculation.

ejaculation. The expulsion of male semen, usually at the climax (orgasm) of the sexual act.

Electra complex. Excessive emotional attachment of a daughter to her father.

emasculate. To castrate; to deprive of manliness or masculine vigor.

embryo. The unborn young in its early stage of development—in man, from one week following conception to the end of the second month.

emission. Discharge of semen from the male penis, especially when involuntary, as during sleep (nocturnal emission).

endemic. Pertaining to or prevalent in a particular district or region; pertaining to a disease that has a low incidence but is constantly present in a given community.

endocrine gland. A gland that secretes its product (hormone) directly into the bloodstream.

endometriosis. The aberrant presence of endometrial tissue (uterus lining) in other parts of the female pelvic cavity, such as in the Fallopian tubes or on the ovaries, bladder, or intestines.

endometrium. The mucous membrane that lines the cavity of the uterus in the female.

epididymis. The network of tiny tubes in the male that connects the testicles with the sperm duct.

episiotomy. Incision in a woman's perineum to facilitate the birth of a child.

epispadia. A congenital defect in males in which the opening (meatus) of the urethra is on the upper surface of the penis instead of at its tip. *Cf.* HYPOSPADIA.

epithelium (adj. **epithelial**). The outer layer of cells covering the internal and external surfaces of the body.

erection. The stiffening and enlargement of the penis (or clitoris), usually as a result of sexual excitement.

erogenous zone. A sexually sensitive area of the body, such as the mouth, lips, breasts, nipples, buttocks, genitals, or anus.

erotic. Pertaining to sexual love or sensation; sexually stimulating.

estrogen. A steroid hormone producing female sex characteristics and affecting the functioning of the menstrual cycle.

estrus. A recurrent period of sexual receptivity in female animals, marked by intense sexual urge.

eunuch. A castrated male.

eunuchoid. Having the physical characteristics of a eunuch without actually being castrated.

exhibitionism. A sexual deviation in which the individual—usually male—suffers from a compulsion to expose his genitals publicly.

extragenital. Originating or lying outside the genital organs.

extramarital. Literally, outside of marriage; usually used in reference to adulterous sexual intercourse.

Fallopian tube. The oviduct or egg-conducting tube that extends from each ovary to the uterus in the female.

fellatio. The act of taking the penis into the mouth and sucking it for erotic purposes.

fertility. The state of being capable of producing young; the opposite of *sterility*.

fertilization. The union of egg (ovum) and sperm (spermatozoon), which results in conception.

fetishism. A sexual deviation in which sexual gratification is achieved by means of an object, such as an article of clothing, that bears sexual symbolism for the individual.

fetus. In humans, the unborn child from the third month after conception until birth.

fibrillation. Spontaneous contraction of individual muscle fibers no longer under control of a motor nerve.

follicle. The small sac or vesicle near the surface of the ovary in the female that contains a developing egg cell (ovum).

foreplay. The preliminary stages of sexual intercourse, in which the partners usually stimulate each other by kissing, touching, and caressing.

foreskin. The skin covering the tip of the male penis or female clitoris; prepuce.

fornication. Sexual intercourse between two unmarried persons (as distinguished from *adultery,* which involves a person who is married to someone other than his coital partner).

fourchette. The fold of mucous membrane at the posterior junction of the labia majora in the female.

frenulum. A delicate, tissue-thin fold of skin that connects the foreskin with the under surface of the glans penis; frenum.

frenulum clitoridis. The clitoral prepuce.

frenum. See FRENULUM.

frigidity. Coldness, indifference, or insensitivity on the part of a woman to sexual intercourse or sexual stimulation; inability to experience sexual pleasure or gratification.

frottage. A sexual deviation in which orgasm is induced by rubbing against an individual of the opposite sex, usually a stranger.

fundus. The base or part of a hollow organ farthest from its mouth.

gene. The basic carrier of hereditary traits, contained in the chromosomes.

genital organs (or **genitals** or **genitalia**). The sex or reproductive organs.

germ cell. The sperm (spermatozoon) or egg (ovum).

gerontosexuality. A sexual disorder in which a young person chooses an elderly person as the subject of his sexual interest.

gestation. Pregnancy; the period from conception to birth.

glans clitoridis. The head of the female clitoris.

glans penis. The head of the male penis.

gonad. A sex gland; a testicle (male) or ovary (female).

gonorrhea. A venereal disease, transmitted chiefly through coitus, that is a contagious catarrhal inflammation of the genital mucous membrane.

Graafian follicle. A small sac or pocket in the female ovary in which the egg (ovum) matures and from which it is discharged at ovulation.

gynecologist. A physician specializing in the treatment of the problems of the female sexual and reproductive organs.

gynecomastia. Female-like development of the male breasts.

heredity. The transmission of bodily traits and characteristics or of diseases from parents to offspring.

hermaphrodite. An individual possessing both male and female sex glands (ovary and testicle) or sex gland tissue of both sexes. *Cf.* PSEUDOHERMAPHRODITE.

heterosexuality. Sexual attraction to, or sexual activity with, members of the opposite sex; the opposite of *homosexuality*.

hirsutism. Abnormal hairiness, especially in women.

homologous. Corresponding in position, structure, or origin to another anatomical entity.

homosexuality. Sexual attraction to, or sexual activity with, members of one's own sex; the opposite of *heterosexuality*.

hormone. A chemical substance produced by an endocrine gland that has a specific effect on the activities of other organs in the body.

hydrocele. An accumulation of fluid in the male scrotum.

hymen. The membranous fold that partly covers the external opening of the vagina in most virgin females; the maidenhead.

hyperplasia. The abnormal multiplication or increase in the number of cells in a tissue. *Cf.* HYPERTROPHY.

hypertrophy. The abnormal enlargement of a bodily organ due to an increase in size of its constituent cells. *Cf.* HYPERPLASIA.

hypospadia. A congenital defect in males in which the opening (meatus) of the urethra is on the underside of the penis instead of at its tip. *Cf.* EPISPADIA. In female hypospadia, the urethra opens into the vagina.

hysterectomy. Surgical removal of the female uterus, either through the abdominal wall or through the vagina.

hysterotomy. Incision into the uterus.

impotence. Disturbance of sexual function in the male that precludes satisfactory coitus; more specifically, inability to achieve or maintain an erection sufficient for purposes of sexual intercourse.

impregnation. The act of fertilization or fecundation; making pregnant.

incest. Sexual relations between close relatives, such as father and daughter, mother and son, or brother and sister.

interstitial cells. Specialized cells in the testicles that produce the male sex hormones.

intromission. The insertion of the male penis into the female vagina.

invert. A homosexual; one who is sexually attracted to persons of his own sex.

involution. An inward curvature; a shrinking or return to a former size, as of the uterus after childbirth; the regressive alterations in the body or its parts characteristic of the aging process.

kleptomania. An irresistible compulsion to steal, usually without any use for the article stolen.

labia majora (sing. **labium majus**). The outer and larger pair of lips of the female external genitals (vulva).

labia minora (sing. **labium minus**). The inner and smaller pair of lips of the female vulva.

lactation. The manufacture and secretion of milk by the mammary glands in a mother's breasts.

lesbian. A female homosexual.

libido. Sexual drive or urge.

maculopapular. Spotted and raised or elevated.

maidenhead. The hymen.

masochism. A sexual deviation in which an individual derives sexual gratification from having pain inflicted on him.

masturbation. Self-stimulation of the genitals through manipulation; autoeroticism.

meatus. An opening, such as at the end of the urethral passage in the male penis.

menarche. The onset of menstruation in girls, occurring in late puberty and ushering in the period of adolescence.

menopause. The period of cessation of menstruation in the human female, occurring usually between the ages of 45 and 55; climacteric; change of life.

menstruation. The discharge of blood from the uterus through the vagina that normally recurs at approximately four-week intervals in women between the ages of puberty and menopause.

miscarriage. Spontaneous expulsion of a fetus from the onset of the fourth to the end of the sixth month of pregnancy.

Monilia. A yeast-like infective organism (fungus) causing itching and inflammation of the female vagina.

monogamy. Marriage between one man and one woman.

mons veneris (or **mons pubis**). A triangular mound of fat at the symphysis pubis of a woman, just above the vulval area.

mucoid. Resembling mucus.

mucosa. A mucous membrane; a thin tissue that has a moist surface from the secreting of mucus.

mucus (adj. **mucous**). The thick, slippery fluid secreted by mucous membranes.

multipara (adj. **multiparous**). A woman who has given birth to two or more children.

myoma (pl. **myomas** or **myomata**). A tumor consisting of muscle tissue that grows in the wall of the uterus; also called *fibroid.*

myotonia. Increased muscular tension.

narcissism. Excessive self-love; sexual excitement through admiration of one's own body.

necrophilia. A sexual deviation in which an individual has a morbid sexual attraction to corpses.

nocturnal emission. An involuntary male orgasm and ejaculation of semen during sleep; a "wet dream."

nullipara (adj. **nulliparous**). A woman who has never borne a viable child.

nymphomania. Excessive sexual desire in a woman.

obscene. Disgusting, repulsive, filthy, shocking—that which is abhorrent according to accepted standards of morality.

obsession. A neurosis characterized by the persistent recurrence of some irrational thought or idea, or by an attachment to or fixation on a particular individual or object.

obstetrician. A physician specializing in the care of women during pregnancy, labor, and the period immediately following delivery.

Oedipus complex. Excessive emotional attachment, involving conscious or unconscious incestuous desires, of a son in relation to his mother.

onanism. Withdrawal of the male penis from the female vagina before ejaculation; *coitus interruptus.*

oophorectomy. The surgical removal of an ovary or ovaries.

oral eroticism. Pleasurable sensations centered in the lips and mouth.

orgasm. The peak or climax of sexual excitement in sexual activity.

orgasmic platform. The area comprising the outer third of the vagina and the labia minora, which displays marked vasocongestion in the plateau phase of the female sexual response cycle (term used by Masters and Johnson).

os. A mouth or orifice, as the external os of the cervix *(os externum uteri).*

ovary. The female sex gland, in which the ova are formed.

oviduct. The Fallopian or uterine tube through which the egg (ovum) descends from the ovary to the uterus.

ovulation. The release of a mature, unimpregnated ovum from one of the Graafian follicles of an ovary.

ovum (pl. **ova**). An egg; the female reproductive cell, corresponding to the male spermatozoon, that after fertilization develops into a new member of the same species.

paraphilia. Sexual deviations; aberrant sexual activity.

paresis. A chronic syphilitic inflammation of the brain and its enveloping membranes, characterized by progressive mental deterioration and a generalized paralysis that is sometimes fatal.

parthenogenesis. Reproduction by the development of an egg without its being fertilized by a spermatozoon.

parturition. Labor; the process of giving birth.

pathogenic. Causing disease.

pathological. Pertaining to a diseased or abnormal physical or mental condition.

pederasty. Male sexual relations with a boy; also sexual intercourse via the anus.

pedophilia. A sexual deviation in which an adult engages in or desires sexual activity with a child.

penis. The male organ of copulation and urination.

penis captivus. A condition in humans in which it is alleged that the shaft of the fully introduced penis is tightly encircled by the vagina during coitus and cannot be withdrawn. Most authorities say this condition occurs only in animals, notably the dog.

perineum (adj. **perineal**). The area between the thighs, extending from the posterior wall of the vagina to the anus in the female and from the scrotum to the anus in the male.

peritoneum (adj. **peritoneal**). The strong, transparent membrane lining the abdominal cavity.

perversion. Sexual deviation from normal; paraphilia.

petting. Sexual contact that excludes coitus.

Peyronie's disease. A condition, usually in men of middle age or older, in which the penis develops a fibrous ridge along its top or sides, causing curvature.

phallus. The male penis, usually the erect penis.

phimosis. Tightness of the foreskin of the male penis, so that it cannot be drawn back from over the glans.

pituitary. Known as the "master gland" and located in the head, it is responsible for the proper functioning of all the other glands, especially the sex glands, the thyroid, and the adrenals.

placenta. The cake-like organ that connects the fetus to the uterus by means of the umbilical cord, and through which the fetus is fed and waste products are eliminated; the afterbirth.

polyandry. The form of marriage in which one woman has more than one husband at one time.

polygamy. The form of marriage in which a spouse of either sex may possess a plurality of mates at the same time.

polygyny. The form of marriage in which one man has more than one wife at the same time.

pornography. The presentation of sexually arousing material in literature, art, motion pictures, or other means of communication and expression.

postpartum. Occurring after childbirth or after delivery.

potent. Having the male capability to perform sexual intercourse; capable of erection.

precocious sexuality. Awakening of sexual desire at a prematurely early age.

pregnancy. The condition of having a developing embryo or fetus in the body; the period from conception to birth or abortion.

premature ejaculation. Ejaculation prior to, just at, or immediately after intromission; *ejaculatio praecox.*

prenatal. Existing or occurring before birth.

prepuce. Foreskin.

priapism. Persistent abnormal erection of the penis in males, usually without sexual desire.

progesterone. The female hormone (known as the pregnancy hormone) that is produced in the yellow body or corpus luteum, and whose function is to prepare the uterus for the reception and development of a fertilized ovum.

promiscuous. Engaging in sexual intercourse with many persons; engaging in casual sexual relations.

prophylactic. A drug or device used for the prevention of disease, often specifically venereal disease.

prostate. The gland in the male that surrounds the urethra and the neck of the bladder.

prostitute. A person who engages in sexual relationships for payment.

prudish. Extremely or falsely modest.

pseudocyesis. False pregnancy.

pseudohermaphrodite. An individual who has both male and female external sex organs, usually in rudimentary form, but who has the sex glands (ovary or testicle) of only one sex, and is thus fundamentally male or female. *Cf.* HERMAPHRODITE.

psychogenic. Of psychic or emotional origin; functional.

puberty (or **pubescence**). The stage of life at which a child turns into a young man or young woman: *i.e.,* the reproductive organs become functionally operative and secondary sex characteristics develop.

pudendum (pl. **pudenda**). The external genitalia, especially of the female (the mons pubis, labia majora, labia minora, and the vestibule of the vagina).

pyromania. A compulsion, usually sexually oriented, to start fires.

rape. Forcible sexual intercourse with a person who does not give consent or who offers resistance.

rectocele. A hernia in females in which part of the rectum protrudes into the vagina.

refractory period. A temporary state of psychophysiologic resistance to sexual stimulation immediately following an orgasmic experience (term used by Masters and Johnson).

retrograde ejaculation. Backward ejaculation in males into the posterior urethra and bladder, instead of into the anterior urethra and out through the meatus of the penis.

retroversion. The tipping of an entire organ backward.

rhythm method. A method of birth control that relies on the so-called "safe period" or infertile days in a woman's menstrual cycle.

sadism. The achievement of sexual gratification by inflicting physical or psychological pain upon the sexual partner.

"safe period." The interval of the menstrual cycle when the female is presumably not ovulating.

saliromania. A sexual deviation, found primarily in men, that is characterized by the desire to damage or soil the body or clothes of a woman or a representation of a woman.

salpingectomy. Surgical removal of a Fallopian tube from a woman.

satyriasis. Excessive sexual desire in a man.

scoptophilia (or **scotophilia**). A sexual deviation in which a person achieves sexual gratification by observing sexual acts or the genitals of others. *Cf.* VOYEURISM.

scrotum. The pouch suspended from the groin that contains the male testicles and their accessory organs.

secondary sex characteristics. The physical characteristics—other than the external sex organs—that distinguish male from female.

seduction. Luring a female (sometimes a male) into sexual intercourse without the use of force.

semen. The secretion of the male reproductive organs that is ejaculated from the penis at orgasm and contains, in the fertile male, sperm cells.

seminal vesicles. Two pouches in the male, one on each side of the prostate, behind the bladder, that are attached to and open into the sperm ducts.

seminiferous tubules. The tiny tubes or canals in each male testicle that produce the sperm.

serology. The study of antigen and antibody reactions in blood serum tests.

sex drive. Desire for sexual expression.

sex flush. The superficial vasocongestive skin response to increasing sexual tensions that begins in the plateau phase (term used by Masters and Johnson).

sex gland. A gonad; the testicle in the male and the ovary in the female.

sex hormone. A substance secreted by the sex glands directly into the bloodstream, *e.g.,* androgens (male) and estrogens (female).

sex organ. The genital or reproductive organs, usually the male penis or the female vulva or vagina.

sex skin. The skin of the labia minora in the female, which shows a discoloration response in the plateau phase of the sexual response cycle.

sexual inadequacy. Any degree of sexual response that is not sufficient for the isolated demand of the moment or for a protracted period of time; frequent or total inability to experience orgasm.

sexual intercourse. Coitus; the union of the male and female genitals.

sexual outlet. Any of the various ways by which sexual tension is released through orgasm.

smegma. A thick, cheesy, ill-smelling accumulation of secretions under the foreskin of the penis or around the clitoris.

sodomy. A form of paraphilia, variously defined by law to include sexual intercourse with animals and mouth-genital or anal contact between humans.

somatic. Pertaining to the body, as distinct from the psyche or mind; organic, as distinguished from functional or psychosomatic.

sperm (or **spermatozoon**). The mature reproductive cell (or cells) capable of fertilizing the female egg and causing impregnation.

sperm duct. The tube or duct in males that conveys the sperm from the epididymis to the seminal vesicles and urethra; the vas deferens.

spermatic cord. The structure in males, by which the testicle is suspended, containing the sperm ducts, nerves, and veins.

spermatogenesis. The process of sperm formation.

spermatozoon (pl. **spermatozoa**). A mature male germ cell.

sphincter. A ring-like muscle that closes a natural orifice.

sterility. The inability to produce offspring.

sterilization. Any procedure (usually surgical) by which an individual is made incapable of reproduction.

stricture. The abnormal narrowing of a canal, duct, or passage.

"sweating" phenomenon. The appearance of little droplets of fluid on the walls of the vagina early in the excitement phase of the female sexual response cycle.

symphysis pubis. The articulation between the pubic bones in the lower abdomen.

syphilis. Probably the most serious venereal disease, it is usually acquired by sexual intercourse with a person in the infectious stage of the disease and is caused by invasion of the spirochete Treponema pallidum.

systemic. Spread throughout the body; affecting all body systems and organs.

taboo. An absolute prohibition based on religion, tradition, social usage, or superstition.

telegony. The alleged appearance in the offspring of one sire of characteristics derived from a previous sire or mate of the female.

testicle. The testis; the male sex gland.

testis (pl. **testes**). The male sex gland or gonad, which produces spermatozoa.

testosterone. The male testicular hormone that induces and maintains the male secondary sex characteristics.

thrombosis. The clogging of a blood vessel as the result of the formation of a blood clot within the vessel itself.

transsexualism. A compulsion or obsession to become a member of the opposite sex through surgical changes.

transvestism. A sexual deviation characterized by a compulsive desire to wear the garments of the opposite sex; cross dressing.

trichomoniasis. An infection of the female vagina caused by infestation of the microorganism Trichomonas and characterized by inflammation, usually resulting in a vaginal discharge and itching and burning.

troilism (or **triolism**). A sexual deviation in which, ordinarily, three people (two men and a woman or two women and a man) participate in a series of sexual practices.

tumescence. The process of swelling or the condition of being swollen.

umbilical cord. The flexible structure connecting the fetus and the placenta; navel cord.

undescended testicle. A developmental defect in males in which the testicles fail to descend into the scrotum; cryptorchidism.

urethra. The duct through which the urine passes from the bladder and is excreted outside the body.

urethrocele. Protrusion of the female urethra through the vaginal wall; a hernia.

urologist. A physician specializing in the treatment of the diseases and disorders of the urinary tract of both sexes, as well as of the genital tract of the male.

uterine tube. The Fallopian tube, which extends from each ovary to the uterus in the female.

uterus. The hollow, pear-shaped organ in females within which the fetus develops; the womb.

vagina. The canal in the female, extending from the vulva to the cervix, that receives the penis during coitus and through which an infant passes at birth.

vaginal barrel. The vaginal cavity in women.

vaginal lubrication. A clear fluid (like sweat) that appears on the walls of the vaginal barrel within a few seconds after the onset of sexual stimulation.

vaginal orgasm. A term of ambiguous meaning, apparently referring to an orgasm that a woman allegedly can achieve vaginally without any clitoral stimulation.

vaginismus. Strong muscular contractions within the vagina, preventing intromission of the penis when intercourse is attempted.

vaginitis. Inflammation of the female vagina, usually as a result of infection.

varicocele. A swelling or enlargement of the veins in the male spermatic cord.

vas deferens (or **ductus deferens.**) The sperm duct(s) in males, leading from the epididymis to the seminal vesicles and the urethra.

vasectomy. A surgical procedure for sterilizing the male involving removal of the vas deferens, or a portion of it.

vasocongestion. Congestion of the blood vessels, especially the veins in the genital area.

venereal disease. A contagious disease communicated mainly by sexual intercourse, such as syphilis or gonorrhea.

verumontanum. A small mound in the portion of the male urethra passing through the prostate, which contains the openings of the ejaculatory ducts.

vestibule. The area surrounding and including the opening of the vagina in the female.

virginity. The physical condition of a girl or woman before first intercourse.

voyeurism. A sexual deviation in which a person achieves sexual gratification by observing others in the nude. *Cf.* SCOPTOPHILIA.

vulva. The external sex organs of the female, including the mons veneris, the labia majora, the labia minora, the clitoris, and the vestibule.

Wassermann test. A blood test used to determine whether or not a person has syphilis.

womb. The uterus in the female.

zoophilia. A sexual deviation that involves an abnormal degree of affection for animals. *Cf.* BESTIALITY.

zygote. The single cell resulting from the union of two germ cells (sperm and egg) at conception; the fertilized egg (ovum).

Bibliography

1. *A prescription for family planning: the story of enovid.* New York: G. D. Searle and Co., 1964.
2. Adams, C. R. An informal preliminary report on some factors relating to sexual responsiveness of certain college wives. In *Sexual behavior and personality characteristics* (M. F. DeMartino, Ed.). New York: Grove Press, 1966.
3. Alexander, M. M. Is the nose a sex organ? *Sexology* 31:266-268, 1964.
4. ————. Sex and stealing. *Sexology* 31:636-640, 1965.
5. ————. The overdue baby. *Sexology* 31:410-412, 1965.
6. Allen, C. Perversions, sexual. In *The encyclopedia of sexual behavior,* Vol. II (A. Ellis and A. Abarbanel, Eds.). New York: Hawthorn Books, 1961.
7. ————. The prostitute's customers. *Sexology* 33:10-12, 1966.
8. Allen, G. H. The damaging effect of prudery. *Sexology* 32:463-464, 1966.
9. Anderson, W. J. *How to understand sex.* Minneapolis: T. S. Denison & Co., 1966.
10. Anthony, Rey. *The teenager's guide to sexual awareness.* Tucson: Seymour Press, 1963.
11. APHA Western Branch Conference Report. *Public health report* 77:1000-1004, 1962.
12. Appell, Clara, and Appell, M. Why mothers don't breast-feed. *Sexology* 32:302-304, 1965.
13. Arey, L. B. *Developmental anatomy.* Philadelphia: W. B. Saunders Co., 1937.
14. Armstrong, Eunice B. The possibility of sexual happiness in old age. In *Advances in sex research* (H. Beigel, Ed.). New York: Harper & Row, 1963.
15. Austerman, W., and Beach, P. D. True hermaphroditism with report of two cases. *J. of Urol.* 85:345-351, 1961.
16. Aycock, L. The medical management of premature-ejaculation. *J. of Urol.* 62:361-362, 1949.
17. Ball, T. L. *Gynecologic surgery and urology.* St. Louis: C. V. Mosby Co., 1957.
18. Barr, M. L., and Bertram, E. G. A morphological distinction between neurones of male and female, and the behavior of the nucleolar satellites during accelerated nucleoprotein synthesis. *Nature* 163:676, 1949.
19. Beach, F. Experimental studies of mating behavior in animals. In *Sex research: new developments* (J. Money, Ed.). New York: Holt, Rinehart, & Winston, 1965.
20. Beigel, H. G. (Ed.) *Advances in sex research.* New York: Harper & Row, 1963.
21. Beigel, H. G. *Encyclopedia of sex education.* New York: Daye, 1952.
22. ————. False beliefs about reproduction. *Sexology* 31:334-336, 1964.
23. ————. Imaginary rape. *Sexology* 31:675-677, 1965.
24. ————. Outmoded sex laws should be changed. *Sexology* 32:341-343, 1965.
25. ————. The danger of orgasm worship. *Sexology* 30:232-234, 1963.
26. Bell, R. R. *Marriage and family interaction.* Homewood, Ill.: Dorsey Press, Inc., 1963.
27. Bell, R. R., and Blumberg, L. Courtship intimacy and religious background. *Marriage and family living* 21:356-360, 1959.

28. ———. Courtship stages and intimacy attitudes. *Family life coordinator,* March: 60-63, 1960.
29. Bell, R. R., and Buerkle, J. V. Mother and daughter attitudes to premarital sexual behavior. *Marriage and family living* 23:340-342, 1961.
30. Belt, E. Sterilization: can it be undone? *Sexology* 28:313-317, 1961.
31. Benjamin, H. Prostitution. In *The encyclopedia of sexual behavior,* Vol. II (A. Ellis and A. Abarbanel, Eds.). New York: Hawthorn Books, 1961.
32. Benjamin, H., and Masters, R. E. L. *Prostitution and morality.* New York: Julian Press, 1964.
33. Berg, L., and Street, R. *Sex methods and manners.* New York: McBride, 1953.
34. Bergler, E. *Counterfeit-sex.* New York: Grove Press, 1961.
35. Berke, J. E. The man who hated sex. *Sexology* 32:12-14, 1965.
36. Bickers, W. Sperm migration and uterine contraction. *Fertility and sterility* 11:286-290, 1960.
37. Bieber, I., *et al. Homosexuality: a psychoanalytic study.* New York: Basic Books, 1962.
38. Blank, H., and Rake, G. *Viral and rickettsial diseases.* Boston: Little, Brown, 1955.
39. Blau, S. Venereal diseases. In *The encyclopedia of sexual behavior,* Vol. II (A. Ellis and A. Abarbanel, Eds.). New York: Hawthorn Books, 1961.
40. Bonaparte, Marie. *Female sexuality.* New York: Grove Press, 1953.
41. Boyd, H. Eleven-year survival of an advanced abdominal pregnancy. *Obst. and Gyn.* 25:128-129, 1965.
42. Branson, Helen K. Triolism: sex on exhibition. *Sexology* 26:374-376, 1960.
43. ———. Where did you learn about sex? *Sexology* 29:609-610, 1963.
44. Brecher, Ruth, and Brecher, E. (Eds.). *An analysis of human sexual response.* New York: New American Library, 1966.
45. Briggs, D. K. Chromosomal anomalies in hermaphroditism and other sexual disorders. In *Advances in sex research* (H. Beigel, Ed.). New York: Harper & Row, 1963.
46. Bromley, Dorothy, and Britten, Florence. *Youth and sex.* New York: Harper, 1938.
47. Brown, D. G. Female orgasm and sexual inadequacy. In *An analysis of human sexual response* (Ruth Brecher and E. Brecher, Eds.). New York: New American Library, 1966.
48. ———. Transvestism and sex-role inversion. In *The encyclopedia of sexual behavior,* Vol. II (A. Ellis and A. Abarbanel, Eds.). New York: Hawthorn Books, 1961.
49. **Brown, J. A.** (Medical Director, Almeda Clinic, Houston, Texas). Personal communication. May 25, 1967.
50. Burgess, E. W., and Wallin, P. *Engagement and marriage.* Chicago: Lippincott, 1953.
51. Buxton, C. L., and Engle, E. T. Time of ovulation. *Amer. J. of Obst. and Gyn.* 60:3, 1950.
52. Calderone, Mary S. Abortion, disease of society. *Sexology* 30: 604-606, 1964.
53. ———. Contraception, teenagers, and sexual responsibility. *J. of sex research* 2:37-40, 1966.
54. ———. Sex education for young people—and for their parents and teachers. In *An analysis of human sexual response* (Ruth Brecher and E. Brecher, Eds.). New York: New American Library, 1966.

55. ———. The sex information and education council of the U.S. *J. of marriage and the family* 27:533-534, 1965.
56. Callieri, B. Destructive love. *Sexology* 31:311-313, 1964.
57. Caprio, F. S. *Female homosexuality: a modern study of lesbianism.* New York: Grove Press, 1954.
58. ———. *The modern woman's guide to sexual maturity.* New York: Grove Press, 1959.
59. ———. *The sexually adequate male.* New York: Citadel, 1952.
60. ———. *Variations in sexual behavior.* New York: Grove Press, 1955.
61. Caprio, F. S., Mozes, E., and Dengrove, E. *Sex education library.* New York: Health Publications, 1964.
62. Carbary, Lorraine J. The fascinating facts about twins. *Sexology* 32:478-481, 1966.
63. Cavanagh, D., McLeod, A., and Ferguson, J. Carcinoma of cervix among women in their twenties. *J.A.M.A.* 195:834-836, 1966.
64. Charny, C. W. The husband's sexual performance and the infertile couple. *J.A.M.A.* 43 of No. 2:185, 1963.
65. Chesser, E. *Love without fear.* New York: Signet, 1949.
66. Christensen, H. T., and Carpenter, G. R. Timing patterns in the development of sexual intimacy: an attitudinal report on three modern western societies. *Marriage and family living* 24:30-35, 1962.
67. Christopherson, W. M., and Parker, J. E. Relation of cervical cancer to early marriage and child bearing. *New Eng. J. of Med.* 273:235-239, 1965.
68. Ciociola, G. Eleven kinds of virility. *Sexology* 29:299-301, 1962.
69. Clark, L. Fluid tumors of the scrotum. *Sexology* 29:118-121, 1962.
70. ———. How long to make a baby? *Sexology* 33:478-481, 1967.
71. ———. *Illustrated sex atlas.* New York: Health Publications, 1964.
72. ———. Painful intercourse. *Sexology* 32:194-196, 1965.
73. ———. *Sex and you.* Indianapolis: Bobbs-Merrill, 1949.
74. ———. Sterility in the female. *Sexology* 26:308-314, 1959.
75. ———. Your personal questions answered. *Sexology* 30:35-44, 1963.
76. ———. Your personal questions answered. *Sexology* 30:179-188, 1963.
77. ———. Your personal questions answered. *Sexology* 30:251-260, 1963.
78. ———. Your personal questions answered. *Sexology* 31:251-261, 1964.
79. ———. Your personal questions answered. *Sexology* 31:611-621, 1965.
80. ———. Your personal questions answered. *Sexology* 31:827-837, 1965.
81. ———. Your personal questions answered. *Sexology* 33:467-477, 1967.
82. Coleman, J. *Abnormal psychology and modern life.* Chicago: Scott, Foresman, 1964.
83. Corry, J. Current sexual behavior and attitudes. In *An analysis of human sexual response* (Ruth Brecher and E. Brecher, Eds.). New York: New American Library, 1966.
84. Corsini, R. J. Puritis ani: an incident in psychotherapy. *Voices* 1:103-104, 1965.
85. Cory, D. W. Homosexuality. In *The encyclopedia of sexual behavior,* Vol. I. (A. Ellis and A. Abarbanel, Eds.). New York: Hawthorn Books, 1961.
86. Cory, D. W., and LeRoy, J. P. A radically new sex law. *Sexology* 30:374-376, 1964.
87. Crawley, L. Q., Malfetti, J. L., Stewart, E. I., and Vas Dias, N. *Reproduction, sex, and preparation for marriage.* Englewood Cliffs, N. J.: Prentice-Hall, 1964.
88. Cuber, J. F., with Harroff, Peggy B. *The significant Americans.* New York: Appleton-Century, 1966.

89. Curtis, M. Oral-contraceptives feminization of a normal male infant. *Obst. and Gyn.* 23:295-296, 1964.

90. Cutter, F. Myths about sex offenders. *Sexology* 29:172-176, 1962.

91. ———. The crime of incest. *Sexology* 29:744-746, 1963.

92. Dalven, J. Bizarre menstrual bleeding. *Sexology* 30:676-678, 1964.

93. Davis, Katherine B. *Factors in the sex life of twenty-two hundred women.* New York: Harper, 1929.

94. Davis, Maxine. *The sexual responsibility of women.* New York: Permabooks, 1959.

95. Dearborn, L. W. Masturbation. In *Sexual behavior and personality characteristics* (M. F. DeMartino, Ed.). New York: Grove Press, 1966.

96. Dedman, Jean. The relationship between religious attitude and attitude toward premarital sex relations. *Marriage and family living* 21:171-176, 1959.

97. DeMartino, M. F. Dominance-feeling, security-insecurity, and sexuality in women. In *Sexual behavior and personality characteristics* (M. F. DeMartino, Ed.). New York: Grove Press, 1966.

98. ——— (Ed.). *Sexual behavior and personality characteristics.* New York: Grove Press, 1966.

99. Dengrove, E. Myth of the captive penis. *Sexology* 31:447-449, 1965.

100. Deschin, Celia S. Teen-agers and venereal disease: a sociological study of 600 teen-agers in NYC social hygiene clinics. *Amer. J. Nurs.* 63:63-67, 1963.

101. Dickinson, R. L. *Atlas of human sex anatomy.* Baltimore: Williams & Wilkins, 1949.

102. *Dorland's illustrated medical dictionary* (23rd ed.). Philadelphia: W. B. Saunders, 1955.

103. Duffy, J. Masturbation and clitoridectomy. *J.A.M.A.* 19:246-248, 1963.

104. ———. Masturbation and clitoris amputation. *Sexology* 30:668-671, 1964.

105. Duggan, H. E. Effect of X-ray therapy on patients with Peyronie's disease. *J. of Urol.* 91:572-573, 1964.

106. Eagle, H. The spirochetes. In *Bacterial and mycotic infections of man* (R. J. Dubos, Ed.). Philadelphia: Lippincott, 1952.

107. Eastman, N. J., and Hellman, L. M. *Williams obstetrics* (12th ed.). New York: Appleton-Century-Crofts, 1961.

108. Ehrmann, W. *Premarital dating behavior.* New York: Holt, 1959.

109. ———. Premarital sexual intercourse. In *The encyclopedia of sexual behavior,* Vol. II. (A. Ellis and A. Abarbanel, Eds.). New York: Hawthorn Books, 1961.

110. Eichenlaub, J. E. *Abortions, fact and fancy. Sexology* 30:155-157, 1963.

111. ———. *The marriage art.* New York: Dell, 1961.

112. Ellis, A. Constitutional factors in homosexuality: a re-examination of the evidence. In *Advances in sex research* (H. G. Beigel, Ed.). New York: Harper & Row, 1963.

113. ———. Frigidity. In *The encyclopedia of sexual behavior,* Vol. I. (A. Ellis and A. Abarbanel, Eds.). New York: Hawthorn Books, 1961.

114. ———. *If this be sexual heresy.* New York: Lyle Stuart, 1963.

115. ———. Masturbation. In *Sexual behavior and personality characteristics* (M. F. DeMartino, Ed.). New York: Grove Press, 1966.

116. ———. Myths about sex compatibility. *Sexology* 28:652-655, 1962.

117. ———. *Sex and the single man.* New York: Lyle Stuart, 1963.

118. ———. Sex offenders, the psychology of. In *The encyclopedia of sexual behavior,* Vol. II. (A. Ellis and A. Abarbanel, Eds.). New York: Hawthorn Books, 1961.

119. ———. *Sex without guilt.* New York: Hillman Periodicals, 1959.
120. ———. *Suppressed.* Chicago: New Classics House, 1965.
121. ———. *The American sexual tragedy.* New York: Lyle Stuart, 1962.
122. ———. *The art and science of love.* New York: Lyle Stuart, 1960.
123. ———. *The folklore of sex.* New York: Grove Press, 1961.
124. ———. *The intelligent woman's guide to man-hunting.* New York: Lyle Stuart, 1963.
125. ———. The sex revolution. *Sexology* 32:660-664, 1966.
126. ———. *The theory and practice of rational-emotive psychotherapy.* New York: Lyle Stuart, 1964.
127. Ellis, A., and Abarbanel, A. *The encyclopedia of sexual behavior,* Vol. I. New York: Hawthorn Books, 1961.
128. ———. *The encyclopedia of sexual behavior,* Vol. II. New York: Hawthorn Books, 1961.
129. Ellis, A., and Brancale, R. *The psychology of sex offenders.* Springfield, Ill.: Charles C. Thomas, 1956.
130. Ellis, A., and Sagarin, E. *Nymphomania.* New York: Gilbert Press, 1964.
131. English, O. S. Sexual adjustment in marriage. In Modern marriage and family *living* (M. Fishbein and Ruby Kennedy, Eds.). New York: Oxford University Press, 1957.
132. Falk, G. J. The truth about sex offenders. *Sexology* 32:271-273, 1965.
133. Fischer, I. C. Reproduction, human. In *The encyclopedia of sexual behavior,* Vol. II. (A. Ellis and A. Abarbanel, Eds.). New York: Hawthorn Books, 1961.
134. Fisher, C., Gross, J., and Zuch, J. Cycle of penile erection synchronous with dreaming (REM) sleep. *Arch. of Gen. Psychiat.* 12:29-45, 1965.
135. Flanagan, Geraldine Lux. *Nine months of life.* New York: Simon & Schuster, 1962.
136. Ford, C. S., and Beach, F. A. *Patterns of sexual behavior.* New York: Harper, 1951.
137. ———. Self-stimulation. In *Sexual behavior and personality characteristics* (M. F. DeMartino, Ed.). New York: Grove Press, 1966.
138. Frank, L. K. *The conduct of sex.* New York: Grove Press, 1963.
139. Freeman, R., Whelpton, P. K., and Campbell, A. A. *Family planning, sterility, and population growth.* New York: McGraw-Hill, 1959.
140. Fromme, A. *Sex and marriage.* New York: Barnes & Noble, 1955.
141. Garrett, R. A. Treat undescended testicle by age six. *J.A.M.A.* 188:34, 1964.
142. Gebhard, P. H., Gagnon, J. H., Pomeroy, W. B., and Christenson, C. V. *Sex offenders.* New York: Harper & Row, and Paul B. Hoeber, Inc., 1965.
143. Gebhard, P. H., Pomeroy, W. B., Martin, C. E., and Christenson, C. V. *Pregnancy, birth, and abortion.* New York: Paul B. Hoeber, Inc., 1958.
144. Geller, J. Progesterone drug may reduce benign prostatic hypertrophy. *J.A.M.A.* 189:32, 1964.
145. Gold, L. N. Psychiatric profile of a firesetter. *J. Sci.* 7:404, 1962.
146. Green, D. S., and Green, Betty. Double sex. *Sexology* 31:561-563, 1965.
147. Greenblat, B. R. *A doctor's marital guide for patients.* Chicago: Budlong Press, 1962.
148. Greene, G. *Sex and the college girl.* New York: Dial Press, 1964.
149. Guttmacher, A. F. Should our abortion laws be changed? *Sexology* 29:436-439, 1963.
150. ———. The attitudes of 3,381 physicians towards contraception and the contraceptives they prescribe. *Human biology* 12:1-12, 1947.

151. Hall, R. E. Therapeutic abortion, sterilization and contraception. *Amer. J. of Obst. and Gyn.* 91:518, 1965.

152. Hamilton, G. V. *Research in marriage.* New York: Albert and Charles Boni, 1929.

153. Hanes, M. V. Ectopic pregnancy following total hysterectomy: report of a case. *Obst. and Gyn.* 23:882-884, 1964.

154. Harlow, H. F., and Harlow, Margaret K. Social deprivation in monkeys. In *Human development* (M. L. Haimowitz and Natalie R. Haimowitz, Eds.). New York: Thomas Y. Crowell, 1966.

155. ———. The effect of rearing conditions on behavior. In *Sex research: new developments* (J. Money, Ed.). New York: Holt, Rinehart, & Winston, 1965.

156. Harper, R. A. Communication problems in marriage and marriage counseling. *Marriage and family living* 20:107-112, 1958.

157. ———. Extramarital sex relations. In *The encyclopedia of sexual behavior,* Vol. I. (A. Ellis and A. Abarbanel, Eds.). New York: Hawthorn Books, 1961.

158. ———. Overcoming impotence. *Sexology* 31:680-682, 1965.

159. ———. Sex tryouts before marriage. *Sexology* 32:724-726, 1966.

160. Herrick, E. H. Is virgin birth possible? *Sexology* 28:590-594, 1962.

161. ———. Telegony. *Sexology* 26:316-318, 1959.

162. Hirsch, E. W. *How to improve your sexual relations.* Chicago: Zeco, 1951.

163. Hollingshead, A. B. *Elmtown's youth.* New York: John Wiley & Sons, 1949.

164. Honigmann, J. J. A cultural theory of obscenity. In *Sexual behavior and personality characteristics* (M. F. DeMartino, Ed.). New York: Grove Press, 1963.

165. Hooker, Evelyn. An empirical study of some relations between sexual patterns and gender identity in male homosexuals. In *Sex research: new developments* (J. Money, Ed.). New York: Holt, Rinehart, & Winston, 1965.

166. ———.The adjustment of the male overt homosexual. *J. Proj. Tech.* 21:18-31, 1957.

167. *J.A.M.A.* Growing older—later. 191:143, 1965.

168. *J.A.M.A.* Antibody's role in infertility studies. 189:32, 1964.

169. Javert, C. T. Role of the patient's activities in the occurrence of spontaneous abortion. *Fertility and sterility* 11:550-558, 1960.

170. Johnson, Virginia E., and Masters, W. H. A product of dual import: intravaginal infection control and contraception control. *Pac. Med. and Surg.* 73:267-271, 1965.

171. Johnson, W. R. *Human sex and sex education.* Philadelphia: Lea & Febiger, 1963.

172. Jones, H. E. Adolescence in our society. In *The adolescent* (J. M. Seidman, Ed.). New York: Holt, Rinehart, & Winston, 1960.

173. Kanin, E. J., and Howard, D. H. Postmarital consequences of premarital sex adjustment. *Amer. Socio. Rev.* Sept.: 197-204, 1957.

174. Kardiner, A. *Sex and morality.* Indianapolis: Bobbs-Merrill, 1954.

175. Karpman, B. *The sexual offender and his offenses.* New York: Julian Press, 1954.

176. Kelly, G. L. Impotency. In *The encyclopedia of sexual behavior,* Vol. I. (A. Ellis and A. Abarbanel, Eds.). New York: Hawthorn Books, 1961.

177. ———. *Sex manual.* Augusta, Ga.: Southern Medical Supply Co., 1959.

178. Kinsey, A. C., Pomeroy, W. B., and Martin, C. E. Concepts in normality and abnormality in sexual behavior. In *Psychosexual development in health and disease* (P. H. Hoch and J. Zubin, Eds.). New York: Grune & Stratton, 1949.

179. Kinsey, A. C., Pomeroy, W. B., Martin, C. E., and Gebhard, P. H. *Sexual behavior in the human female.* Philadelphia: W. B. Saunders, 1953.

180. Kinsey, A. C., Pomeroy, W. B., and Martin, C. E. *Sexual behavior in the human male.* Philadelphia: W. B. Saunders, 1948.

181. Kirkendall, L. A. Obscenity and the U. S. Supreme Court. *Sexology* 32:242-245, 1965.

182. ———. *Premarital intercourse and interpersonal relations.* New York: Julian Press, 1961.

183. ———. Sex drive. In *The encyclopedia of sexual behavior,* Vol. II. (A. Ellis and A. Abarbanel, Eds.). New York: Hawthorn Books, 1961.

184. ———. The problem of pornography. *Sexology* 26:694-696, 1960.

185. ———. The truth about college sex. *Sexology* 31:8-11, 1964.

186. Kirkpatrick, C. *The family as process and institution.* New York: Ronald Press, 1959.

187. Kleegman, Sophia J. Female sex problems. *Sexology* 31:226-229, 1964.

188. ———. Frigidity. *Quart. Rev. Surg. Obst. and Gyn.* 16:243-248, 1959.

189. Kopp, S. B. The character structure of sex offenders. *Amer. J. Psychother.* 16:64-70, 1962.

190. Krauss, L., and Fitzpatrick, T. The treatment of priapism by penile aspiration under controlled hypotension. *J. of Urol.* 85:595-598, 1961.

191. Kronhausen, Phyllis, and Kronhausen, E. *The sexually responsive woman.* New York: Ballantine Books, 1965.

192. Landis, J. T., and Landis, Mary G. *Building a successful marriage.* Englewood Cliffs, N. J.: Prentice-Hall, 1963.

193. Lehfeldt, H. Artificial insemination. In *The encyclopedia of sexual behavior,* Vol. I. (A. Ellis and A. Abarbanel, Eds.). New York: Hawthorn Books, 1961.

194. ———. Contraception. In *The encyclopedia of sexual behavior,* Vol. I. (A. Ellis and A. Abarbanel, Eds.). New York: Hawthorn Books, 1961.

195. ———. The physician's dilemma. *J. of sex research* 2:43-46, 1966.

196. Levie, L. H. Phimosis. *J. of sex research* 1:189-200, 1965.

197. Lewis, G. M. *Practical dermatology for medical students and general practitioners.* Philadelphia: W. B. Saunders, 1955.

198. Le Witter, M., and Abarbanel, A. Aging and sex. In *The encyclopedia of sexual behavior,* Vol. I. (A. Ellis and A. Abarbanel, Eds.). New York: Hawthorn Books, 1961.

199. Licklider, S. Jewish penile carcinoma. *J. of Urol.* 86:98, 1961.

200. Lion, E. G., *et al. An experiment in the psychiatric treatment of promiscuous girls.* San Francisco: Dept. of Public Health, 1945.

201. Lloyd, C. W. *Human reproduction and sexual behavior.* Philadelphia: Lea & Febiger, 1964.

202. Locke, H. J. *Predicting adjustment in marriage.* New York: Holt, 1951.

203. Macdougald, D., Jr. Aphrodisiacs and anaphrodisiacs. In *The encyclopedia of sexual behavior,* Vol. I. (A. Ellis and A. Abarbanel, Eds.). New York: Hawthorn Books, 1961.

204. MacLean, P. D. New findings relevant to the evolution of psychosexual functions of the brain. In *Sex research: new developments* (J. Money, Ed.). New York: Holt, Rinehart, & Winston, 1965.

205. Mann, T. *The biochemistry of semen.* London: Methuen & Co., 1954.

206. Maslow, A. H. Critique and discussion. In *Sex research: new developments* (J. Money, Ed.). New York: Holt, Rinehart, & Winston, 1965.

207. ———. Love in self-actualizing people. In *Sexual behavior and personality characteristics* (M. F. DeMartino, Ed.). New York: Grove Press, 1966.

208. ———. *Motivation and personality.* New York: Harper, 1954.

209. ———. Self-esteem (dominance-feeling) and sexuality in women. In *Sexual behavior and personality characteristics* (M. F. DeMartino, Ed.). New York: Grove Press, 1966.

210. Masters, R. E. L. *Patterns of incest.* New York: Julian Press, 1963.

211. Masters, W. H. The sexual response cycle of the human female: I. Gross anatomic considerations. *Western J. Surg.* 68:57-72, 1960.

212. ———. The sexual response cycle of the human female: II. Vaginal lubrication. *Ann. N. Y. Acad. Sci.* 83:301-317, 1959.

213. Masters, W. H., and Ballew, J. W. The third sex. In *Problems of the middle-aged* (C. G. Vedder, Ed.). Springfield, Ill.: Charles C. Thomas, 1965.

214. Masters, W. H., and Johnson, Virginia E. Counseling with sexually incompatible marriage partners. In *Counseling in marital and sexual problems (A physician's handbook)* (R. H. Clemer, Ed.). Baltimore: Williams & Wilkins, 1965.

215. ———. *Human sexual response.* Boston: Little, Brown, 1966.

216. ———. Intravaginal environment: I. A lethal factor. *Fertility and Sterility* 12:560-580, 1961.

217. ———. *Major questions in human sexual response.* A lecture presented to Harris County Medical Society, March 15, 1967.

218. ———. Orgasm, anatomy of the female. In *The encyclopedia of sexual behavior,* Vol. II. (A. Ellis and A. Abarbanel, Eds.). New York: Hawthorn Books, 1961.

219. ———. Sexual response: Part II. Anatomy and physiology. In *Human reproduction and sexual behavior* (C. W. Lloyd, Ed.). Philadelphia: Lea & Febiger, 1964.

220. ———. The artificial vagina: anatomic, physiologic, psychosexual function. *Western J. Surg.* 69:192-212, 1961.

221. ———. The clitoris: an anatomic baseline for behavioral investigation. In *Determinants of human sexual behavior* (G. W. Winokur, Ed.). Springfield, Ill.: Charles C. Thomas, 1963.

222. ———. The human female: anatomy of sexual response. *Minnesota Med.* 43:31-36, 1960.

223. ———. The physiology of the vaginal reproductive function. *Western J. Surg.* 69:105-120, 1961.

224. ———. The sexual response cycle of the human female: 2. The clitoris: anatomic and clinical considerations. In *Sex research: new developments* (J. Money, Ed.). New York: Holt, Rinehart, & Winston, 1965.

225. ———. The sexual response cycle of the human female: III. The clitoris: anatomic and clinical considerations. *Western J. Surg.* 70:248-257, 1962.

226. ———. The sexual response cycles of the human male and female: comparative anatomy and physiology. In *Sex and behavior* (F. A. Beach, Ed.). New York: John Wiley & Sons, 1965.

227. ———. The sexual response of the human male: I. Gross anatomic considerations. *Western J. Surg.* 71:85-95, 1963.

228. ———. Treatment of the sexually incompatible family unit. *Minnesota Med.* 44:466-471, 1961.

229. ———. Vaginal pH: the influence of the male ejaculate. In *Report of the thirty-fifth Ross conference, endocrine dysfunction and infertility.* Columbus, Ohio: Ross Laboratories, 1960.
230. Mathis, J. L. What doctors don't know about sex. *Med. Econ.* 43:110-115, 1966.
231. McCary, J. L. *An introduction to sexology, a neglected subject.* Houston: Pierre St. Le Macs, 1966.
232. ———. What I would tell my daughter about premarital sex. *Sexology* 32:583-586, 1966.
233. Mead, Margaret. *Coming of age in Samoa.* New York: William Morrow, 1928.
234. Melzack, R. The perception of pain. *Scientific Amer.* 204:41-49, 1961.
235. Menaker, J. S. "Engagement" ovaries. *Sexology* 28:49-53, 1961.
236. Money, J. Judging teenage mores. *J. of sex research* 2:41-42, 1966.
237. ———. Phantom orgasm in the dreams of paraplegic men and women. *Arch. of Gen. Psychiat.* 3:373-382, 1960.
238. ———. Psychosexual differentiation. In *Sex research: new developments* (J. Money, Ed.). New York: Holt, Rinehart, & Winston, 1965.
239. ———. The strange case of the pregnant hermaphrodite. *Sexology* 33:7-9, 1966.
240. Money, J., and Yankowitz, R. The sympathetic-inhibiting effects of the drug ismelin on human male eroticism, with a note on mellaril. *J. of sex research* 3:69-82, 1967.
241. Montagu, A. Myths about birthmarks. *Sexology* 29:734-736, 1963.
242. ———. Myths about menstruation. *Sexology* 29:821-823, 1963.
243. ———. Myths about pregnancy. *Sexology* 30:58-61, 1963.
244. ———. Sex made to order. *Sexology* 30:384-386, 1964.
245. ———. Smoking, pregnancy, and sex. *Sexology* 30:220-222, 1963.
246. Mozes, E. B. Premature ejaculation. *Sexology* 30:274-276, 1963.
247. ———. Stone babies. *Sexology* 30:411-413, 1964.
248. ———. The technique of wooing. *Sexology* 25:756-760, 1959.
249. Mueller, G. O. W. Sex law reform. *Sexology* 31:742-744, 1965.
250. Murdock, G. P. *Our primitive contemporaries.* New York: Macmillan, 1934.
251. ———. *Social structure.* New York: Macmillan, 1949.
252. Netter, F. H. *Reproductive system.* Summit, N. J.: Ciba Pharmaceutical Products, Inc., 1961.
253. Neumann, G. Abortion. In *The encyclopedia of sexual behavior,* Vol. I (A. Ellis and A. Abarbanel, Eds.). New York: Hawthorn Books, 1961.
254. Newman, G., and Nichols, C. R. Sexual activities and attitudes in older persons. *J.A.M.A.* 173:33-35, 1960.
255. Oliver, B. J., Jr. What the rapist is like. *Sexology* 31:849-851, 1965.
256. Platt, R. Reflections on aging and death. *Lancet* 1:1-6, 1963
257. Pereyra, A. J. Relationship of sexual activities to cervical cancer. *Obst. and Gyn.* 17:154-159, 1961.
258. Poffenberger, T. Individual choice in adolescent premarital sex behavior. *Marriage and family living* 22:324-330, 1960.
259. Pomeroy, W. B. Parents and homosexuality, I. *Sexology* 32:508-511, 1966.
260. ———. Parents and homosexuality, II. *Sexology* 32:588-590, 1966.
261. ———. The Masters-Johnson report and the Kinsey tradition. In *An analysis of human sexual response* (Ruth Brecher and E. Brecher, Eds.). New York: New American Library, 1966.
262. ———. The sexual non-conformist. *Sexology* 32:295-296, 1965.
263. ———. Why we tolerate lesbians. *Sexology* 31:652-654, 1965.

264. Posner, L. B., Chidiac, J. E., and Posner, A. C. Pregnancy at age forty and over. *Obst. and Gyn.* 17:194-198, 1961.
265. Pund, E. R., and Von Haam, E. Spirochetal and venereal diseases. In *Pathology* (W. A. D. Anderson, Ed.). St. Louis: C. V. Mosby, 1957.
266. Radzinowicz, L. (Ed.) *Sexual offenses.* London: Macmillan, 1957.
267. Reevy, W. R. Child sexuality. In *The encyclopedia of sexual behavior,* Vol. I (A. Ellis and A. Abarbanel, Eds.). New York: Hawthorn Books, 1961.
268. Reik, T. *Psychology of sex relations.* New York: Grove Press, 1966.
269. Reiser, C. Vasectomy: medical and legal aspects. *J. of Urol.* 79:138-143, 1958.
270. Reiss, I. L. *Premarital sexual standards in America.* Glencoe, Ill.: Free Press, 1960.
271. ———. Sexual codes in teen-age culture. *The Annals,* Nov.:53-62, 1961.
272. ———. Standards of sexual behavior. In *The encyclopedia of sexual behavior,* Vol. II (A. Ellis and A. Abarbanel, Eds.). New York: Hawthorn Books, 1961.
273. Revitch, E., and Weiss, R. G. The pedaphiliac offender. *Dis. Nerv. Sys.* 23:73-78, 1962.
274. Riedman, Sarah R. Change of life. *Sexology* 27:808-813, 1961.
275. Rodgers, D. A., Ziegler, F. J., Prentiss, R. J., and Martin, P. L. Comparisons of nine contraceptive procedures by couples changing to vasectomy or ovulation-suppression medication. *J. of sex research* 1:87-96, 1965.
276. Rowan, R. L. "Honeymoon cystitis" and other bladder problems. *Sexology* 31:118-120, 1964.
277. Rubin, I. Birth control pills for men. *Sexology* 28:12-15, 1961.
278. ———. Common sex myths. *Sexology* 32:512-514, 1966.
279. ———. Good and bad sex research. *Sexology* 33:198-200, 1966.
280. ———. Is there a sex revolution? *Sexology* 32:220-222, 1965.
281. ———. Myths about homosexuality. *Sexology* 30:595-597, 1964.
282. ———. Sex after forty and after seventy. In *An analysis of human sexual response* (Ruth Brecher and E. Brecher, Eds.). New York: New American Library, 1966.
283. ———. Sex needs after 65. *Sexology* 30:769-771, 1964.
284. ———. Sex over 65. *Sexology* 28:622-625, 1962.
285. ———. Sex over 65. In *Advances in sex research* (H. Beigel, Ed.). New York: Harper & Row, 1963.
286. ———. Should students learn birth control? *Sexology* 30:449-451, 1964.
287. ———. Story of the sperm. *Sexology* 28:82-87, 1961.
288. ———. The electric vibrator and frigidity. *Sexology* 31:156-158, 1964.
289. ———. The new Kinsey report. *Sexology* 32:443-446, 1966.
290. ———. Transition in sex values—implications for the education of adolescents. *J. of marriage and the family* 27:185-189, 1965.
291. ———. Will sex abstinence prolong life? *Sexology* 30:158-160, 1963.
292. Rugh, R. Choosing the sex of your child. *Sexology* 29:663-666, 1963.
293. ———. Why you are unique. *Sexology* 29:621-623, 1963.
294. Russell, M. Sterilization. In *The encyclopedia of sexual behavior,* Vol. II (A. Ellis and A. Abarbanel, Eds.). New York: Hawthorn Books, 1961.
295. Rutledge, A. L. Sex during pregnancy. *Sexology* 30:483-485, 1964.
296. Safier, B. *A psychiatric approach to the treatment of promiscuity.* New York: American Social Hygiene Assoc., 1949.
297. Scheinfeld, A. *You and heredity.* New York: Garden City Publishing Co., 1945.

298. Schur, E. (Ed.) *The family and the sexual revolution: selected readings.* Bloomington: Indiana University Press, 1964.
299. Sentnor, M., and Hult, S. Erotic zones—facts and superstitions. *Sexology* 28:76-81, 1961.
300. *Sex endocrinology: a handbook for the medical and allied professions.* Bloomfield: Schering Corporation, Medical Research Division, 1944.
301. *Sexology.* A need for reform. 32:70, 1965.
302. ————. A psychiatrist looks at the problem of obscenity. 27:93, 1960.
303. ————. Babies born from frozen semen. 31:272, 1964.
304. ————. Birth control vaccine. 27:402, 1961.
305. ————. Current research. 28:111, 1961.
306. ————. From the editor's scrapbook. 30: 32-34, 1963.
307. ————. From the editor's scrapbook. 30:408-410, 1964.
308. ————. From the editor's scrapbook. 31:118-120, 1965.
309. ————. From the editor's scrapbook. 31:536-538, 1965.
310. ————. Husbands' pregnancy symptoms. 31:457, 1965.
311. ————. Italy since the Merlin law. 32:744, 1966.
312. ————. Medical science notes. 27:790, 1961.
313. ————. Medical science notes. 27:862, 1961.
314. ————. Medical science notes. 28:70, 1961.
315. ————. Medical science notes. 28:214, 1961.
316. ————. Medical science notes. 28:358, 1961.
317. ————. Ministers and sex. 25:663, 1959.
318. ————. News of the month. 28:197, 1961.
319. ————. News of the month. 28:269, 1961.
320. ————. News of the month. 28:342, 1961.
321. ————. Nonatuplets in Pakistan. 33:270, 1966.
322. ————. Public law and private morality. 31:862, 1965.
323. ————. Science notes. 29:214, 1962.
324. ————. Science notes. 31:139, 1964.
325. ————. Science notes. 31:281, 1964.
326. ————. Science notes. 31:499, 1965.
327. ————. Science notes. 31:715, 1965.
328. ————. Science notes. 32:356, 1965.
329. ————. Science notes. 32:428, 1966.
330. ————. Scrapbook. 32:392, 1966.
331. ————. Sex behavior of older women. 32:734, 1966.
332. ————. Sex in the news. 30:209, 1963.
333. ————. Sex in the news. 31:569, 1965.
334. ————. Sex in the news. 33:67, 1966.
335. ————. Sex in the news. 33:421, 1967.
336. ————. Sex offenders good parole risk. 29:768, 1963.
337. ————. The British sex revolution. 30:733-734, 1964.
338. ————. Sexual maturity and climate. 27:773, 1961.
339. ————. So they say. 28:323, 1961.
340. ————. Sports and menstruation. 27:407, 1961.
341. ————. Story of the sperm. 31:379-381, 1965.
342. ————. Teen-age extramarital conception. 28:178, 1961.
343. ————. The war against poverty. 31:286, 1964.
344. ————. 200,000 vasectomies done each year. 33:417, 1967.
345. ————. Weakness in medical education. 28:557, 1962.

346. Shafer, N. Vaginal discharges. *Sexology* 32:531-533, 1966.
347. Shaffer, J. W. Masculinity-femininity and other personality traits in gonadal aplasia (Turner's syndrome). In *Advances in sex research* (H. Beigel, Ed.). New York: Harper & Row, 1963.
348. Shaw, W. *Operative gynaecology*. Baltimore: Williams & Wilkins, 1954.
349. Sherman, J. K. Freezing human sperm. *Sexology* 31:812-815, 1965.
350. Sherwin, R. V. Laws on sex crimes. In *The encyclopedia of sexual behavior*, Vol. II (A. Ellis and A. Abarbanel, Eds.). New York: Hawthorn Books, 1961.
351. Shettles, L. B. Observations on human spermatozoa. *Bull. Sloane Hosp. for women* 6:48, 1960.
352. ———. The great preponderance of human males conceived. *Amer. J. of Obst. and Gyn.* 89:130-133, 1964.
353. Smith, C. E. Negro-white intermarriage: forbidden sexual union. *J. of sex research* 2:169-177, 1966.
354. Steen, E. B., and Montagu, A. *Anatomy and physiology,* Vol. 2. New York: Barnes and Noble, 1959.
355. Steinhaus, A. H. *Toward an understanding of health and physical education.* Dubuque: William C. Brown Co., 1964.
356. Stiller, R. Common prostate problems. *Sexology* 29:817-819, 1963.
357. ———. Drinking and sex. *Sexology* 31:519-521, 1965.
358. ———. Electrically caused ejaculation. *Sexology* 29:321-322, 1962.
359. ——— (Ed.) *Illustrated sex dictionary*. New York: Health Publications, 1966.
360. ———. The cult of virility. *Sexology* 31:166-168, 1964.
361. ———. The firebug and sex. *Sexology* 31:236-238, 1964.
362. ———. Why girls get pregnant. *Sexology* 33:162-165, 1966.
363. ———. Wife swapping. *Sexology* 27:652-656, 1961.
364. Stokes, W. R., Montagu, A., Money, J., Rutledge, A. L., and Yoder, H. W. Is pornography harmful? *Sexology* 30:16-19, 1963.
365. Stone, A., and Stone, Hannah. *A marriage manual.* New York: Simon & Schuster, 1952.
366. Tarail, M. Sex over 65. *Sexology* 28:440-442, 1962.
367. Tarr, J. D. F., and Lugar, R. R. Early infectious syphilis: male homosexual relations as a mode of spread. *Calif. Med.* 93:35-37, 1960.
368. Te Linde, R. W. *Operative gynecology*. Philadelphia: Lippincott, 1953.
369. Terman, L. M. Correlates of orgasm adequacy in a group of 556 wives. In *Sexual behavior and personality characteristics* (M. F. DeMartino, Ed.). New York: Grove Press, 1966.
370. ———. *Psychological factors in marital happiness*. New York: McGraw-Hill, 1938.
371. The British Council of Churches. *Sex and morality*. London: SCM Press, Ltd., 1966.
372. Thorne, F. C. Ejaculatio praecox. *Dis. of the Nerv. Syst.* 4:273-275, 1943.
373. Thorpe, L. P., Katz, B., and Lewis, R. T. *The psychology of abnormal behavior*. New York: Ronald Press, 1961.
374. Tietze, C. History of contraceptive methods. *J. of sex research* 1:69-85, 1965.
375. Trainer, J. B. *Physiologic foundations for marriage counseling*. St. Louis: C. V. Mosby, 1965.
376. Trice, E. R., Gayle, S., Jr., and Clark, F. A., Jr. The transmission of early infectious syphilis through homosexual practices. *Virginia M. Month.* 87:132-134, 1960.

377. Turner, H. H. A syndrome of infantilism, congenital webbed neck and cubitus valgus. *Endocrinology* 23:566, 1938.
378. Ubell, E. *New York Herald Tribune,* June 17, 1962.
379. Van de Velde, T. H. *Ideal marriage.* New York: Random House, 1957.
380. Vatsyayana. *The kama sutra.* New York: Dutton, 1962.
381. Villee, C. A. *Biology* (3rd ed.). Philadelphia: W. B. Saunders, 1957.
382. Vincent, C. E. *Unmarried mothers.* Glencoe, Ill.: Free Press, 1961.
383. ————. Unmarried mothers: society's dilemma. *Sexology* 28:450-455, 1962.
384. Vizinczey, S. *In praise of older women.* London: Barrie & Rockliff, 1965.
385. Walker, K. Erection disorders. *Sexology* 29:696-698, 1963.
386. Waller, W., and Hill, R. *The family.* New York: Dryden Press, 1951.
387. Wendt, H. *The sex life of the animals.* New York: Simon & Schuster, 1965.
388. Williamson, P. The erotic zones. *Sexology* 27:740-743, 1961.
389. Wood, R. Popular sex superstitions. *Sexology* 29:752-754, 1963.
390. Wright, R. C. The relief of cervical dyspareunia by transvaginal paracervical uterine denervation. *Amer. J. of Obst. and Gyn.* 87:963-967, 1963.
391. Young, W. C., Goy, R. W., and Phoenix, C. H. Hormones and sexual behavior. In *Sex research: new developments* (J. Money, Ed.). New York: Holt, Rinehart, & Winston, 1965.

Index